Microeconomics Workbook: Principles and Practice

ISBN 978-1-60904-907-2

Kari L. Battaglia & Susan L. Dadres

Published by

Stipes Publishing L.L.C.
www.stipes.com

This Workbook belongs to ______________________________

(print your name)

If found, please return to the Economics Department or call ______________

Course Information:

____

____

____

Instructor Information:

____

____

____

Important Dates and Assignments:

____

____

____

____

____

____

____

____

FINAL EXAM on ______________________________

Table of Contents
Microeconomics Workbook
Principles and Practice
2019-2021

Welcome to Microeconomics

The study of economics is divided into Microeconomics and Macroeconomics, with further divisions in areas of specialization like Labor Economics, International Economics, Public Economics, and Industrial Organization. Economists are employed by corporations, banks, nonprofit institutions, and government agencies at all levels. Whether you are interested in pursuing a degree in economics or are just taking an introductory course to become a more informed voter, this workbook will help you master the concepts and skills you need.

Assignments in this workbook include multiple choice, fill-in-the-blank, short answer, graphs, and problems. You are encouraged to complete every assignment, even if your teacher is not collecting it for a grade. All of the assignments provide the kind of practice you need to do well on exams. Practice exams are provided at the end of each unit with answer keys. A good strategy is to take a practice exam as you would a real exam, without referring to the text or your notes, and then check your answers to see if there are any concepts that should be further reviewed before taking a graded exam.

The appendix to chapter 1 includes a review of some basic math concepts that are important in the class, as well as information about graphs. Introductory economics is taught without the use of Calculus, but you will need to use some algebra and geometry and graphs play an important role as a tool for representing relationships such as the relationship between the price of a gallon of gasoline and the number of gallons consumers choose to purchase.

The workbook is designed to give you the information you need to learn in short, easy-to-read chapters, combined with multiple opportunities to practice and apply the material. Good luck with your study of the exciting world of microeconomics!

CHAPTER 1 Introduction to Microeconomics

Economics is a social science that attempts to understand how societies allocate scarce resources to satisfy virtually unlimited wants and needs. Government makes some decisions on behalf of the members of society, such as how much to spend on infrastructure or the military, but many societies also rely on markets to allow buyers and sellers to make decisions about how scarce resources are used. Under certain conditions, free (unregulated) markets promote an efficient allocation of resources, which means society is getting the most it can out of available resources and answering the economic questions of what to produce, how to produce, and for whom to produce in the best possible way.

Microeconomics studies the decisions of individuals, households, and firms. It focuses on the interaction of buyers and sellers in specific markets, the consumption decisions of households, and the production decisions of firms. **Macroeconomics** studies economic aggregates, such as the national unemployment rate, the rate of inflation, and the economy's growth rate, as well as macroeconomic policies designed to promote full employment, price stability, and a healthy rate of economic growth.

Economic analysis can be either positive or normative. **Positive** economics deals with statements about *what is true*, which can be tested against facts. Economists develop and test positive statements by analyzing data, and positive statements require a lot of research. An economist can make a statement, such as "wages increase when workers are more productive." Since this is a statement about what is true, it is a positive statement. However, economists would seek to support the statement with theory and empirical data because it is not possible to know what is really true without conducting research.

Normative economics deals with statements of *what should be* and requires value judgments or personal opinions. For example, "firms should pay workers a higher wage when workers become more productive" is a normative statement. If policymakers, reflecting society's views or goals, express a desire to see an increase in wages, economists conduct research to find out how to achieve this objective. It is up to society to determine what should be through the choice of institutional rules and government policies.

Whether engaged in microeconomic analysis or macroeconomic analysis, positive analysis or normative analysis, economists are concerned with observing behavior, understanding relationships, predicting outcomes, and identifying solutions to economic problems. It is a field of study with enormous practical application.

Economic Theories and Models

In order to identify the relationship between two specific variables, other variables that might influence the relationship are assumed not to change. The term **ceteris paribus** roughly translates as "all other things unchanged." The *ceteris paribus assumption* is used to isolate the relationship between two variables by holding other influences on the relationship constant. For example, an analyst might assume that consumer income and other variables remain the same in order to focus on how a change in the price of gasoline affects how much gas is purchased.

Once a relationship has been identified and tested, a theory can be developed. Economic theories are not necessarily complex; rather, a good economic **theory** explains important relationships. Many economic theories that have been widely accepted and applied take on the status of a "law" (for example, the law of demand, the law of supply, and the law of diminishing returns). Economic **models** are designed to simplify reality in an attempt to explain real-world relationships and predict outcomes. Models are used in a similar fashion in other contexts. For example, if someone wants to give directions to the mall to a friend, they might design a simple model like a map. The model will likely show the most important information, like the streets the friend will use to get to the mall, but will not include every possible detail because too many details would just be distracting and confusing. Economic models take many forms, and those used by governments, academics, and businesses in the real world tend to be fairly complicated mathematical and statistical models that require the use of a computer. A basic economics course, however, uses models based on simple equations, two-dimensional graphs, and tables.

Developing economic theories and building economic models that may be used to help design economic policy requires a disciplined and analytical approach in order to avoid several common pitfalls, or errors, in economic reasoning. These errors, or fallacies, in reasoning can lead to incorrect conclusions; being aware of these fallacies in reasoning can help economists and policy makers avoid them.

The **fallacy of false cause** (**post hoc fallacy or association-causation issue**) occurs when it is assumed that because one event follows another, the first event must have caused the second. In many cases, there may be an association between the two events, but one is not causing the other. An example is the relationship between ice cream sales and criminal activity. In many large cities, an increase in ice cream sales is followed closely by an increase in criminal activity. Concluding that eating ice cream leads to criminal behavior is erroneous. These events are associated because both tend to occur more in the summer, but there is no cause-effect relationship. It is important not to confuse **association,** or **correlation,** with **causation**.

The **fallacy of division** occurs when it is incorrectly assumed that what is good, or true, for the whole is also good, or true, for the parts, or that all of the benefits divide equally. An example of the fallacy of division is concluding that because technological improvement brings benefits to the economy as a whole, it is also beneficial for each segment of society. Improved technology can have adverse effects on specific industries, firms, or individuals. For example, the invention of electricity was harmful to individuals engaged in making and selling candles. In general, economic gains rarely divide evenly, so there are often both winners and losers as a result of change.

The **fallacy of composition** occurs when it is incorrectly assumed that what is good, or true for the individual parts is also good, or true, for the whole. For example, if the government printed $1,000,000 and gave it to Sally, she clearly benefits. What would happen if the government printed $1,000,000 for each person? Most likely, people would stop working, so there would be nothing produced and nothing to consume. Everyone would increase spending, causing prices to rise and causing inflation. This action that would be good for one individual would probably prove to be very harmful for society as a whole.

Scarcity and Economic Resources

The fundamental economic problem is **scarcity**, which exists because there are not enough **resources** to produce everything people want and need. Scarcity means that society faces tradeoffs when making choices about how to use resources. If a large number of capable workers are engaged in national defense, there are fewer workers to provide health care or design new automobiles. Labor is a critically important resource, but there are other kinds of resources used to manufacture goods and provide services. Since there are so many different kinds of resources or **inputs** (also called the **factors of production**), economists classify them into four categories:

- **Land and other natural resources**
- **Labor services**
- **Capital (structures and equipment)**
- **Entrepreneurial ability**

The first category includes **land** as well as timber, water, minerals, and other gifts of nature. These can be further divided into renewable and non-renewable resources. Solar energy is renewable, while oil is non-renewable since it takes millions of years to form naturally.

Labor services represent the physical and mental talents of people. Labor includes the productive efforts of all kinds of workers in all industries, such as manufacturing and retail. Labor is the most significant input in almost every productive endeavor. For most people, labor is the resource they have available to sell, and their income depends on labor earnings (wages).

Capital refers to the structures that have been built and the machines, tools, and equipment that have been produced in the past, which can now be used to produce goods and provide services. A business firm invests in capital when it builds a factory or office building, or acquires new machines, tools, or equipment. In economics, people make investments when they build or purchase physical structures, buy machines and tools, or upgrade equipment in order to start or expand a business. The process of starting or expanding a business generally requires financing, which is why there is such a strong connection between physical capital and financial capital. Keep in mind that if you are asked to provide an example of capital in an economics class, it is not correct to say money or other financial assets.

Entrepreneurs are innovators who start or operate a business with the expectation of earning profit. They organize resources, take risks, offer something new and different to the market, and often see an opportunity before anyone else. In a market economy, entrepreneurs make many of the decisions about how to allocate scarce resources based on consumer demand, and they are motivated to make efficient decisions in order to maximize profits.

Opportunity cost is defined as the value of the next best alternative, or the best option that must be given up when a choice is made. All decisions involve an opportunity cost, which can be measured in terms of foregone activities or in monetary terms. In order to attend college, you might be giving up the chance to work at a full-time job, so the opportunity cost of college could be the salary you are giving up. If you are paying tuition, this is also an opportunity cost since you could use the money for something else if you didn't attend college.

Marginal Analysis

Economists apply **cost-benefit analysis** to many different decisions. It is not enough to demonstrate that a particular action or policy has benefits; the benefits must outweigh the costs for an action to have a positive net benefit. The cost-benefit approach often uses marginal analysis, comparing marginal benefit with marginal cost, in order to focus on proposed changes.

Marginal benefit (MB) is the additional benefit created when an action is taken, such as consuming one more slice of pizza. The benefit or satisfaction received from consumption is called utility. Marginal benefit typically declines as additional units are consumed due to an economic principle called the **law of diminishing marginal utility**.

Marginal cost (MC) is the additional cost incurred when an action is taken, such as producing one more coffee cup. The cost of producing additional units of output reflects the amount paid for resources used in production. Marginal cost typically rises as additional units are produced due to an economic principle called the **law of diminishing marginal returns**.

It is optimal or **efficient** to continue an activity as long as the marginal benefit exceeds the marginal cost, or MB > MC. If MB is declining and MC is rising, it is optimal or efficient to continue an activity up to the point where **MB = MC**, so setting marginal benefit equal to marginal cost is one way of describing the efficiency rule.

To illustrate marginal analysis, consider the decision of how much time to spend studying for an exam. With each extra hour spent studying, the exam grade improves, up to a point. Assume a student who does not study the night before an exam will earn a grade of 60 on the exam. If studying one hour the night before an exam improves the grade from 60 to 75, the marginal benefit of the first hour is the value of an added 15 points. If adding a second hour of study time raises the exam grade from 75 to 82, the marginal benefit of the second hour is the value of an added 7 points. Studying a third hour will add even less than 7 points to the exam grade, and this pattern of declining marginal benefit continues until marginal benefit becomes zero or even negative. The reason for declining marginal benefit is that a rational person will study the most important material first, so once that is mastered, additional study is devoted to less relevant material. Also, after a certain amount of time, fatigue sets in and it becomes harder to concentrate. If a student spends so much time studying that she gives up sleep, the exam score could actually be reduced because a well-rested person performs better than an exhausted person.

The marginal cost of studying an additional hour will likely be low initially, because a low-value activity can be sacrificed first. For example, a student might decide to give up watching a television program in order to free one hour for study time the night before an exam. After that, alternative activities that have a higher value must be sacrificed to free additional study time. As a result, the marginal cost of each successive hour of study time gets higher and higher because an alternative activity with a higher value is given up.

Given the expected patterns of declining marginal benefit and rising marginal cost, the two functions can be represented graphically as shown on the next page.

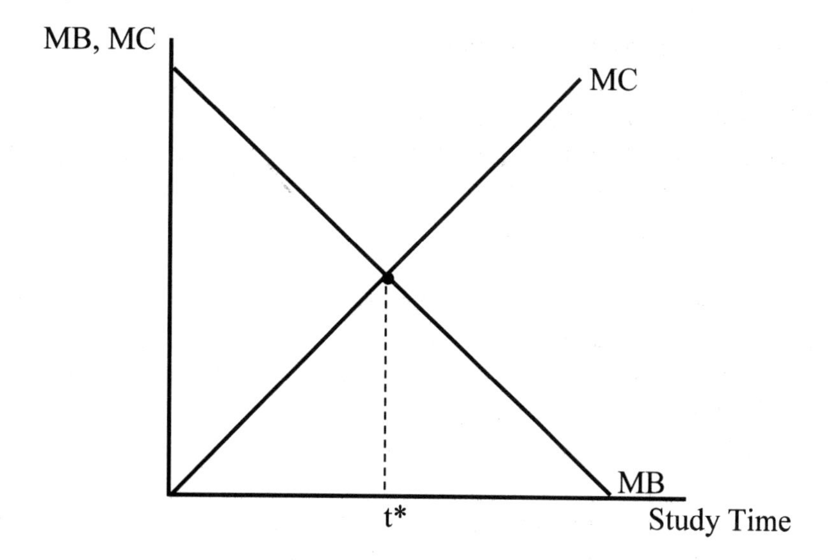

If a student stops studying at a point in time less than t*, where the marginal benefit is still high and the marginal cost is low (MB > MC), she is not making an efficient choice. Efficiency requires that additional time be spent studying when there is a lot to gain and little to lose and the net benefit is positive.

Believe it or not, there is such a thing as studying too much! Going past t* means the marginal benefit of additional study time will be small, so little improvement in the exam grade is expected, but the marginal cost is high, meaning that a big sacrifice is needed. Studying until MC > MB is inefficient because it means giving up high-value activities just to bump an exam grade a tiny bit.

In later chapters, the concept of efficient behavior based on marginal benefit and marginal cost analysis will be given more attention.

Economic Systems

An **economic system** is comprised of the laws, traditions, institutions, and mechanisms that are designed to answer the basic **economic questions** of *what outputs to produce, how to produce the outputs, and who gets to consume the outputs*? Throughout history, societies have developed different ways to answer the economic questions based on tradition or centralized rule (government). An economic system based on free markets is a relatively recent innovation.

Writing his *Inquiry into the Nature and Causes of the Wealth of Nations* in 1776, Adam Smith proposed that a **free market economy** is capable of achieving an efficient allocation of resources without the need for government intervention. Smith wanted to replace the very visible hand of government officials with an **invisible hand** that would guide resources to their best use and generate the best living standards possible given available resources and technology. He argued that a system in which transactions are voluntary, resources are privately owned, and markets are competitive would be more likely to generate an efficient outcome than would a system controlled by government or central planners.

Many of Adam Smith's arguments were directed at **Mercantilists**, who advocated government policies that limited imports and restricted trade. The purpose of the protectionist policies advocated by Mercantilists was to accumulate gold, which they used to judge the wealth of a nation. By contrast, Smith argued that the wealth of a nation could best be judged by the living standards of its citizens, which depended on the outputs produced and available for consumption.

Capitalism is an economic system in which resources are privately owned and decisions about how to use those resources are made by individuals and firms. In a Capitalist, or **free market**, economy, there is **private property** and **decentralized decision-making**. Those who own resources make decisions in pursuit of their own self-interest, such as the pursuit of profit, because as resource owners, they get to keep the proceeds from the sale or use of their resources.

A market system is based on voluntary exchange and incentives to exchange. The existence of **incentives** means that people are motivated through self-interest to make efficient choices and to put resources to their highest-valued use, resulting in an efficient allocation of scarce resources.

In a **command**, or **socialist** economy, government owns or controls most resources and uses central planning to decide how to allocate resources. Rather than relying on incentives, central planners direct resources to certain lines of production and decide who gets the output. In theory, government planners use society's resources to produce the goods and services that members of society want and need most, but it has proven difficult in practice for central planners to anticipate what individuals will most want and need.

Many of the specific objectives of a socialist or communist economy were outlined in *The Communist Manifesto*, written by Karl Marx and Freidrich Engels and published in 1848. Marx believed that a government-controlled or socialist economy would be necessary initially, but that eventually "the state would wither away," leading to a communist system in which each person contributes according to ability and takes according to need. In reality, the transition to Communism has not occurred because countries like China have continued to operate with very strict government controls. Marx envisioned an economy that would operate like a commune, with no real need for authority because individuals choose to do what is best for the society, but socialist countries have proven too large and complex to operate without central planning.

The diagram shows economic systems along a spectrum. At one extreme is a free market, or capitalist, economy, with limited government, which is also called **laissez-faire** (meaning "allow to do" in French). The opposite end of the spectrum, a command economy, involves the highest degree of government control.

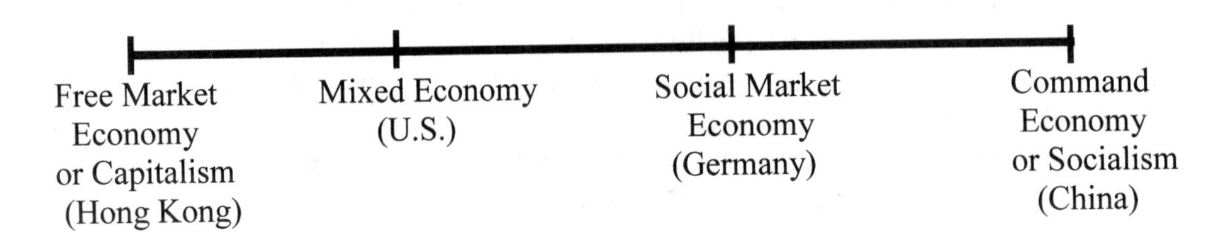

The U.S. has an economic system that is commonly referred to as a **mixed economy** because, although markets play a dominant role and most resources are privately owned, the government goes beyond what Adam Smith envisioned. A minimal amount of government involvement encompasses a legal system (to protect property, enforce contracts, and prosecute criminal activity), infrastructure (roads and bridges), and national defense. In a mixed economy like the U.S., government goes further and provides public education, enacts environmental regulations, provides social insurance, and offers assistance to families in poverty. A **social market** economy, such as Germany, is also a mixed economy like the U.S., but goes further by providing universal health care and tuition-free college.

The Circular Flow Model

The **circular flow model**, which was developed in the mid-eighteenth century in France, was one of the first models designed to explain economic relationships. In the simplest version of the model, the economy consists of two sectors (business and household) and two markets (product and resource).

Households demand goods and services, like food and medical care, in **product markets**. Households also supply labor services and other inputs, such as the drilling rights to land they own, in **resources markets**. Firms supply goods and services in the **product market** and demand inputs in **resource markets**.

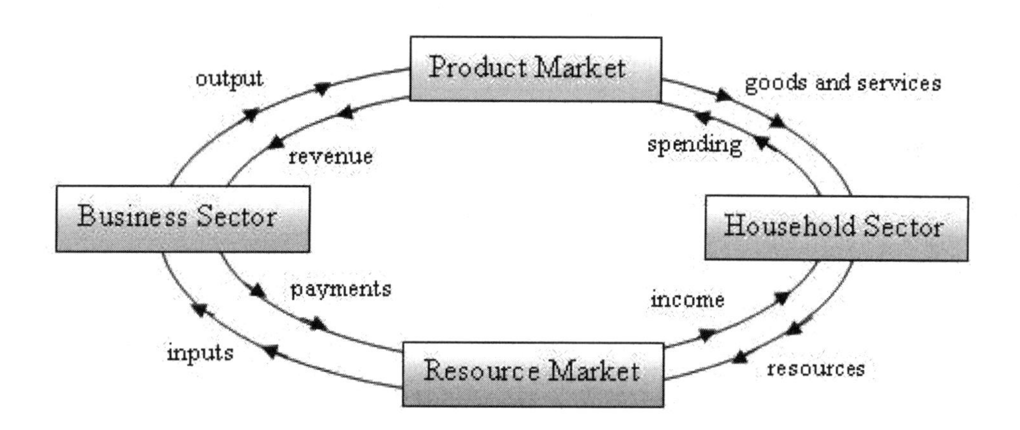

The circular flow model illustrates that households exchange resources for income in the resource market, and then spend income on goods and services in the product market. Business firms make payments for the use of inputs in the resource market and use those inputs to produce output, which is sold in the product market.

The outer circle represents a **real** flow, which is the flow of goods and services as well as the flow of resources. The inner circle a represents a **monetary** flow, which is the flow of money spent by households to purchase the output produced by firms as well as the flow of money spent by firms to pay for the resources owned by households, thus generating income for households.

The simplest version of the circular flow model implicitly assumes that households spend all their income. In reality, households **save** part of their income, and these savings flow into the financial market. In financial markets, those who have saved money are the suppliers of loanable funds, while those who wish to borrow money are the demanders of loanable funds.

The circular flow model can be extended to include a financial market that connects the decisions of savers (or lenders) and borrowers. The model can also be extended to include the public sector, or government, as well as the foreign sector. Some textbooks show a diagram with all of these additions, but it does get very complicated, so this section will only mention the other extensions without modifying the diagram beyond the basic two-sector, two-market version.

Government levies many kinds of taxes, on both households and business firms, and uses tax revenues to pay for national defense, roads and highways, education, police and fire protection, and many other goods and services. In the U.S., nearly 20 percent of the labor force is employed by the public sector and over one-third of total output in the U.S. is purchased by the government (local, state, and federal).

Finally, the circular flow model can be extended by adding the foreign sector. Some of the goods and services produced in an economy are **exported**, or sold in other countries, and some of the goods and services purchased by an economy are **imported**, or purchased from other countries. A country experiences a **trade surplus** when the value of exports exceeds the value of imports; a **trade deficit** when the value of imports exceeds the value of exports; and a **trade balance** when the value of exports equals the value of imports.

NAME Drew Doller SECTION#____________

PRINT LAST NAME, FIRST NAME

ECONOMIC CONCEPTS

1. Macroeconomics focuses on:
   a. concepts, while microeconomics focuses on math and graphs
   b. the decisions and behaviors of individual households, firms, and markets.
   c. the measurement and analysis of the economy as a whole.
   d. politics, while microeconomics focuses on business.

C

2. Microeconomics focuses on:
   a. math and graphs, while macroeconomics focuses on concepts.
   b. the decisions and behaviors of individual households, firms, and markets.
   c. the measurement and analysis of the economy as a whole.
   d. business, while macroeconomics focuses on politics.

B

3. Economics is ***best*** defined as a social science that studies how:
   a. societies allocate scarce resources to satisfy the most important needs of each individual.
   b. governments allocate scarce resources to satisfy the most important needs of each individual.
   c. societies allocate scarce resources to satisfy virtually unlimited wants and needs.
   d. governments allocate scarce resources to satisfy virtually unlimited wants and needs.

C

4. "Two large business firms that control a market should not be allowed to merge together" is an example of a:
   a. normative microeconomic statement.
   b. positive microeconomic statement.
   c. normative macroeconomic statement.
   d. positive macroeconomic statement.

C

5. Economic models are:
   a. simplifications of reality that describe or predict real world behaviors and outcomes.
   b. useful in macroeconomics but not in microeconomics because all individuals are not the same.
   c. based primarily on anecdotal evidence and built using normative economic tools.
   d. helpful in understanding how a market system works but of little use when explaining the behavior of households and firms.

A

6. The *ceteris paribus* assumption is used to:
   a. quantify economic relationships by assuming constant values for the variables under consideration.
   b. isolate the relationship between two variables by holding other influences on the relationship constant.
   c. explain the difference between an economic theory and an economic model.
   d. separate normative economics from positive economics.

B

NAME____SECTION#______________

PRINT LAST NAME, FIRST NAME

7. Assuming that everyone in the country is better off when a bridge is built in Alaska to serve a small community is an example of the:
   a. fallacy of composition.
   b. fallacy of division.
   c. fallacy of false cause.
   d. fallacy of ceteris paribus.

8. A sick person is more likely to make others sick in winter when everyone spends more time indoors. Concluding that sickness is the result of cold weather is an example of the:
   a. fallacy of composition.
   b. fallacy of division.
   c. fallacy of false cause.
   d. fallacy of ceteris paribus.

9 Assuming that a policy designed to reduce the national rate of unemployment is going to benefit a specific individual living in Michigan is an example of the:
   a. fallacy of composition.
   b. fallacy of division.
   c. fallacy of false cause.
   d. fallacy of ceteris paribus.

10. Scarcity exists because:
   a. society's ability to produce goods and services exceeds its wants and needs.
   b. society's wants and needs exceed its ability to produce goods and services.
   c. there are too many different kinds of goods and services that can be produced.
   d. few people can tell the difference between wants and needs.

NAME____SECTION#______________

PRINT LAST NAME, FIRST NAME

ECONOMIC TERMS

Write "Micro" in the blanks to the left of microeconomic topics and "Macro" in the blanks to the left of macroeconomic topics.

________ 1. The effect of a tax cut on national spending, output, and employment

________ 2. The reasons explaining an increase in the cost of college tuition

________ 3. The impact of an increase in the hourly wage paid to workers on the hiring decisions of a local business

Write the letter "P" in the blanks to the left of **positive** statements and the letter "N" in the blanks to the left of **normative** statements.

_________ 4. An increase in the demand for gasoline is expected to cause an increase in the price of gasoline, ceteris paribus.

_________ 5. Government should lower the tax on gasoline to reduce transportation costs for low-income workers.

_________ 6. An increase in the number of gas stations will most likely put downward pressure on the price of gasoline.

_________ 7. Government should raise the tax on gasoline to discourage people from driving so much.

Write the letters "PHoc" next to examples illustrating the post hoc fallacy, the letters "Comp" next to examples illustrating the fallacy of composition, and the letters "Div" next to examples illustrating the fallacy of division.

________ 8. Alexandra owns a business that was facing tough competition from foreign suppliers. When trade restrictions were enacted, she was able to charge a higher price and earn more profit. Alexandra concludes that trade restrictions must be good for the economy as a whole because she is better off as a result when trade restrictions were enacted.

________ 9. The economic model of international trade shows that free trade between nations can improve average living standards in a nation as a whole. After analyzing this model, Ali concludes that each individual member of society will be better off when trade restrictions are eliminated and free trade occurs.

________10. John has observed that his stock portfolio performs best in those years when his favorite football team makes the playoffs. Therefore, he purchases more stock when his team is winning and sells off his stock when his team is losing.

NAME____SECTION#________________
PRINT LAST NAME, FIRST NAME

THE CIRCULAR FLOW MODEL

Fill in the missing information:

The household sector includes consumers and workers (labor), as well as owners of other factors of production. The business sector includes many different organizations, from grocery stores to steel mills.

1. Consumers purchase goods and services in the ____________________ market.

2. Workers obtain employment in the ____________________ market.

3. Firms employ workers in the ____________________ market.

4. Firms earn revenue by selling output in the ____________________ market.

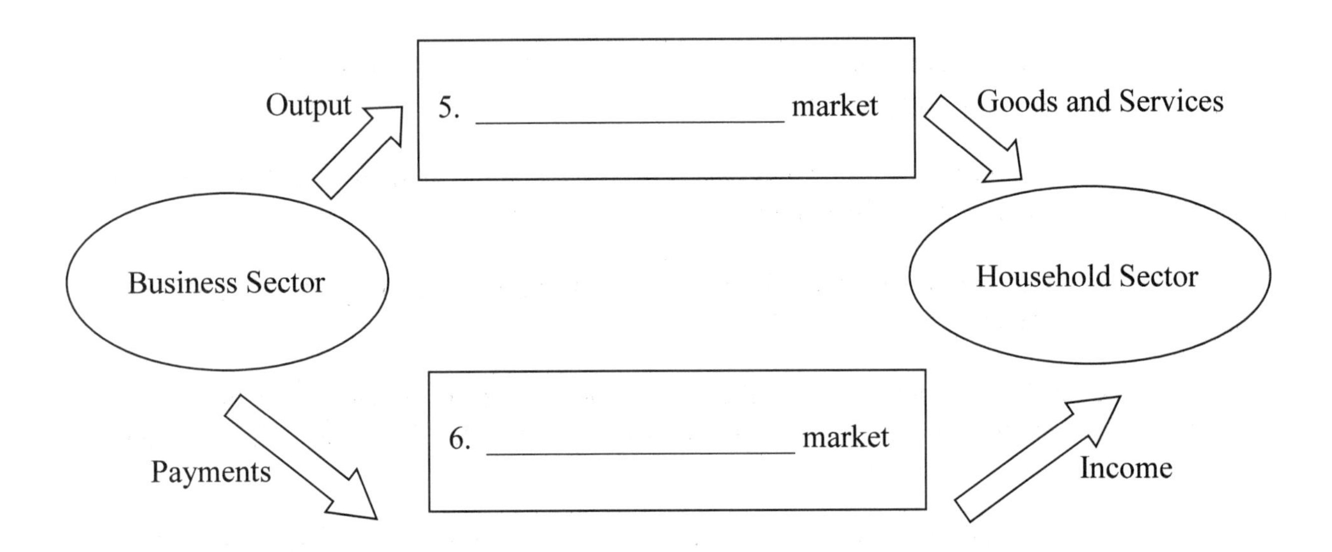

The diagram above shows that business firms produce output, which becomes the goods and services purchased by households.

7. The sale of output generates ____________________ for business firms.

8. The difference between total revenue and total cost is called ____________________.

The diagram above shows that business firms make payments to households, giving households income.

9. The part of income used to purchase goods and services is called ____________________.

10. The income that remains after consumers purchase output is called ____________________.

NAME____SECTION#______________

PRINT LAST NAME, FIRST NAME

ECONOMIC CONCEPTS

1. Beth quit her job as a computer programmer for a large corporation to begin her own computer repair business. To do this, she took $10,000 out of her retirement fund and hired her brother, Will, on an hourly basis. As a factor of production, Beth is best classified as _______________, and Will is best classified as _______________.
   a. an entrepreneur; labor
   b. labor; an entrepreneur
   c. capital; labor
   d. an entrepreneur; capital

2. Which of the following is ***not*** an example of the factor of production called capital?
   a. Computers used in a local bank
   b. Cash registers at a restaurant
   c. An office building
   d. Deposits in a corporate bank account

3. Land, as a resource category, includes all of the following ***except***:
   a. timber and minerals
   b. the climate
   c. entrepreneurial innovation
   d. solar energy

4. If Jakob decides to go see the new *Avengers* movie, his opportunity cost includes:
   a. only the amount of money spent at the movies.
   b. only the value of his time.
   c. both the amount of money spent at the movies and the value of his time.
   d. neither the amount of money spent at the movies nor the value of his time.

5. Emma graduated from college and is currently engaged in a job search. She believes that the marginal benefit of additional search is falling, while the marginal cost is rising. Efficiency requires that Emma continue her search as long as:
   a. marginal benefit is positive.
   b. marginal benefit exceeds marginal cost.
   c. marginal cost is positive.
   d. marginal cost exceeds marginal benefit.

6. A command economy is characterized by:
   a. a system of private property.
   b. central planning to direct resources.
   c. decentralized decision-making.
   d. all of the above.

7. A free market economy is characterized by:
   a. government ownership of property.
   b. centralized decision-making.
   c. economic incentives such as the profit motive.
   d. all of the above.

NAME____SECTION#________________
PRINT LAST NAME, FIRST NAME

8. In the circular flow model, the household sector _____ goods and services in _____ markets.
   a. demands; product
   b. supplies; product
   c. demands; resource
   d. supplies; resource

9. In the circular flow model, the business sector _____ the factors of production (inputs) in _____ markets.
   a. demands; product
   b. supplies; product
   c. demands; resource
   d. supplies; resource

10. In the circular flow model, firms in the business sector _____ goods and services in product markets and _____ inputs in resource markets.
   a. demand; demand
   b. supply; supply
   c. demand; supply
   d. supply; demand

Appendix: Math and Graphs

Economics relies on mathematical analysis, but introductory courses only require students to apply their knowledge of arithmetic, fractions and percentages, basic algebra, graphing functions, and some geometry. Graphs are frequently used in economics to illustrate and analyze relationships between variables.

Most of the mathematical calculations required for this course involve only addition, subtraction, multiplication, or division of dollar amounts (prices, costs, etc.) and unit amounts (quantities). Students are often encouraged to use a non-programmable calculator to perform calculations. It may be necessary to memorize formulas for some of the relationships. For example, to calculate average total cost, it may be necessary to memorize that average total cost is equal to total cost divided by the quantity produced. If a firm pays a total of \$200 in costs to produce 50 units of output, then average total cost is equal to \$200/50, or \$4, at this output level. Some students regard these relationships or formulas as basic common sense, but it depends on the student's background and experience. If you encounter assignment questions involving numbers and have difficulty knowing what to do, an equation sheet or set of note cards might be helpful.

Sometimes, it is necessary to use basic algebra to solve for an unknown. As an example, suppose the information that average total cost (ATC) is equal to \$4 when output (Q) is 50 units is provided, but you are asked to calculate total cost (TC) at this level of output. Knowing the relationship between total cost and average total cost presented in the previous paragraph, a student could then write the formula and algebraically solve for the unknown, as shown below.

$$ATC = \frac{TC}{Q} \quad \text{so} \quad \$4 = \frac{TC}{50}$$

Rewriting the formula to solve for TC reveals that (\$4)(50) = TC = \$200.

Some professors administer math pre-tests to determine if students are prepared for advanced courses. One such pre-test includes this algebra section (note that you will not be expected to solve these equations in this introductory class, but will be expected to have mastered this skill, along with many others, if you take advanced economics):

Solve each equation

1. $8x - 2 = -9 + 7x$

2. $-8 = -(x+4)$

3. $-18 - 6k = 6(1+3k)$

4. $-(1 + 7x) - 6(-7 - x) = 36$

5. $5n + 34 = -2(1-7n)$

Graphs

Basic economic analysis focuses on the relationship between two variables, and the relationship can be graphed on a Cartesian plane. A Cartesian plane is divided into four quadrants; most graphs in economics use only the first quadrant (quadrant I) because negative values of many economic variables do not make sense. In quadrant I, both variables are greater than zero. When two variables are functionally related, one of them is dependent upon the other. The **independent variable**, usually denoted X and plotted on the horizontal axis, has a value that can change freely. The value of the **dependent variable**, usually denoted Y and plotted on the vertical axis, changes in response to a change in the independent variable. Since the value of the dependent variable depends on the value of the independent variable, a function is often written as Y = f(X) or variable Y is a function of variable X. As an example, TC = f(Q) indicates that a firm's total cost is a function of the quantity of output produced by the firm.

A **direct**, or **positive**, relationship exists when a change in the independent variable causes the dependent variable to change in the *same* direction. This means that an increase in the value of X leads to an increase in the value of Y and a decrease in the value of X leads to a decrease in the value of Y, assuming X is the independent variable and Y is the dependent variable. The differing values for the independent variable and corresponding values for the dependent variable can be expressed as a point on a two-dimensional graph. Each point has two coordinates – the X (horizontal) coordinate, and the Y (vertical) coordinate – which are given parenthetically as (X,Y). Direct relationships are graphed as curves (or straight lines) that slope upward to the right.

The graph of the line between the two points (2,1) and (5,4) is shown in quadrant I of the Cartesian plane below. The upward-sloping line represents a positive (direct) relationship between the variables X and Y.

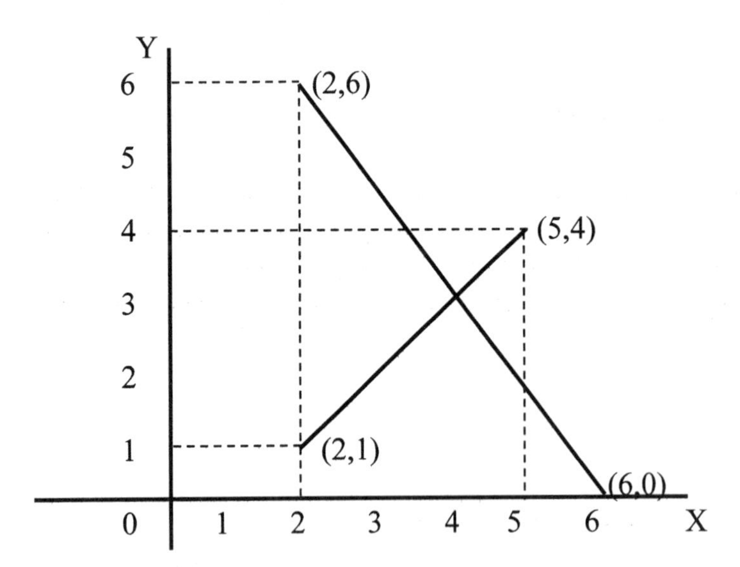

An **inverse**, or **negative**, relationship exists when a change in the independent variable causes the dependent variable to change in the *opposite* direction. This means that an increase in the value of X leads to a decrease in the value of Y and a decrease in the value of X leads to an increase in the value of Y, assuming X is the independent variable and Y is the dependent variable. Inverse relationships are graphed as curves (or straight lines) that slope downward to the right. The line between the two points (2,6) and (6,0) is graphed on the Cartesian plane on the previous page. This downward-sloping line represents a negative (inverse) relationship between the variables X and Y.

The direction of the line between any two points indicates the type of relationship that exists between the two variables. If a direct relationship exists, then the curve or line will slope upward to the right. Frequently, this relationship needs to be quantified. In other words, by how much will the dependent variable increase as a result of the increase in the independent variable? The **slope** of the line between the two points provides this information. Slope measures the change in the variable on the vertical axis in response to a one unit change in the variable on the horizontal axis. Slope can be expressed as:

$$\text{slope} = \frac{\text{vertical change}}{\text{horizontal change}} = \frac{\text{rise}}{\text{run}} = \frac{\Delta Y}{\Delta X} = \frac{Y_2 - Y_1}{X_2 - X_1}$$

Slope is constant along a straight line but varies from point to point along a curve. The slope of a horizontal line is zero while the slope of a vertical line is undefined, or infinity. The graph below shows a direct relationship between the quantity of ice cream cones sold and the total revenue received by the ice cream parlor. In this instance, the quantity of ice cream cones sold is the independent variable and total revenue is the dependent variable. Total revenue is found by multiplying the number of ice cream cones sold by the price of each cone.

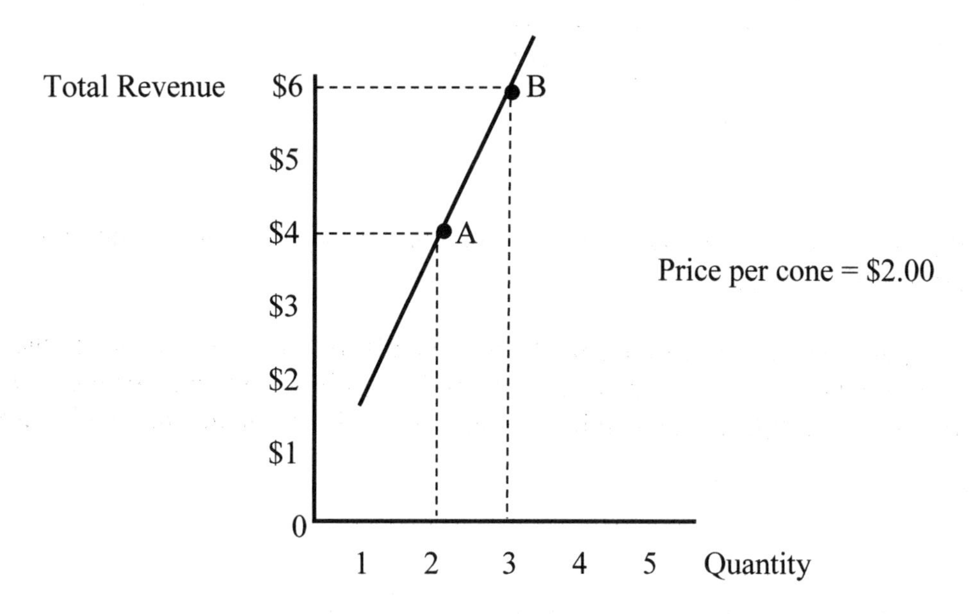

The slope of this line is found by dividing the vertical change by the horizontal change between any two points on the line. The coordinates for point A are (2, 4) and the coordinates for point B are (3, 6). Using the formula above, slope = $(Y_2 - Y_1)/(X_2 - X_1) = (6\text{-}4)/(3\text{-}2) = 2$. The slope of this line is positive 2. This means that for every 1 unit increase in the quantity of ice cream cones sold, total revenue will increase by $2.

Geometry

The math pre-test previously mentioned also includes a section on basic geometry, primarily the area of a triangle. Questions from the pre-test include:

1. Find the area of an acute triangle with a base of 15 inches and a height of 4 inches.

2. Find the area of a right triangle with a base of 6 centimeters and a height of 9 centimeters.

3. The area of a triangular-shaped mat is 18 square feet and the base is 3 feet. Find the height.

There are several applications where the ability to calculate the area of a square, rectangle, or triangle will be very important, even at the introductory level. As an example, find the area of a right triangle with a height equal to 8 feet and a base equal to 10 feet. The diagram below helps visualize the problem.

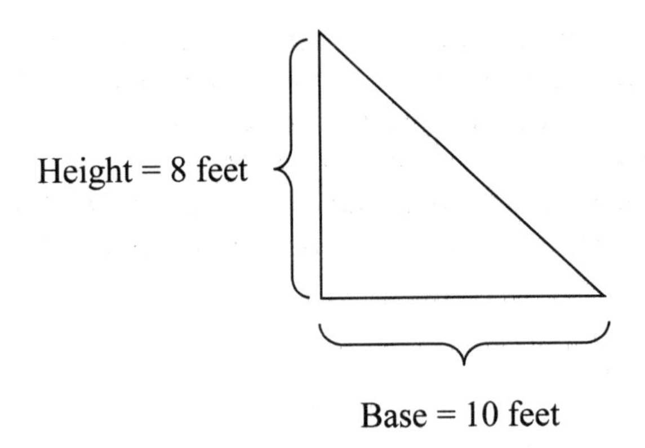

The formula for the area of a triangle is ½(base)(height), so for this example the solution is area = ½(10 feet)(8 feet) = 40 square feet.

The graphs on the next page illustrate a number of calculations and corresponds to the kind of problems that will be encountered in chapters 6 and 7 as well as some later chapters. It might be helpful to review this appendix again before working on the problems that require these calculations.

Practice calculating the shaded areas and check your work using the answers provided.

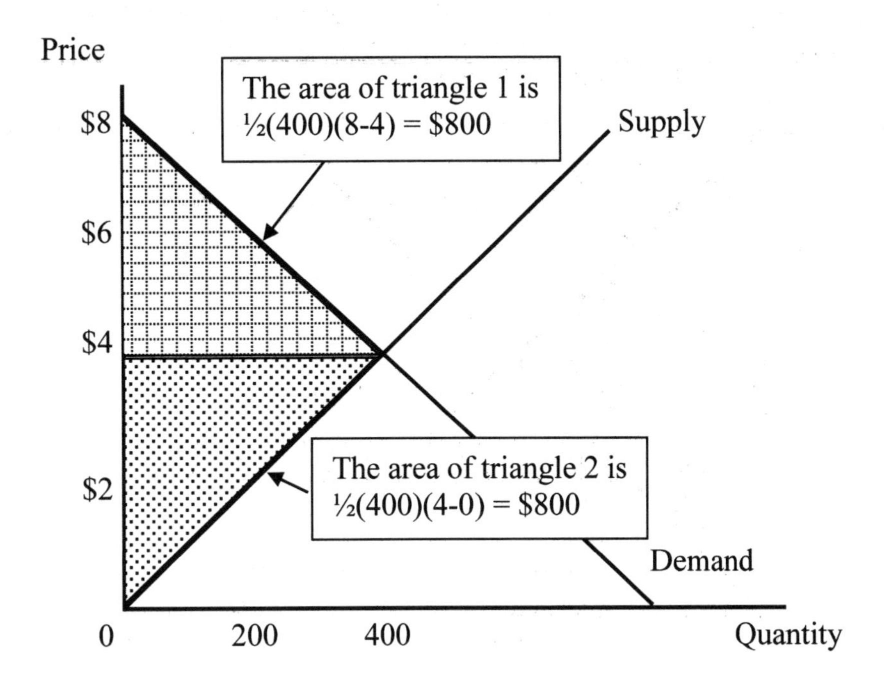

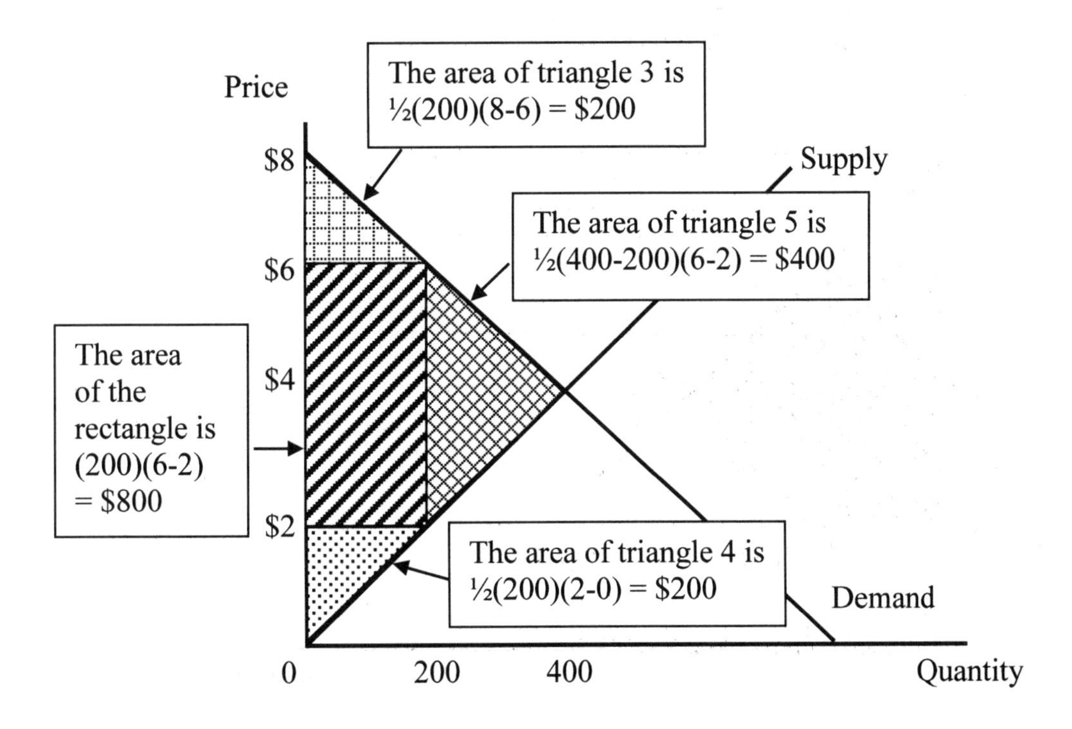

Similar diagrams are provided on the next page with the answers left out so you can practice.

Fill in the values for each of the shaded areas identified below.

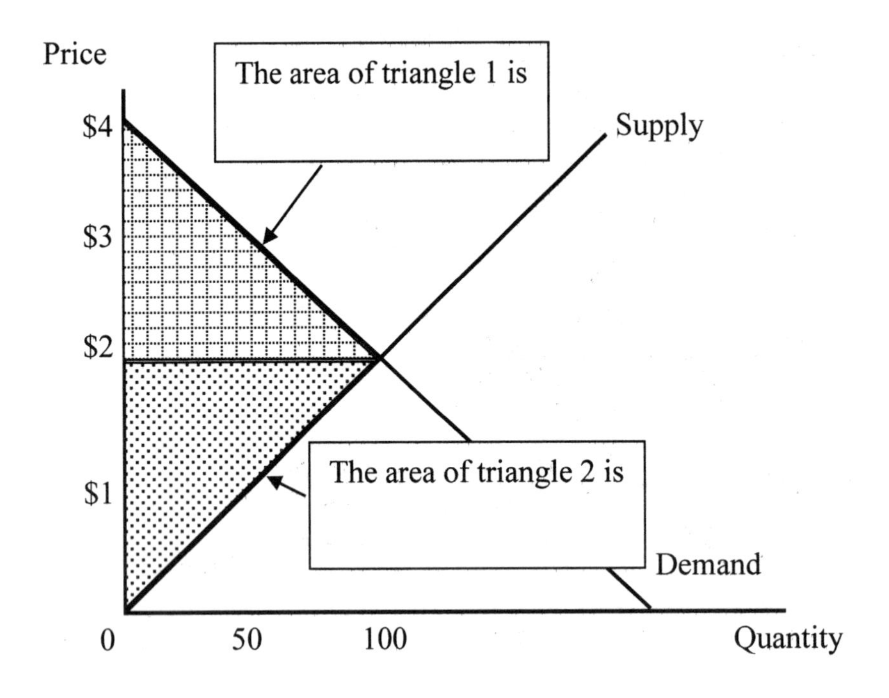

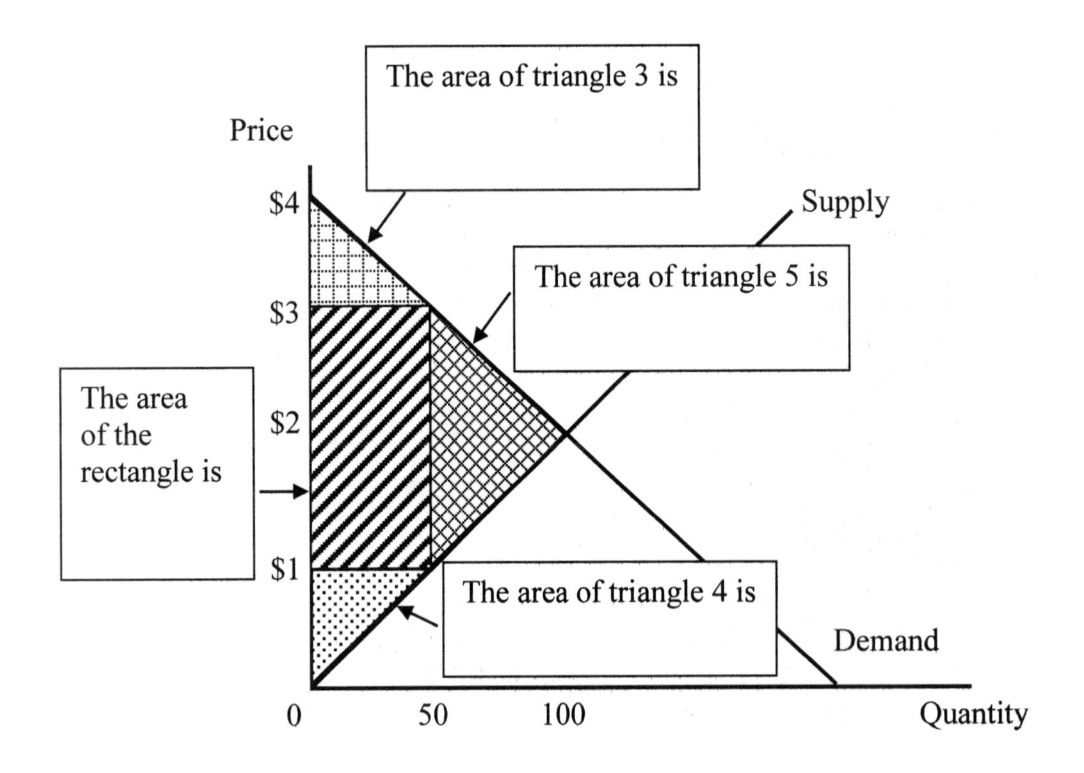

NAME____SECTION#______________
PRINT LAST NAME, FIRST NAME

MATH AND GRAPHS

Use the information in the table below to answer questions 1 through 3.

Labor	Quantity of Output
0	0
1	25
2	55
3	75

1. The chart shows that the relationship between the number of workers hired (labor) and the amount of output produced (quantity of output) is:
   a. direct
   b. inverse
   c. impossible to determine
   d. both direct and inverse

2. Output per worker is equal to _____ when three workers are hired.
   a. 0. b. 25. c. 55. d. 75.

3. When the second worker is hired, output increases by _____ units.
   a. 0. b. 25. c. 30. d. 55.

Use the graph depicting the number of candy bars purchased on the Y axis and the number of sodas purchased on the X axis to answer questions 4 and 5

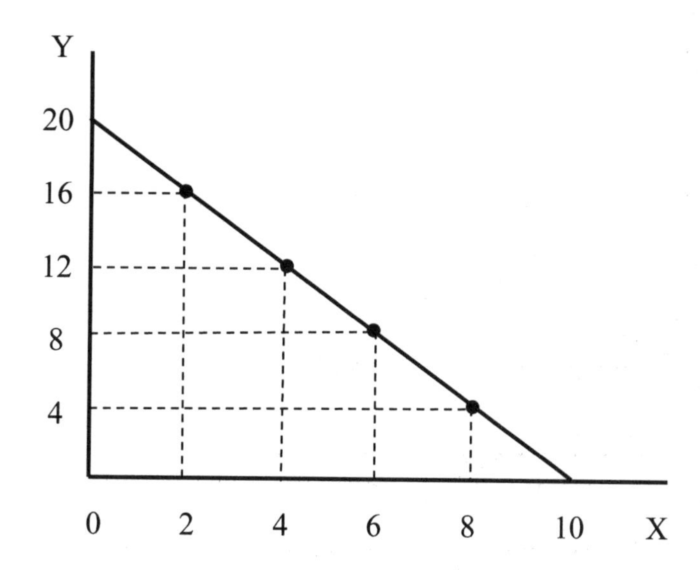

4. The slope of the function graphed is equal to:
   a. ½. b. 2. c. -½. d. -2.

5. If the price of a candy bar is $1 and the price of a soda is $2, a consumer with $20 to spend could afford to purchase _____ candy bars and _____ sodas.
   a. 20; 10
   b. 12; 4
   c. 12; 12
   d. 4; 10

NAME______________________________ SECTION#______________

PRINT LAST NAME, FIRST NAME

6. A downward-sloping line illustrates:
   a. a direct (positive) relationship between two variables.
   b. an inverse (negative) relationship between two variables.
   c. that the two variables represented by the line are not related.
   d. a relationship that might be either direct (positive) or inverse (negative).

7. An upward-sloping line illustrates a(n) __________ relationship, indicating that as the value of one variable increases, the value of the other variable __________.
   a. direct (positive); increases
   b. direct (positive); decreases
   c. inverse (negative); increases
   d. inverse (negative); decreases

8. Research indicates that increasing aerobic exercise leads to better cardiovascular health, especially among middle-aged persons. This implies cardiovascular health is the __________ variable, and exercise and cardiovascular health are __________ related.
   a. independent; directly (positively)
   b. independent; inversely (negatively)
   c. dependent; directly (positively)
   d. dependent; inversely (negatively)

Use the graph below to answer questions 9 and 10

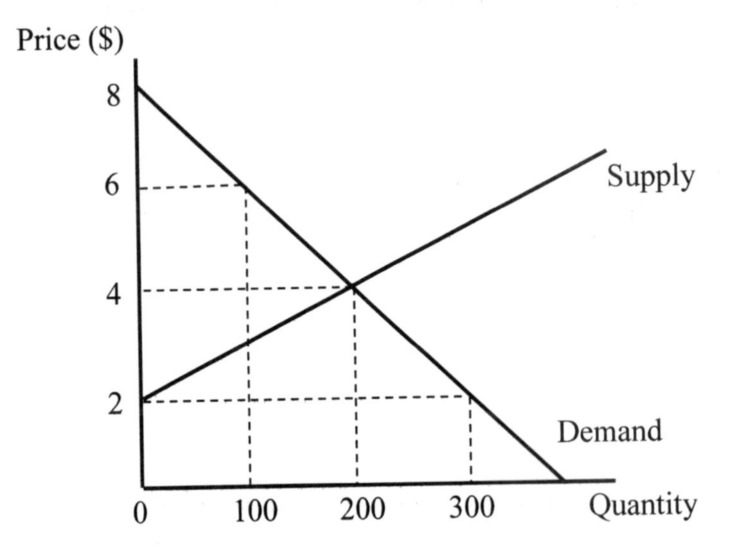

9. If price is $4, the area between the demand curve and price is equal to:
   a. 200 b. 400 c. 600 d. 800

10. If price is $4, the area between the supply curve and price is equal to:
   a. 200 b. 400 c. 600 d. 800

CHAPTER 2 The Production Possibilities Model

The production possibilities model illustrates the choices available to a society based on current production capabilities. The choices can be presented graphically if there are only two products, although it might seem unrealistic to assume only two products can be made.

Sometimes in economics (especially at the introductory level), it is useful to make simplifying assumptions, even knowing that they are not realistic. In the real world, there are too many different ways to use resources to count them all. To focus on making choices and identifying trade-offs, this model narrows down all the choices to only two. For most students, there are an unlimited number of future occupations to consider, but when it is time to do some research and make a decision, it makes sense to first narrow down the choices. Similarly, in looking at a society's production possibilities, narrow down the choices and analyze specific trade-offs, such as whether to devote more resources to building up the military or to improving the average person's living standards (the traditional "guns versus butter" example).

Scarcity forces all societies to make decisions about what to produce from available resources and technology. A **production possibilities frontier (PPF)** illustrates the possible combinations of two types of output that can be produced given available resources and technology. The specific assumptions needed to draw a PPF are:

1) available resources (labor, capital, etc.) are fixed,
2) production technology does not change,
3) available resources are fully employed, and
4) production is efficient.

Straight-Line PPF: Constant Opportunity Cost

Suppose an economy produces two outputs, jeans and denim skirts, and currently has 40 yards of fabric, 4 huge spools of thread, 2 sewing machines, 2 workers, and 1 week for production. The table below is a **production possibilities schedule** and shows some of the possible combinations of jeans and skirts.

Combination	Jeans	Skirts
A	0	40
B	5	30
C	10	20
D	15	10
E	20	0

If all resources are used to produce skirts, then output is 0 jeans and 40 skirts, which is combination A. If all resources are instead used to produce jeans, output is 20 jeans and 0 skirts, which is combination E. The schedule identifies other possibilities assuming resources are divided between jean production and skirt production (points B, C, and D). The combination of 20 jeans and 20 skirts, for example, cannot be produced given current resources and technology. The combination of 5 jeans and 5 skirts is possible, but would not use available resources fully.

The attainable combinations that fully use available resources can be plotted as points on a graph and connected to form a production possibilities frontier (PPF), as shown below. Points outside the PPF are currently unattainable, and points inside the PPF, such as point F, indicate unemployment or inefficiency. An economy producing at a point inside the PPF would need to either reduce unemployment or improve efficiency to move to a more desirable point on the PPF.

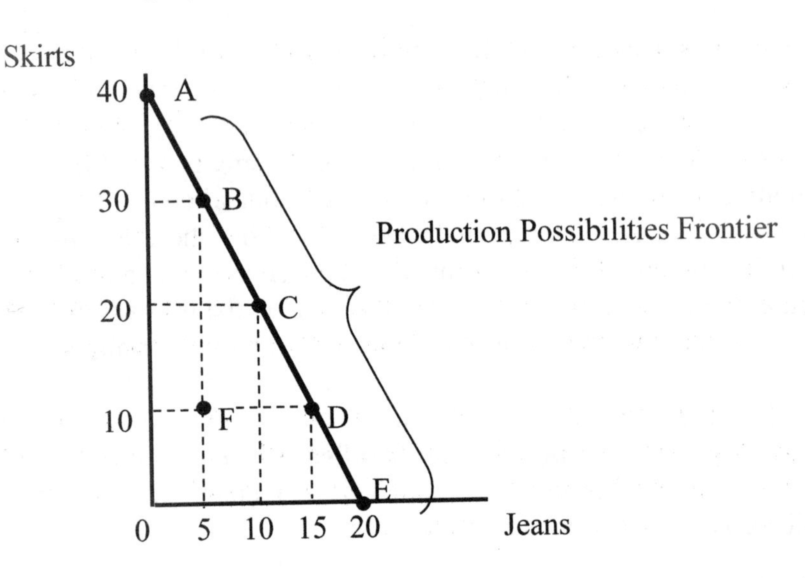

The above PPF is a straight line with a slope equal to -2, indicating that the **opportunity cost** of 1 pair of jeans is equal to 2 skirts. When the PPF is linear, opportunity cost is **constant**. This occurs because the resources used to produce jeans and skirts are equally well suited to producing both types of output.

Bowed-Outward PPF: Increasing Opportunity Cost

Increasing opportunity costs are encountered when resources are not well suited to all types of production. This means that continuing to increase the production of one output entails giving up increasingly larger amounts of the other output. When opportunity cost is increasing, the production possibilities frontier will bow outward and be concave to the origin.

Land is a resource that is usually not equally well suited to producing all outputs. Some land is not as good for growing crops but may be fine for grazing cows, for example. The table below shows different combinations of corn and cows that can be produced on a particular area of land, assuming some of the land is better for crops like corn.

Combination	Corn	Cows
A	14	0
B	12	1
C	9	2
D	5	3
E	0	4

If all available land is planted in corn, the economy can produce 14 units of corn but will have no cows, as represented by combination A. To graze one cow, land has to be taken away from corn production, which occurs when moving from combination A to combination B. Combination B is 1 cow and 12 units of corn; cows increased by 1 unit but corn decreased by 2 units, from 14 to 12, when moving from combination A to combination B. The **opportunity cost** of the first cow is 2 units of corn because that land will not be available for corn production if cows are put on it. The land least suited to corn production will be the first land given to the cows since the cows can graze on any land. Moving to combination C means devoting more land to cows and less to corn. The land given to the cows could have produced 3 units of corn (12 – 9), so the opportunity cost of the second cow is 3 units of corn.

Continuing to add cows means yet more land is taken away from the production of corn. The last unit of land given over to cow grazing is the best suited to corn production, so the opportunity cost of the fourth cow is 5 units of corn. Notice that the opportunity cost of continuing to increase the number of cows is increasing: the number of corn units that must be given up to gain 1 additional cow increases as we move from point A to point B to point C to point D to point E.

The production possibilities schedule on the previous page illustrates increasing opportunity cost; graphing this data will yield a PPF that is bowed outward, as shown below.

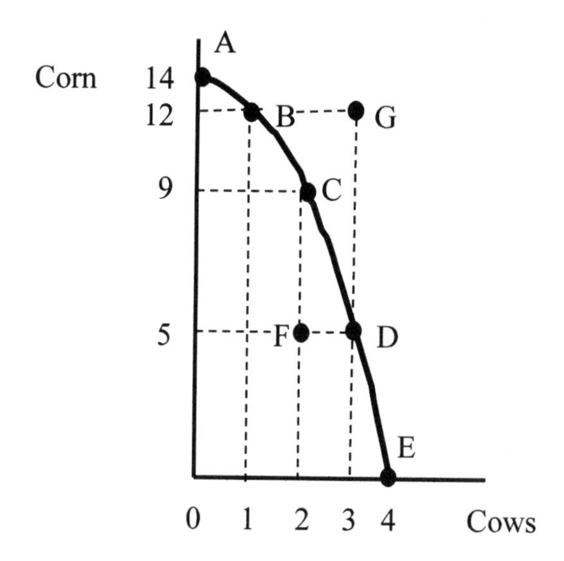

The combination of 5 units of corn and 2 cows (point F in the above graph) is a point inside the PPF; if any combination inside the PPF, such as point F, is produced, it means that some land is not being used (unemployment) or that land is not being efficiently allocated.

The combination of 12 units of corn and 3 cows (point G in the above graph) is a point outside the PPF, so it is currently unattainable because only so much can be produced assuming all of the available land is being efficiently used. Although points outside the PPF like point G are currently unattainable, conditions could change in the future. In a growing economy, more resources, more productive resources, or improved technology lead to an outward shift of the PPF, so point G could be attained after economic growth has occurred.

The Law of Increasing Opportunity Cost

The graph below illustrates different production possibilities assuming the two possible products are guns and butter. Each point on the PPF reflects the assumptions of the model (fixed resources and technology, full employment, and efficient production). If this society is currently producing at a point on its PPF (such as point B, point C, or point D), increasing the production of guns can be accomplished only by decreasing the production of butter. Because the PPF is bowed-outward, it reflects increasing opportunity cost.

Moving from point B to point C means giving up 2 units of butter to produce an additional gun, since butter production falls from 11 units to 9 units. Moving from point C to point D means giving up 4 units of butter to produce a fourth gun, since butter production falls from 9 units to 5 units. The opportunity cost of the fourth gun is higher than the opportunity cost of the third gun because resources are shifted from butter production to gun production in an efficient manner, with those most suitable for gun production being shifted first.

The opportunity cost of producing more guns increases as resources are shifted away from producing butter and society moves down along the PPF, reflecting the **law of increasing opportunity cost**. The same conclusion holds if resources are shifted in the opposite direction.

Starting at point D and moving to point C, the trade-off is a gain of 4 units of butter and a loss of 1 gun; therefore, the opportunity cost per unit of butter is one-fourth of a gun. Moving from point C to point B means giving up another gun, but gaining only 2 units of butter, so the opportunity cost per unit of butter is one-half of a gun on this segment. Since ½ is greater than ¼, the opportunity cost of producing more butter increases as society moves up along the PPF and gives up guns.

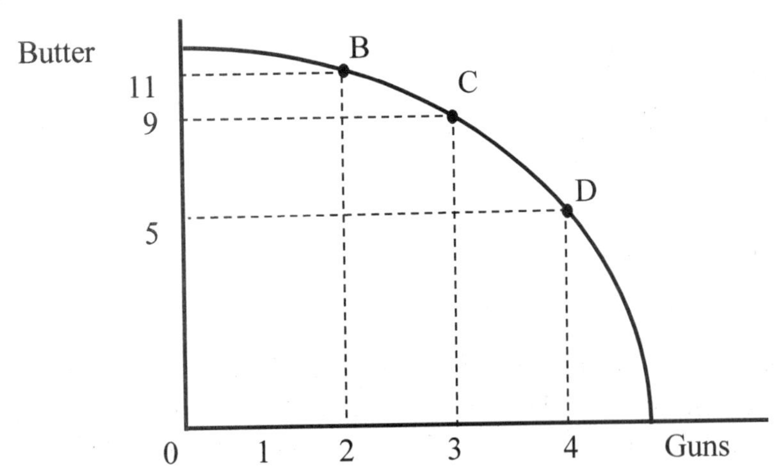

The **marginal rate of transformation** is the absolute value of the slope of the PPF and is a measure of the opportunity cost of producing one more unit of the product represented on the horizontal axis (guns in the above graph). Since the slope of a curved function is equal to the slope of a line drawn tangent to the function and since lines drawn tangent become steeper as society moves down and to the right along the PPF, the marginal rate of transformation is increasing when the PPF is bowed outward and is constant when the PPF is a straight line.

Economic Growth

When an economy is producing at a point on its production possibilities curve, the economy is using its resources fully and efficiently. Points A, B, C, and D in the graph below are all on the PPF and represent full employment and efficient use of resources.

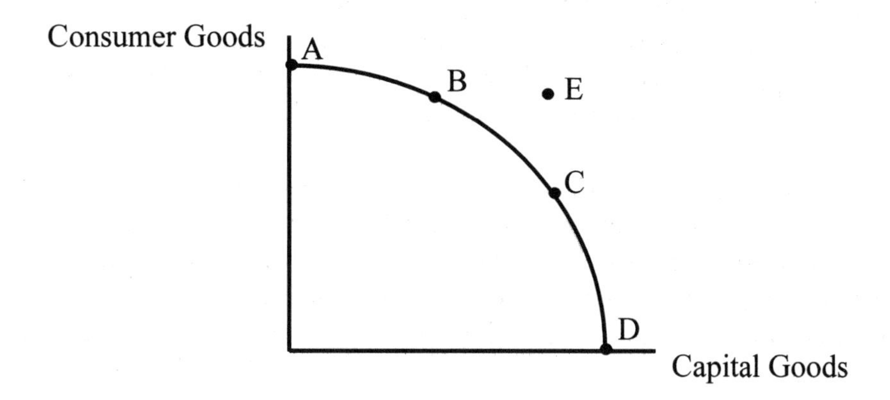

Point E lies outside the PPF and is therefore unattainable given current resources and technology. Although the model assumes fixed resources and technology when drawing a curve, this does not imply that resources and technology actually remain fixed as time passes. When there is a change in the quantity or quality (productivity) of resources or an improvement in technology, the PPF is likely to shift outward. The increase in output that is possible following an outward shift of the PPF is referred to as **economic growth** within the model.

If a society produces more capital goods (machines, tools, and equipment) by shifting resources away from consumer goods (food, clothing, and entertainment), there is a movement along the PPF, such as from point B to point C. This does not correspond to economic growth since the PPF did not shift. If a society is able to produce at point E following an increase in the labor force, an increase in the capital stock, or improved technology, economic growth has occurred and it is not necessary to give up consumer goods in order to produce more capital goods.

Since producing more capital goods can result in an increase in the capital stock (assuming depreciation of capital is not too high), and an increase in the capital stock is one of the factors that can contribute to growth, a society producing at a point like C is likely to experience stronger growth in the future than a society producing at point B.

Economic growth is a long-term process that permits increased production of goods and services and improved material standards of living. In the production possibilities model, economic growth requires an increase in the quantity of resources (land, labor, capital, and entrepreneurial ability), an increase in the productivity of those resources, an improvement in technology, or a combination of these changes.

An increase in a country's population leads to an increase in its labor force. The quality of workers can also improve over time, as investment in human capital (education and training) makes them more productive. When a country has more workers or has more productive workers, the country's ability to produce goods and services increases, ceteris paribus, resulting in an outward shift of the country's PPF and economic growth. Similarly, when firms invest in capital, there are more factories, machines, and tools with which to produce goods and services. An increase in the capital stock is another way a country can achieve economic growth. Finally, spending on research and development (R&D) promotes invention, resulting in improved technology. Technological improvements can result in economic growth by making workers more productive or by making it possible to produce and use more advanced machines and tools.

Whether caused by an increase in the quantity or quality of resources or an improvement in technology, economic growth shifts the production possibilities frontier outward. If the production possibilities frontier shifts outward from PPF_1 to PPF_2 in the graph below, the economy is able to produce more of both types of output. If the source of economic growth is an increase in the quantity of resources, then these additional resources are equally well-suited to the production of wheat or the production of automobiles, based on the type of shift.

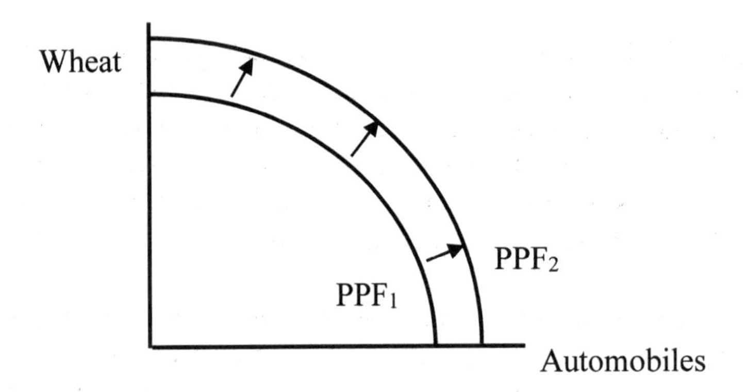

In other cases, growth may be industry-specific. The PPF may rotate outward from one of the axes, as shown by the shift from PPF_3 to PPF_4 in the graph below. The shift below implies that the economy added additional resources or technological know-how that are specific to the automobile industry. However, society could choose to take advantage of these new resources by freeing up resources to grow more wheat, as indicated by the move from point A to point B.

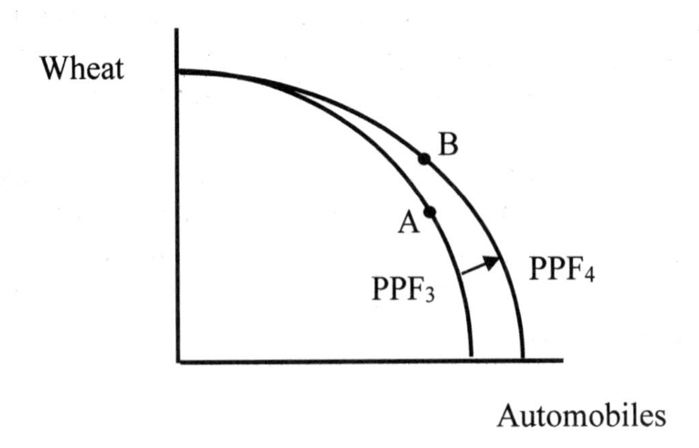

Optimal Production

Production possibilities frontiers identify the combinations of outputs an economy is able to produce; however, the model does **not** identify which combination is **best**, or **optimal**, for society. Additional information about consumer demand is needed to identify the optimal point on society's PPF.

For example, if a PPF is drawn showing different combinations of beef and vegetables a society can produce, but every member of society is a vegetarian, the optimal combination corresponds to the maximum possible production of vegetables, assuming the society is not able to trade beef for vegetables with another society.

If a society can engage in **international trade**, it is no longer constrained to consuming the same items it produces, so further analysis is needed. The production possibilities model is applied to the study of international trade in the next chapter.

Efficiency

Economists sometimes distinguish between **technical efficiency** and **economic efficiency** (also known as allocative efficiency). Technical efficiency is achieved when producers are making as much output as they can with available resources and technology, so each point on a PPF is technically efficient. Economic efficiency is achieved when society is producing the point on the PPF that is optimal or best, as described in the previous section. The production possibilities model does not reveal the optimal point, so additional tools of analysis are needed to identify economic efficiency.

Practice

The production possibilities schedule below gives some of the combinations of cars and computers that can be produced in a given time period, assuming full employment and efficient production. Graph the combinations in the grid below and label points A through F.

Combination	Cars	Computers
A	0	60
B	1	56
C	2	48
D	3	36
E	4	20
F	5	0

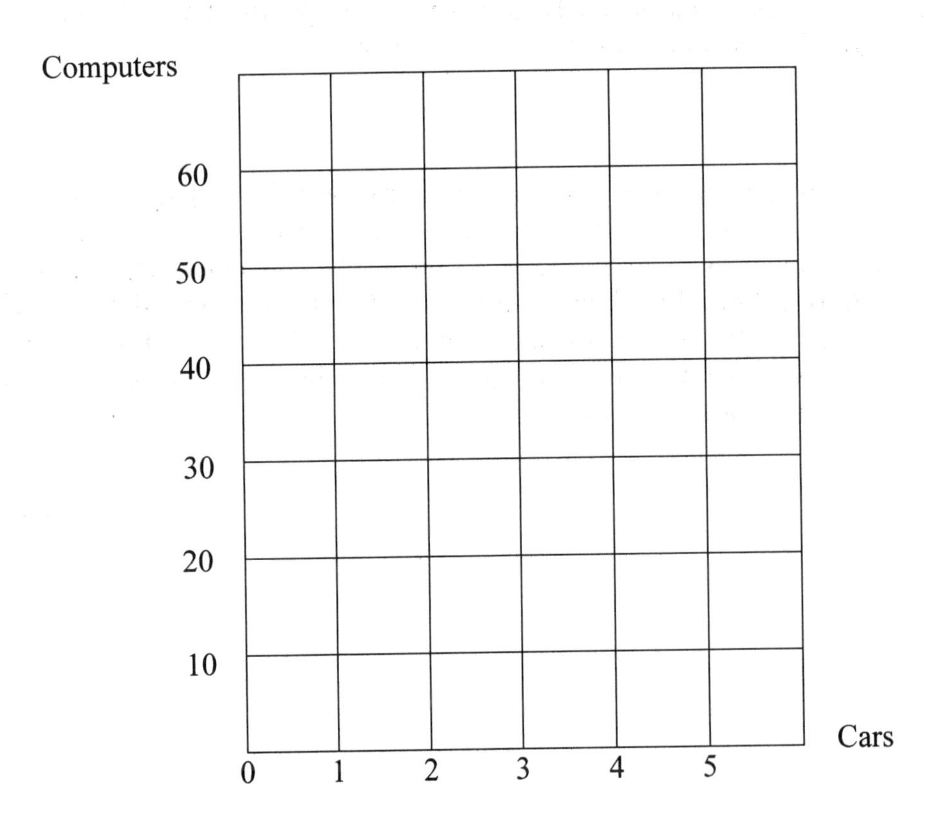

Questions

a) Does the opportunity cost of producing an additional car increase as more cars are produced?

b) If output is 3 cars and 30 computers, is this society efficiently and fully employing resources?

c) Is this society able to produce 4 cars and 30 computers with current resources and technology?

NAME____SECTION#_______________

PRINT LAST NAME, FIRST NAME

THE PRODUCTION POSSIBILITIES FRONTIER

The production possibilities schedule below gives some of the combinations of tanks and trucks that can be produced in a given time period, assuming full employment and efficient production. Mark the horizontal axis with the number of tanks, increasing by 1 each time, and the vertical axis with the number of trucks, increasing by 5 each time. Plot the combinations shown in the chart below and label points A through F.

Combination	Tanks	Trucks
A	0	30
B	1	28
C	2	25
D	3	20
E	4	12
F	5	0

Trucks

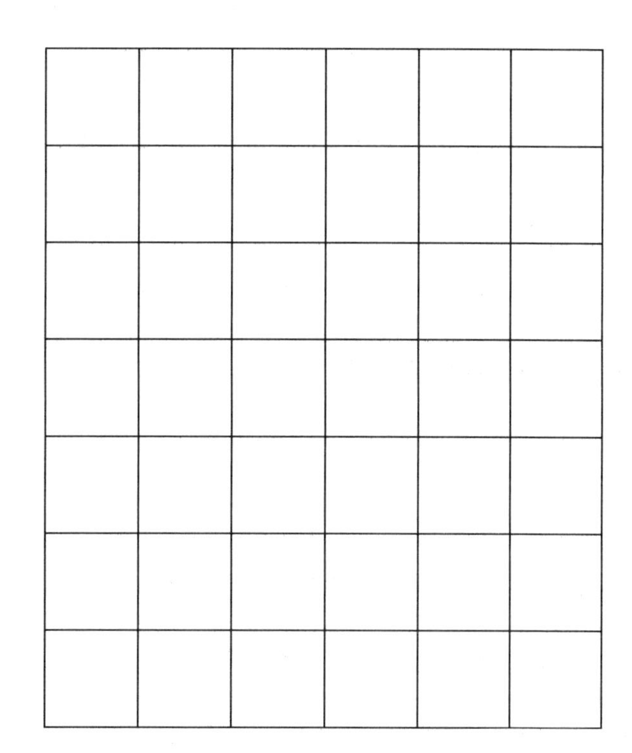

Tanks

Is this PPF a straight line or bowed outward? ______________________________

Fill in the opportunity costs, as measured in trucks:

When moving from point:	A to B	B to C	C to D	D to E	E to F
…the opportunity cost is:					

NAME____SECTION#______________

PRINT LAST NAME, FIRST NAME

THE PRODUCTION POSSIBILITIES FRONTIER

Use the graph below to fill in the blanks.

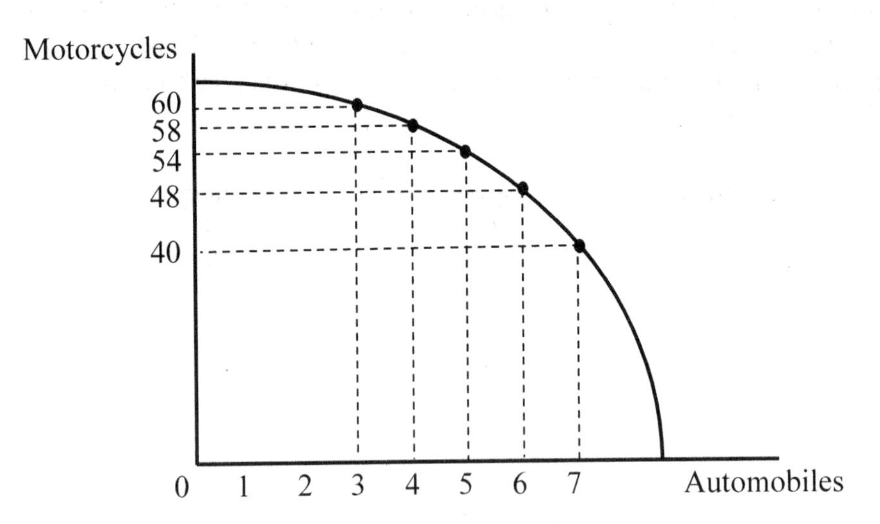

1. Assuming full employment and technical efficiency, if this society produces 60 motorcycles, it can produce ______________ automobiles. If automobile production is increased to 4, motorcycle production must be reduced to ______________.

2. The opportunity cost of the fourth automobile is ______________ motorcycles, while the opportunity cost of the fifth automobile is ______________ motorcycles.

3. The opportunity cost of the sixth automobile is ______________ motorcycles, while the opportunity cost of the seventh automobile is ______________ motorcycles.

4. The opportunity cost of producing more automobiles ______________ as more automobiles are produced, reflecting the law of ______________ opportunity costs.

5. A combination of 48 motorcycles and 5 automobiles reflects ____________________ or ____________________.

NAME Drew Dollar SECTION#____________
PRINT LAST NAME, FIRST NAME

PRODUCTION POSSIBILITIES MODEL

1. A production possibilities frontier for two outputs is drawn assuming that:
   a. opportunity cost is fixed, but the quantity and quality of resources changes.
   b. both outputs use the same quantity of each resource, but the technology differs.
   c. the amount of resources currently available for production is fixed.
   d. the technology available can only be applied to producing one of the outputs.

C

Use the graph below to answer questions 2 through 4.

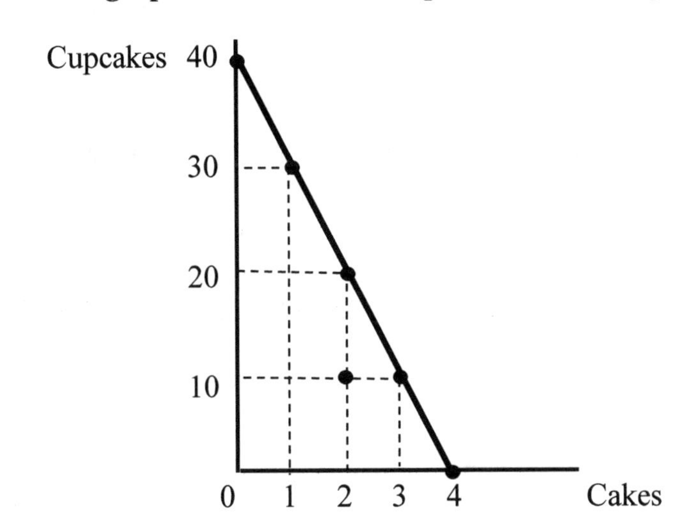

2. This production possibilities frontier is _______, illustrating ________ opportunity costs.
   a. linear; constant
   b. linear; increasing
   c. bowed outward; constant
   d. bowed outward; increasing

A

3. The opportunity cost of each additional cake:
   a. is constant and equal to 1 cupcake.
   b. is constant and equal to 10 cupcakes.
   c. is constant and equal to 40 cupcakes.
   d. increases as more cakes are produced.

B

4. If the combination of 10 cupcakes and 2 cakes is produced:
   a. available resources are fully employed.
   b. available resources are efficiently employed.
   c. cake production can be increased to 3 with no loss in cupcake production.
   d. cake production can be increased to 4 with no loss in cupcake production.

C

NAME____SECTION#_______________

PRINT LAST NAME, FIRST NAME

Use the production possibilities schedule below to answer questions 5 through 8.

Combination	School Buses	Army Tanks
A	14	0
B	12	1
C	9	2
D	_____	3
E	0	4

5. The opportunity cost of the first army tank is _____ school buses, and the opportunity cost of the second army tank is _____ school buses.
   a. 1; 2 b. 2; 3 c. 3; 4 d. 4; 5

6. If the opportunity cost of the third army tank is 4 school buses, how many school buses can be produced at combination D?
   a. 13 b. 9 c. 5 d. 0

7. If the opportunity cost of the third army tank is 4 school buses, the opportunity cost of the fourth army tank is:
   a. 2 school buses.
   b. 3 school buses.
   c. 4 school buses.
   d. 5 school buses.

8. Ceteris paribus, this economy can produce 4 army tanks if it produces:

   a. 14 school buses.
   b. 12 school buses
   c. 9 school buses.
   d. 0 school buses.

9. A point ***inside*** a production possibilities frontier represents:
   a. a combination that is currently unattainable.
   b. efficiency and full employment.
   c. inefficiency or unemployment.
   d. increasing opportunity cost.

10. A point ***outside*** a production possibilities frontier represents:
    a. a combination that is currently unattainable.
    b. efficiency and full employment.
    c. inefficiency or unemployment.
    d. increasing opportunity cost.

NAME____SECTION#______________
PRINT LAST NAME, FIRST NAME

PRODUCTION POSSIBILITIES

Use the graph below to answer questions 1 through 5.

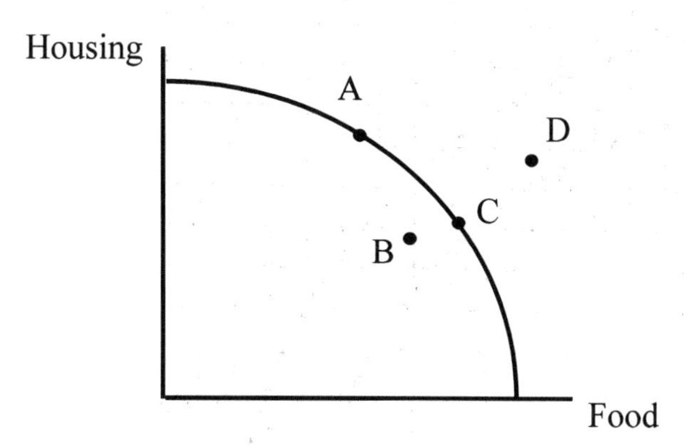

1. Which point corresponds to a combination of food and housing that is currently unattainable?
   a. A b. B c. C d. D

2. Which point illustrates inefficiency or unemployment?
   a. A b. B c. C d. D

3. Which points illustrate efficiency and full employment?
   a. A and B b. B and C c. A and C d. B and D

4. Shifting resources from food production to housing production could cause the economy to move from point _____ to point _____.
   a. A; C b. C; A c. B; C d. C; D

5. If the PPF is a straight line, opportunity cost __________ as resources are shifted from producing housing to food production; when the PPF is bowed outward, opportunity cost __________ as resources are shifted from producing housing to food production.
   a. remains constant; remains constant
   b. increases; increases
   c. remains constant; increases
   d. increases; remains constant

6. In the production possibilities model, economic growth is illustrated by:
   a. an inward shift of the production possibilities frontier.
   b. an outward shift of the production possibilities frontier.
   c. the straight-line shape of the production possibilities frontier.
   d. the bowed-outward shape of the production possibilities frontier.

NAME____SECTION#______________
PRINT LAST NAME, FIRST NAME

Use the graph below to answer questions 7 through 10.

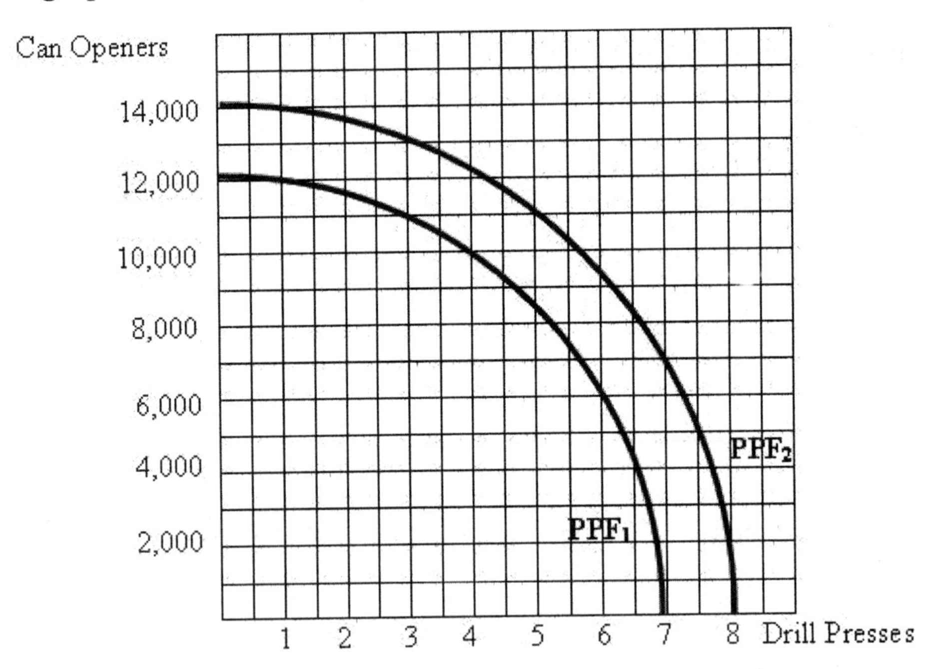

7. On PPF_1, all of the following output combinations are currently attainable ***except***:
   a. 12,000 can openers and 0 drill presses.
   b. 10,000 can openers and 6 drill presses.
   c. 4,000 can openers and 6 drill presses.
   d. 0 can openers and 7 drill presses.

8. On PPF_1, the opportunity cost of the 7th drill press is approximately ____ can openers.
   a. 2,000 b. 4,000 c. 6,000 d. 8,000

9. An increase from PPF_1 to PPF_2 makes it possible to produce approximately ____ additional can openers if 7 drill presses are produced.
   a. 2,000 b. 4,000 c. 5,000 d. 7,000

10. All of the following events would lead to a shift from PPF_1 to PPF_2 ***except***:
    a. Improved technology
    b. An increase in the size of the labor force
    c. A decrease in the capital stock caused by depreciation of machines and tools
    d. Greater investment in education leading to a more productive workforce

CHAPTER 3 International Trade

The debate surrounding international trade is constantly in the news, and people have different views about whether government should place restrictions on imports from other nations or pursue a free trade policy. The debate involves many different issues, but economic analysis focuses on the notion that world consumption can increase if each country specializes according to comparative advantage and engages in free trade.

The U.S. economy is inextricably linked to the rest of the world. This can easily be seen by the significance of both **imports** and **exports** in our economy. The United States currently exports more than ten percent of total domestic output and imports an even higher percentage. When exports exceed imports, a **trade surplus** exists. When imports exceed exports, a **trade deficit** exists. The balance of trade between the U.S. and our trading partners has been of concern in recent decades because of our persistently large trade *deficits*.

Countries can erect **trade barriers** to restrict international trade. Two common trade barriers are quotas and tariffs. A **quota** is a legal limit on the quantity of a product that can be imported from other countries. A **tariff** is a tax levied on imports. Both tend to raise the price of imported goods, leading to a reduction in imports. Arguments in favor of restricting trade include protecting industries vital to national defense, protecting domestic jobs, and protecting infant industries. Those who argue against free trade are often said to take a **protectionist** stance on trade since the goal is to protect domestic workers and firms from foreign competition.

The main argument favoring free trade is that nations can potentially gain by specializing in certain outputs, exporting some of their output, and importing goods and services produced elsewhere at lower cost. The economic model of international trade, which is the main focus of this chapter, demonstrates the potential for gains from trade.

A country has an **absolute advantage** in the production of a particular output if it can produce more of the output in a given time period than another country. A country has a **comparative advantage** in the production of a particular output if it can produce the output at a lower opportunity cost than another country. The economic argument for free trade is based on the **principle of comparative advantage**. Specifically, it is possible for every country participating in free trade to benefit when each country specializes according to its comparative advantage.

In free trade equilibrium, nations export the goods and services that they are best suited to produce (those for which they have a comparative advantage) and import goods and services that their trading partners are best suited to produce. Both countries can gain from specialization and trade even when one country has a huge resource advantage, or an absolute advantage in the production of all outputs that could be produced by both countries. A specific example using production possibilities for two countries is presented in the next section to illustrate.

Consider a simple example in which there are two countries, Tropico and Parador; both can produce two outputs, food and clothing. For simplicity, assume that each country has constant opportunity cost resulting in linear PPFs.

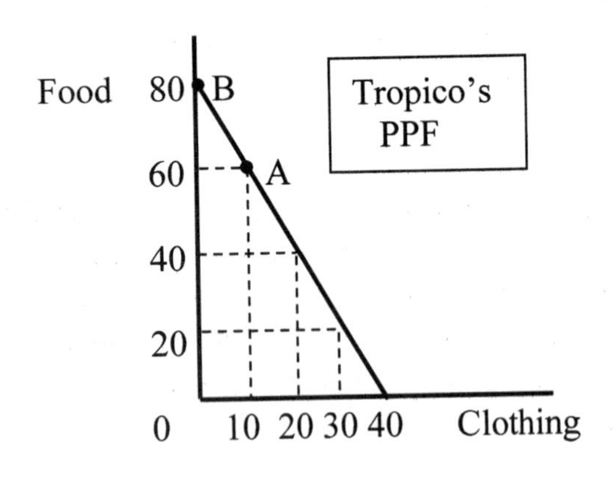

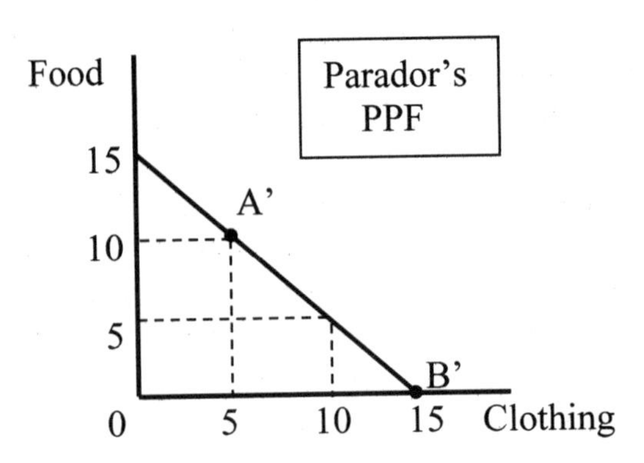

If Tropico does *not* engage in trade, it will choose the most desirable combination of food and clothing to produce based on what consumers prefer. Assume Tropico has determined that 60 food and 10 clothing, as represented by **point A** on its PPF, is the best option available when there is no trade. Similarly, Parador will produce at the point on its PPF it prefers to consume; assume the combination of 10 food and 5 clothing, as represented by **point A'** on Parador's PPF, is their preferred option when there is no trade. If the two countries produce at points A and A', world production is **70 food and 15 clothing**.

At first, it might seem that there is no reason for Tropico to trade with Parador, since it can produce more food and more clothing. However, *world production and consumption are both potentially higher when countries specialize according to comparative advantage, and then trade with each other.*

A country has a **comparative advantage** in the production of the output for which it has the **lowest opportunity cost**. To determine where each country's comparative advantage lies, calculate the opportunity cost of producing each output.

Recall from the previous chapter that the opportunity cost of the output on the horizontal axis is equal to the absolute value of the slope of the PPF. In Tropico, the opportunity cost of one unit of clothing is two units of food, while the opportunity cost of one unit of clothing is equal to one unit of food in Parador. The opportunity cost of one unit of food is equal to one-half unit of clothing in Tropico and one unit of clothing in Parador.

Assume complete specialization according to comparative advantage, which means Tropico produces only food (output = 80 food, represented by point B) and Parador produces only clothing (output = 15 clothing, represented by point B'). In the no-trade equilibrium, world production was 70 food and 15 clothing; with complete specialization, world production is 80 food and 15 clothing. If the two countries specialize and trade, world consumption will increase and the potential gain is 10 units of food.

The gains from trade are divided between countries when the **terms of trade** are set. In the table below, the terms of trade are 1.5 food per unit of clothing. In the chart, after both countries specialize and produce according to their comparative advantage, Tropico exports 15 units of food, but since it produced 80 units, it keeps 65 units for its own consumption. Parador imports 15 units of food and exports 10 units of clothing in exchange. Both countries are better off as a result of free trade.

Consumption and Production if no Trade	Production if there is Specialization According to Comparative Advantage	Units of Output Traded Imports (+) Exports (-)	Consumption with Free Trade
60 food 10 clothing	80 food 0 clothing	-15 food +10 clothing	65 food 10 clothing
10 food 5 clothing	0 food 15 clothing	+15 food -10 clothing	15 food 5 clothing

Compare these two columns to calculate the gains from trade for both countries: each country is able to consume an additional 5 units of food with no loss of clothing

Another way to formulate the trade problem starts with the number of hours required to produce one unit of output rather than the number of units of an output a country can produce using available resources.

The table below indicates how much time is needed to produce either one unit of food or one unit of clothing in each country.

Hours needed to produce one unit of:

	Food	**Clothing**
Tropico	3 hours	6 hours
Parador	16 hours	16 hours

Because Tropico can produce food using much less time, compared to Parador, it has an **absolute advantage** in the production of food. Tropico also has an absolute advantage in the production of clothing. However, as demonstrated above, Tropico can potentially gain by trading with Parador as long as both countries specialize according to comparative advantage.

Tropico can produce either 2 units of food or 1 unit of clothing in 6 hours, so Tropico's opportunity cost of 1 unit of clothing is equal to 2 units of food, while the opportunity cost of 1 unit of food is ½ unit of clothing.

Parador can produce either 1 unit of food or 1 unit of clothing in 16 hours, so Parador's opportunity cost for 1 unit of clothing is equal to 1 unit of food, and the opportunity cost of 1 unit of food is 1 unit of clothing.

The opportunity cost of clothing is lower in Parador, so Parador should specialize in producing clothing. The opportunity cost of food is lower in Tropico, so Tropico should specialize in producing food. With free trade, Tropico should export food and import clothing, while Parador should export clothing and import food.

It is possible to transform the above problem back into the production possibilities problem shown in the first part of the chapter by assuming that the total number of hours available to both countries is a fixed amount. If both countries have 240 hours to use, Tropico can produce either 80 units of food (since each unit requires 3 hours) or 40 units of clothing (since each unit requires 6 hours). Note that these production numbers match up with the production possibilities frontier shown for Tropico and the beginning of the chapter. Likewise, Parador can produce either 15 units of food or 15 units of clothing in 240 hours, since each unit of food or clothing requires 16 hours for them, so their production possibilities frontier also matches the graph presented previously.

Specialization is complete in simple examples used to illustrate the principle of comparative advantage due to the assumption that each nation has constant opportunity cost (linear PPFs). More realistically, when each country has a bowed-outward production possibilities frontier, reflecting the law of increasing opportunity cost, free trade equilibrium occurs before specialization is complete.

The result that countries can benefit by specializing and trading also applies to individual situations. Suppose, for example, that Rose opens her own legal practice after graduating from law school. Because she typed so many papers while in college, Rose can type over 100 words per minute. She hires Robert as her legal assistant, but Robert can only type 60 words per minute. In this example, Rose has an absolute advantage in typing because she is faster than Robert. When it comes to specialization, though, Rose should leave the typing to Robert and focus on winning legal cases. Similarly, a country might sometimes gain by importing products from another country even when it has an absolute advantage in those products.

Many argue that there are good reasons to restrict trade using tariffs or import quotas. This debate cannot be fully resolved based on the results reached in this chapter, but the conclusions reached here are an important part of the debate surrounding trade policy.

NAME______________________________________SECTION#__________

PRINT LAST NAME, FIRST NAME

INTERNATIONAL TRADE

1. The economic argument supporting free trade is based on the principle of:
   a. absolute advantage.
   b. comparative advantage.
   c. protection.
   d. tariffs and quotas.

Use the graphs below to answer questions 2 through 5.

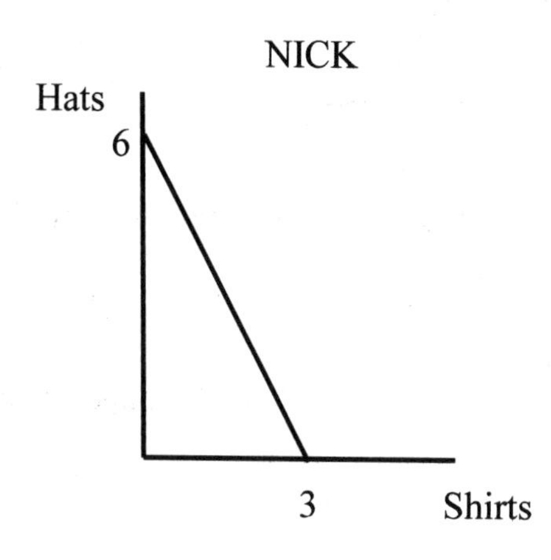

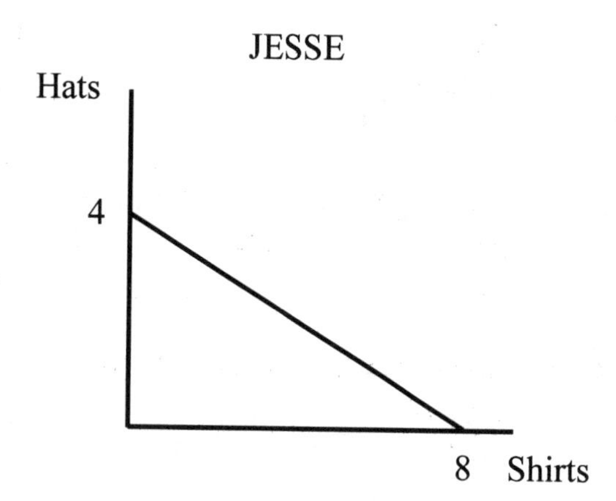

2. Nick has to give up ________ hat(s) to produce 3 shirts, which means that the opportunity cost of 1 shirt is equal to ________ hat(s) for Nick.
   a. 3; 2 b. 6; 2 c. 3; ½ d. 6; ½

3. Jesse has to give up ________ hat(s) to produce 8 shirts, which means that the opportunity cost of 1 shirt is equal to ________ hat(s) for Jesse.
   a. 4; 2 b. 8; 2 c. 4; ½ d. 8; ½

4. If Nick and Jesse specialize according to comparative advantage and produce efficiently, they will produce a combined total of:
   a. 10 hats and 11 shirts.
   b. 6 hats and 8 shirts.
   c. 5 hats and 5½ shirts.
   d. 4 hats and 3 shirts.

5. A legal limit on the quantity of a product that can be imported from other countries is called:
   a. a tariff.
   b. a trade treaty.
   c. an export subsidy.
   d. a quota.

6. A tax levied on imports is called:
   a. a tariff.
   b. a trade treaty.
   c. an export subsidy.
   d. a quota.

NAME____ SECTION#______________

PRINT LAST NAME, FIRST NAME

Use the graphs below to answer questions 7 through 10.

ALEX

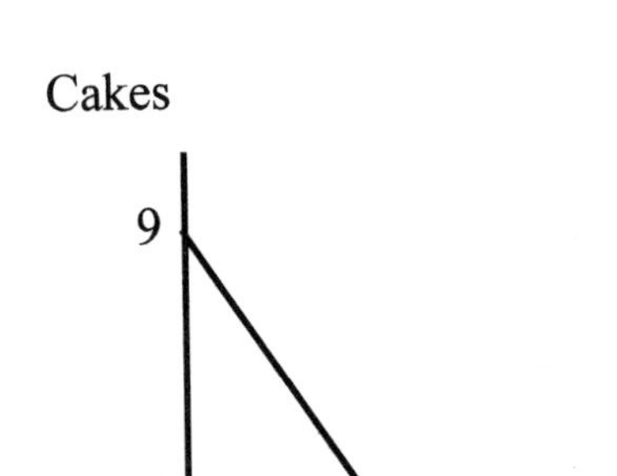

PAM

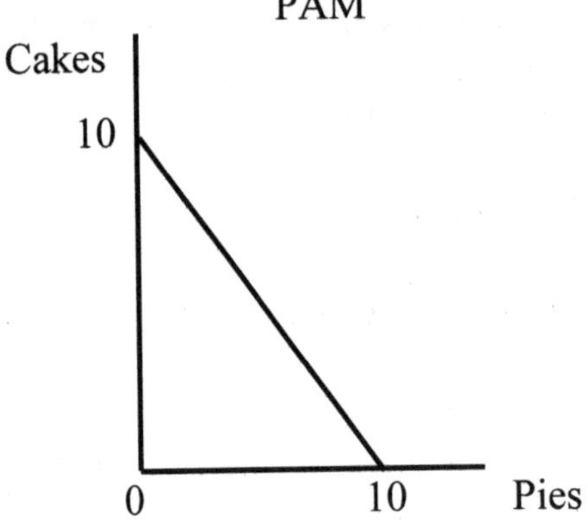

7. For Alex, the opportunity cost of 1 pie is _______ cake(s); for Pam, the opportunity cost of 1 pie is _______ cake(s).
   a. 2/3; 1 b. 2/3; 2 c. 1½; 1 d. 1½; 2

8. For Alex, the opportunity cost of 1 cake is _______ pie(s); for Pam, the opportunity cost of 1 cake is _______ pie(s).
   a. 2/3; 1 b. 2/3; 2 c. 1½; 1 d. 1½; 2

9. Alex has a comparative advantage in _____ and Pam has a comparative advantage in _____.
   a. cakes; pies
   b. pies; cakes
   c. cakes; cakes
   d. pies; pies

10. If Alex and Pam specialize according to comparative advantage, their combined output will be:
    a. 9 cakes and 10 pies.
    b. 19 cakes and 16 pies.
    c. 10 cakes and 6 pies.
    d. 15 cakes and 20 pies.

NAME____SECTION#______________
PRINT LAST NAME, FIRST NAME

GAINS FROM SPECIALIZATION AND TRADE

Jack and Jill are stranded on an island. In order to survive, they must use their labor skills to catch fish and pick bananas. The charts below show the maximum amounts of fish and bananas each can produce per period, assuming no change in available resources or technology.

Jack		**Jill**	
Fish	Bananas	Fish	Bananas
80	0	30	0
40	20	15	30
0	40	0	60

Use the data to graph production possibilities frontiers for each individual (include all numbers):

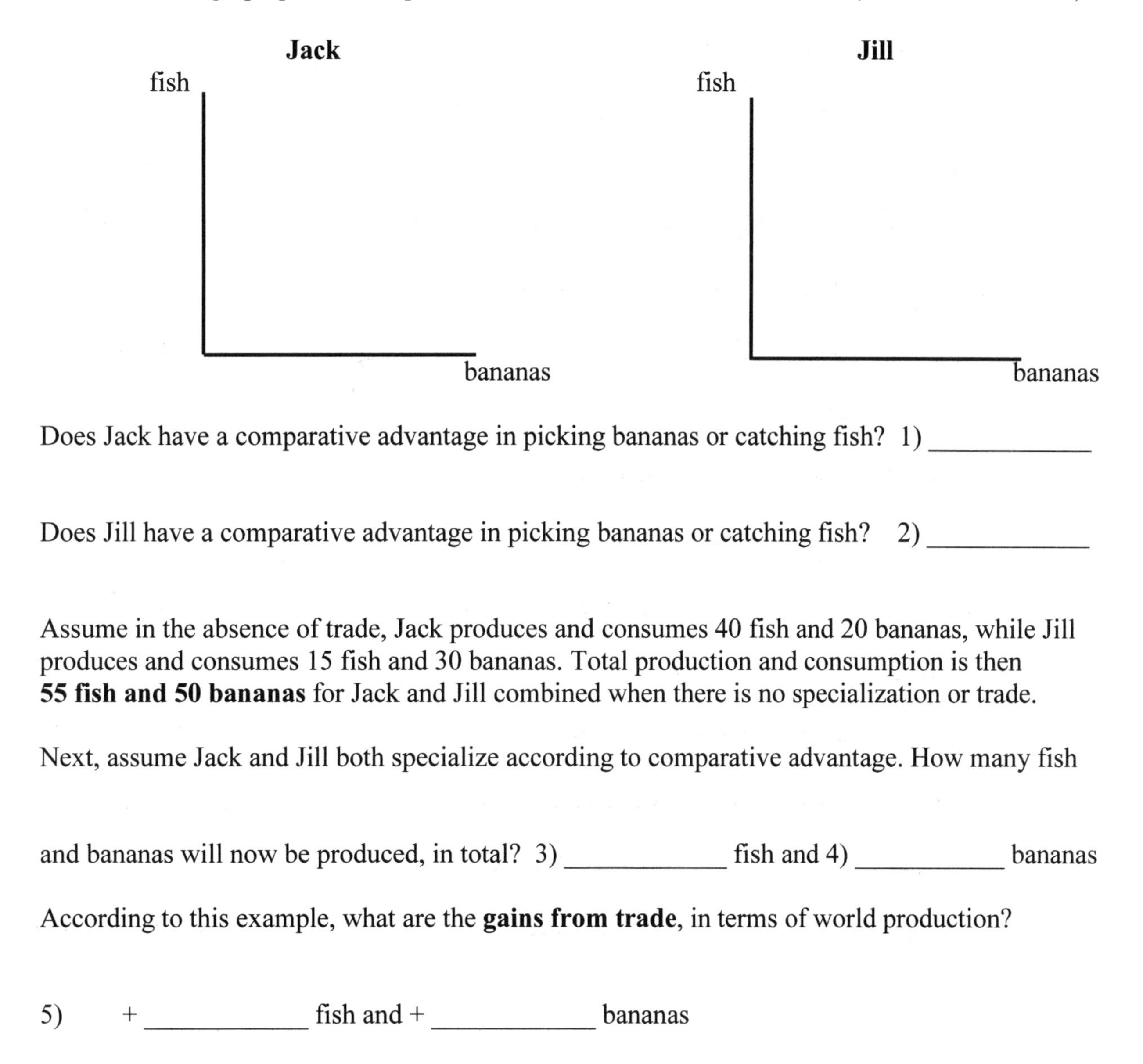

Does Jack have a comparative advantage in picking bananas or catching fish? 1) ___________

Does Jill have a comparative advantage in picking bananas or catching fish? 2) ___________

Assume in the absence of trade, Jack produces and consumes 40 fish and 20 bananas, while Jill produces and consumes 15 fish and 30 bananas. Total production and consumption is then **55 fish and 50 bananas** for Jack and Jill combined when there is no specialization or trade.

Next, assume Jack and Jill both specialize according to comparative advantage. How many fish

and bananas will now be produced, in total? 3) ___________ fish and 4) ___________ bananas

According to this example, what are the **gains from trade**, in terms of world production?

5) + ___________ fish and + ___________ bananas

NAME____SECTION#______________
PRINT LAST NAME, FIRST NAME

SPECIALIZATION AND TRADE

Use the table below to fill in the blanks.

Assume there are two countries, Alpha and Beta, and two products, bells and whistles. Assume the same amount of time is used in both countries to produce the outputs shown in the PPFs below. Both countries have constant opportunity cost.

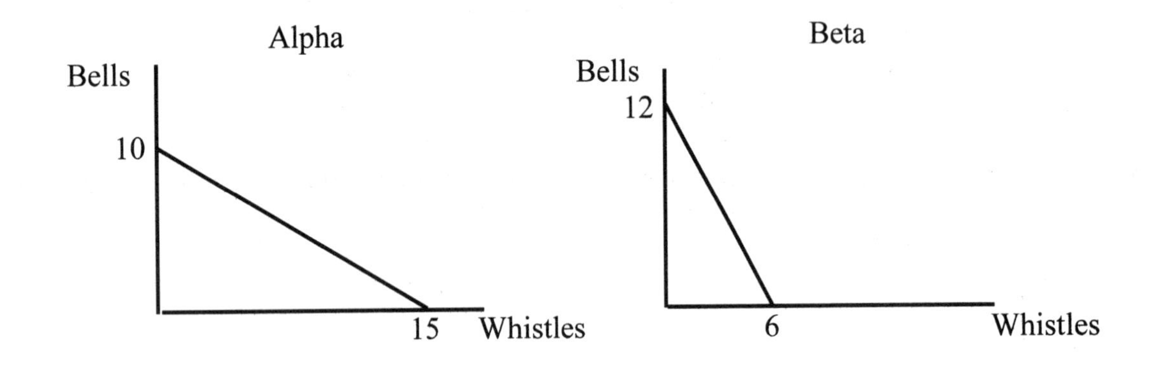

1) For Alpha, the opportunity cost of one bell is equal to _______________ whistles and the opportunity cost of one whistle is equal to _______________ bells.

2) For Beta, the opportunity cost of one bell is equal to _______________ whistles and the opportunity cost of one whistle is equal to _______________ bells.

3) Alpha has a comparative advantage in the production of _____________________ and Beta has a comparative advantage in the production of _____________________.

4) If both countries specialize according to comparative advantage, total output will be equal to _______________ bells and _______________ whistles.

5) Assuming total output was 5 bells plus 7.5 whistles in Alpha, and 6 bells plus 3 whistles in Beta, total output without specialization and trade was equal to _______________ bells and _______________ whistles. Comparing total output with and without specialization and trade leads to the conclusion that the gains from trade in this example were + _______________ bells and + _______________ whistles.

NAME____SECTION#______________

PRINT LAST NAME, FIRST NAME

INTERNATIONAL TRADE

1. Goods and services produced in Canada and consumed in the U.S. are ________ for the U.S. and ________ for Canada.
   a. exports; imports
   b. exports; exports
   c. imports; exports
   d. imports; imports

2. When a country imports less than it exports, it is:
   a. experiencing a trade deficit.
   b. experiencing a trade surplus.
   c. maintaining a balance of trade.
   d. not specializing according to comparative advantage.

Use the graphs below to answer questions 3 and 4.

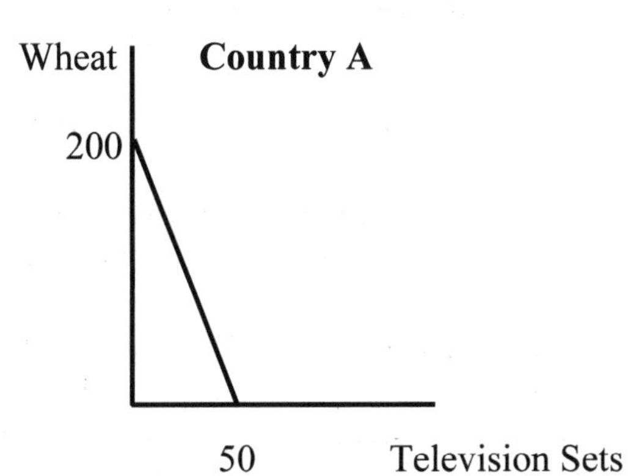

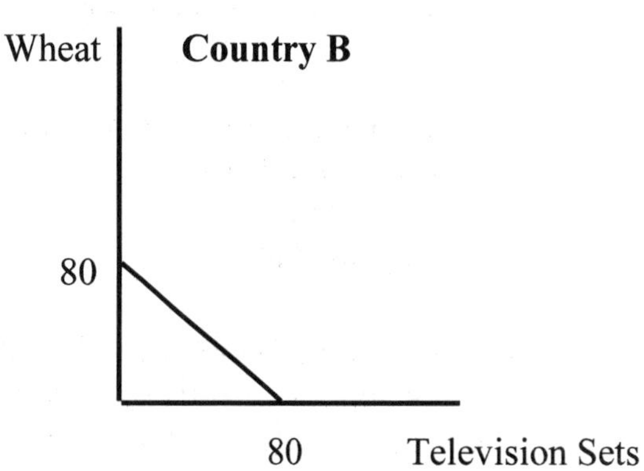

3. Assume output was initially 100 wheat and 25 TV's in Country A and 40 wheat and 40 TV's in Country B. If both countries specialize according to comparative advantage, their combined production of wheat changes from 140 to _____ and their combined production of TV's changes from 65 to _____.
   a. 280; 130 b. 200; 80 c. 80; 50 d. 200; 50

4. Assuming specialization and free trade and using the data in the previous question, if Country A imports 40 TV's and exports 80 wheat, consumption in Country A will be:
   a. 200 wheat and 40 TV's.
   b. 280 wheat and 90 TV's.
   c. 120 wheat and 80 TV's.
   d. 120 wheat and 40 TV's.

5. If Paul's opportunity cost per dream catcher is 3 pot holders, but Kaitlyn's opportunity cost per dream catcher is 2 pot holders, then:
   a. Paul has an absolute advantage in the production of dream catchers.
   b. Paul has a comparative advantage in the production of dream catchers.
   c. Kaitlyn has an absolute advantage in the production of dream catchers.
   d. Kaitlyn has a comparative advantage in the production of dream catchers.

NAME____SECTION#_______________
PRINT LAST NAME, FIRST NAME

6. If Paul is able to produce a greater number of dream catchers per hour than Kaitlyn, then:
   a. Paul cannot have a comparative advantage in the production of dream catchers.
   b. Paul has an absolute advantage in the production of dream catchers.
   c. Kaitlyn cannot have a comparative advantage in the production of dream catchers.
   d. Kaitlyn has an absolute advantage in the production of dream catchers.

Use the graphs below to answer questions 7 and 8.

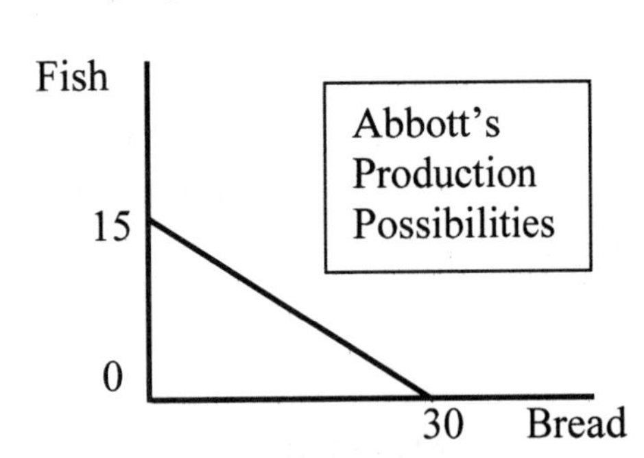

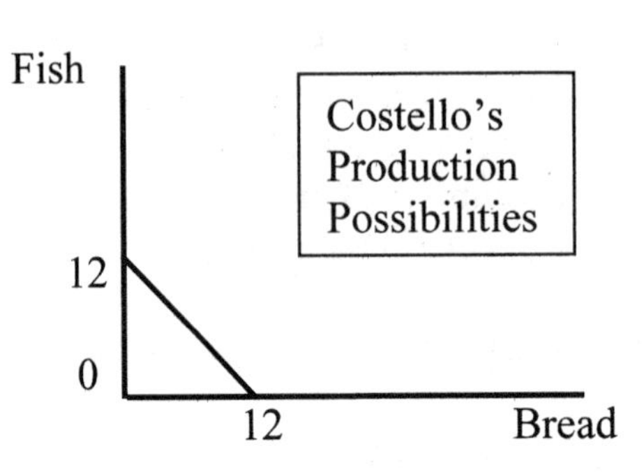

7. Abbott and Costello could benefit from specialization and trade if Abbott produces _____ and Costello produces _____.
   a. fish; bread
   b. bread; fish
   c. both fish and bread; nothing
   d. nothing; both fish and bread

8. Assume that in the absence of trade, Abbott produces and consumes 5 units of fish plus 20 units of bread, while Costello produces and consumes 6 units of fish and 6 units of bread. If they specialize according to comparative advantage, total production of fish changes from 11 fish to ____ fish and total bread production changes from 26 to ____.
   a. 12; 15   b. 12; 30   c. 15; 12   d. 15; 30

Use the table below to answer questions 9 and 10.

Time needed to produce one unit of:

	Wheat	Corn
Farmer Jones	10 hours	5 hours
Farmer Smith	4 hours	8 hours

9. In a time period of 40 hours, Farmer Jones is able to produce either _____ units of wheat or _____ units of corn.
   a. 4; 8   b. 8; 4   c. 5; 10   d. 10; 5

10. In a time period of 40 hours, Farmer Smith is able to produce either _____ units of wheat or _____ units of corn.
   a. 4; 8   b. 8; 4   c. 5; 10   d. 10; 5

CHAPTER 4 Demand and Supply

In a capitalistic economy, market forces answer the three fundamental economic questions of **what to produce, how to produce**, and **for whom to produce**. A market is comprised of all of the buyers and sellers interacting to satisfy a goal. The basic market model of demand and supply assumes that the goal of sellers in their market interactions is to maximize profit, and the goal of buyers is to maximize their satisfaction. The basic model also assumes that large quantities of a product are bought and sold (exchanged) at a specific price.

A market for a particular good or service exists when there is **both** a demand and a supply. There is a **demand** when potential buyers are both willing and able to make purchases. There is a **supply** when potential sellers are both willing and able to make output available. Demand can exist without supply; for example, people can be willing and able to pay for luxury trips to the moon, but if no one is supplying such trips, there is no effective market. Supply can exist without demand; for example, a firm might be willing and able to sell chocolate-covered pickles, but if no one is demanding these snacks, there is no effective market. When demand and supply occur simultaneously, a market emerges.

Law of Demand

Demand models the behavior of buyers in markets. The decision to buy any item is made by taking a lot of information into account, such as the price asked, the amount the buyer has to spend, and the availability of substitutes for an item. Assuming that the main factors that influence buying decisions are held constant except price, the model starts by showing how buyers respond to a change in the price of an item. A demand function gives the relationship between **price** and **quantity demanded,** ceteris paribus (holding everything else constant).

The relationship between the price of a particular product and the quantity demanded of that product may be shown graphically, in equation form, or as selected points displayed in a table. The following table is a **demand schedule** that shows the quantity demanded of constant-quality pizzas in a hypothetical college town, at different prices per pizza, assuming all factors that influence the decision of how many pizzas to buy are held constant except price.

Price $ Per Pizza	Quantity Demanded 1,000s Pizzas per year
$12	0
10	20
8	40
6	60
4	80
2	100

Notice that as the price per pizza falls, the quantity demanded of pizzas increases, and vice-versa. The **Law of Demand** states that a decrease in price causes quantity demanded to increase and an increase in price causes quantity demanded to decrease, ceteris paribus. In other words, price and quantity demanded are **inversely** (negatively) related, ceteris paribus.

When the demand function is plotted on a graph, the quantity is on the horizontal axis, and the price is on the vertical axis, by convention. The resulting curve (or straight line) will slope downward to the right. The graph below shows the demand curve for pizza in the hypothetical college town, using the data from the demand schedule on the previous page. Decreasing price from $8 to $6 causes quantity demanded to increase from 40,000 to 60,000 pizzas per year; this kind of change is referred to as a **movement along** the demand curve, from point A to point B, not a change in demand.

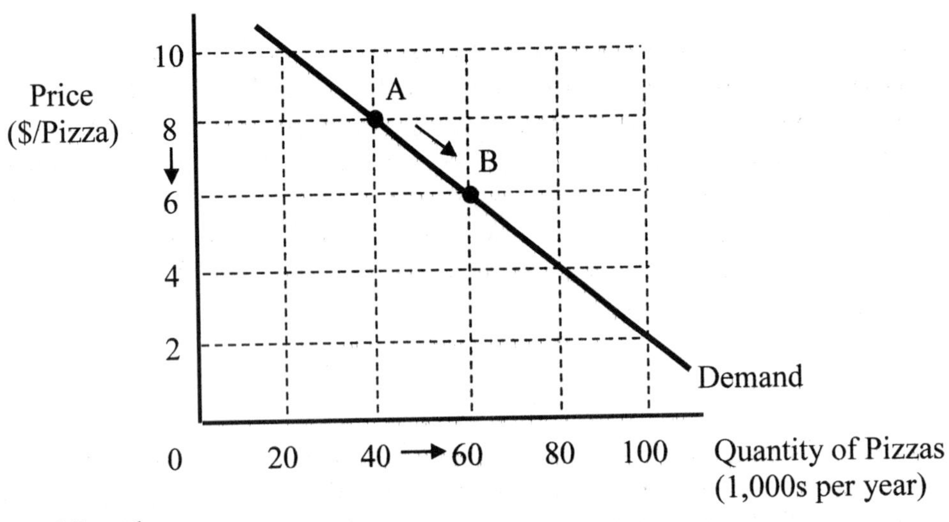

Law of Supply

Supply models the behavior of sellers in markets. In a perfectly competitive market, each individual seller takes the market price as given. Sellers take into account many factors other than price, including the cost of raw materials and the wages paid to workers, when deciding how much output to supply. Assuming that the main factors that influence selling decisions are held constant except price, the model starts by showing how sellers respond to a change in the price of an item. A supply function gives the relationship between **price** and **quantity supplied,** ceteris paribus (holding everything else constant).

The relationship between the price of a particular product and the quantity supplied of that product may be shown graphically, in equation form, or as selected points displayed in a table. The following table is a **supply schedule** that shows the quantity supplied of constant-quality pizzas in a hypothetical college town, at different prices per pizza, assuming all factors that influence the decision of how many pizzas to sell are held constant except price.

Price $ Per Pizza	Quantity Supplied 1,000s Pizzas per year
$12	120
10	100
8	80
6	60
4	40
2	20

Notice that as the price per pizza falls, the quantity supplied of pizzas decreases, and vice-versa. The **Law of Supply** states that a decrease in price causes quantity supplied to decrease and an increase in price causes quantity supplied to increase, ceteris paribus. In other words, price and quantity supplied are **directly** (positively) related, ceteris paribus.

When the supply function is plotted on a graph, the quantity is on the horizontal axis, and the price is on the vertical axis, by convention. The resulting curve (or straight line) will slope upward to the right. The graph below shows the supply curve for pizza in the hypothetical college town, using the data from the supply schedule on the previous page. Decreasing price from \$8 to \$6 causes quantity supplied to fall from 80,000 to 60,000 pizzas per year; this kind of change is referred to as a **movement along** the supply curve, from point C to point B, not a change in supply.

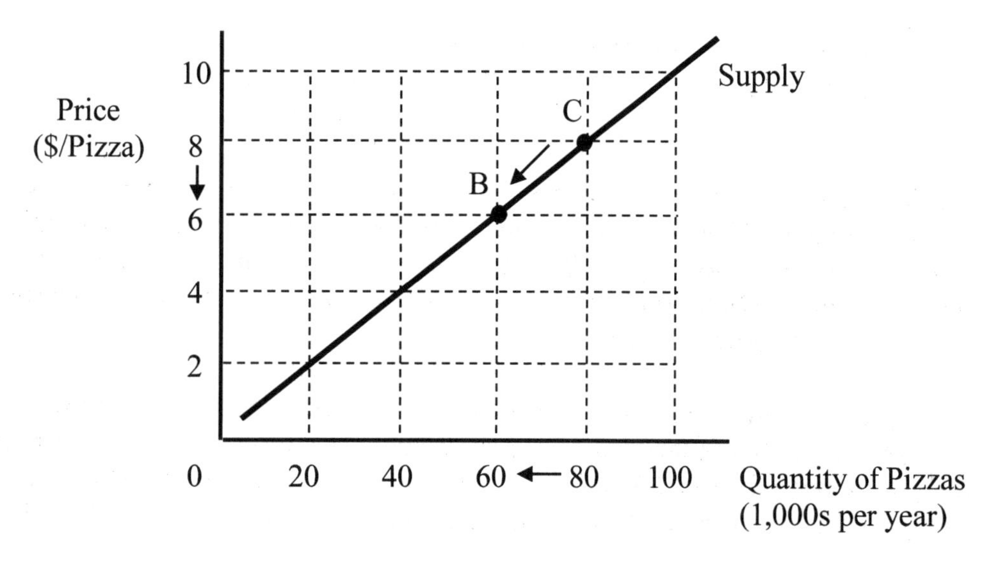

Market Equilibrium

A market is in equilibrium when the plans of buyers and sellers coincide. Specifically, a market is in equilibrium at the price for which **quantity demanded is equal to quantity supplied**. The table below shows that at the prices of \$12 and \$10, quantity supplied exceeds quantity demanded (which creates a market surplus), while at the prices of \$4 and \$2, quantity demanded exceeds quantity supplied (which creates a market shortage). At the price of \$6, quantity demanded and quantity supplied are both 60,000, so this is market equilibrium.

Price $ Per Pizza	Quantity Demanded 1,000s Pizzas per year	Quantity Supplied 1,000s Pizzas per year
$12	0	120
10	20	100
8	40	80
6	60	60
4	80	40
2	100	20

The demand curve and the supply curve can be graphed in the same space to easily identify market equilibrium, which occurs at the point where supply and demand intersect.

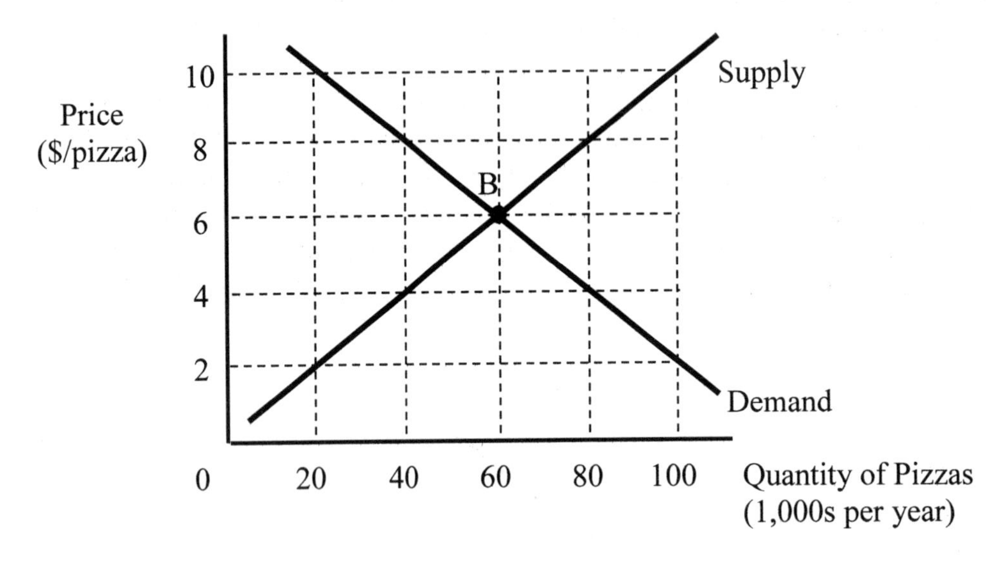

Point B, which corresponds to a price of $6, is the only point that lies on both the demand and supply curves. At a price of $6, quantity demanded is 60,000 pizzas, and quantity supplied is 60,000 pizzas. The price at which quantity demanded equals quantity supplied is referred to as the **market-clearing**, or **equilibrium, price**. In this market for pizzas, $6 is the **equilibrium price,** and 60,000 is the **equilibrium quantity**.

Whenever quantity supplied exceeds quantity demanded, there is a **market surplus**. The size of the surplus is measured by subtracting the quantity demanded from the quantity supplied. At a price of $8, which is above the equilibrium price, the quantity supplied is 80,000 pizzas, and the quantity demanded is 40,000 pizzas, resulting in a surplus of 40,000 pizzas at the $8 price.

Whenever quantity demanded exceeds quantity supplied, there is a **market shortage**. The size of the shortage is found by subtracting quantity supplied from quantity demanded. At a price of $2, which is below the equilibrium price, quantity demanded is 100,000 pizzas and quantity supplied is 20,000 pizzas. There is a shortage of 80,000 pizzas at the $2 price.

In summary, any price above equilibrium is associated with a surplus, and any price below equilibrium is associated with a shortage. When the price is at the equilibrium value (where supply and demand intersect), the quantity demanded equals the quantity supplied, and there is neither a surplus nor a shortage.

Notice that it is <u>not</u> correct to say that demand is equal to supply. Demand is the entire downward-sloping curve, and quantity demanded is one amount associated with a particular price, shown by one point on the demand curve. Likewise, supply means the entire function, and quantity supplied means a particular number of units that firms are willing and able to sell at a particular price.

Observation of real-world markets reveals that there is a strong tendency for price to fall when a surplus exists and for price to rise when a shortage exists, provided there are no legal restrictions preventing price changes (examples of such legal restrictions will be analyzed in chapter 7). Given these tendencies, it is reasonable to expect the price to gravitate toward the market-clearing (equilibrium) value, where the supply curve and the demand curve intersect. However, there is no reason to conclude that product prices do not change. The model is extended to explain why product prices change over time as a result of events that cause demand, supply, or both to shift.

Factors that Shift Demand

The law of demand specifies an inverse relationship between price and quantity demanded, ceteris paribus, and a demand curve shows this relationship. The demand curve on the left (below) shows that the quantity demanded is Q_1 when the price is P_1, and that the quantity demanded increases to Q_2 when the price falls to P_2. The change in price causes a **movement along** the demand curve from point A to point B. The only factor that causes a movement along demand is a change in the price of the product. Furthermore, a change in the price of this product does not cause the demand for this product to change or shift.

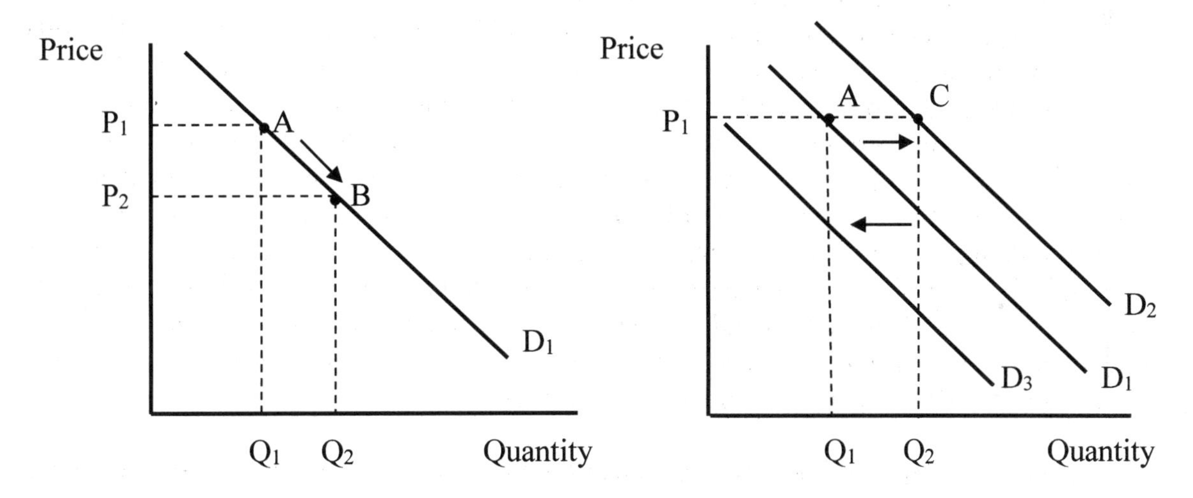

A change in demand occurs when a non-price factor that influences demand changes. The non-price factors are held constant when the demand curve is drawn. A change in demand is graphed as a shift of the demand curve. The graph on the right shows changes in demand. The rightward shift from D_1 to D_2 illustrates an **increase in demand**. As demand increases, or shifts to the right, consumers are willing and able to purchase more of this product at every price. For example, if the price is P_1, consumers want to buy Q_2 units rather than Q_1 (this is shown as a shift from point A to point C in the graph). A **decrease in demand** is shown by a leftward shift of the entire demand curve, such as from D_1 to D_3, in the graph on the right.

There are many events that cause demand curves to shift. Some events cause demand to increase and shift to the right. Other events cause demand to decrease and shift to the left. Some of the events that frequently explain demand shifts are listed on the next page, but keep in mind that a change in the price of the product represented in the graph cannot be responsible for a shift, only for a movement along the demand curve (change in quantity demanded).

Generally, a market demand curve shifts as a result of a change in:

- Tastes and Preferences
- Income
- The price of related goods
- The number of buyers
- Expectations (of buyers)

Fashion trends, diet fads, and reports linking certain products to cancer or other serious side effects can affect consumer **tastes and preferences**. For example, if you read a report that drinking more milk improves your metabolism and helps you lose weight, you might purchase more milk. Changes in tastes and preferences can cause the demand for some products to increase because they are healthier or more fashionable, while causing the demand for other products to decrease. For example, when skirts are fashionable, the demand for pants might fall. Often, we can attribute known changes in demand to changes in tastes and preferences, if no other explanation presents itself.

Income is another major factor that influences buying decisions. The relationship between income and demand depends on the type of good being considered. For **normal goods,** increases in income lead to increases in demand, and decreases in income lead to decreases in demand. Most goods are normal goods. For example, if your income increases, you may purchase more meals in restaurants. Your demand for restaurant meals increases as a result of the increase in your income; the price of restaurant meals did not change – your income changed, and that is why your demand changed. For **inferior goods,** demand decreases when income increases, and demand increases when income decreases. For example, generic canned goods are perceived by many consumers as being of lower quality than name-brand canned goods, but they are also less expensive than name-brand alternatives. If consumers switch to generic canned goods following a decrease in income, and the demand for generic canned goods increases as a result, then the generic canned goods are an inferior good.

To summarize, the four possible shifts that might occur as a result of a change in income:

- Demand shifts to the right (increases) following an increase in income for a normal good
- Demand shifts to the right (increases) following a decrease in income for an inferior good
- Demand shifts to the left (decreases) following a decrease in income for a normal good
- Demand shifts to the left (decreases) following an increase in income for an inferior good

The demand for a product may change, or shift, as a result of a change in the **price of a related good**. **Substitute goods** are two items that perform the same basic function. If corn and beans are **substitutes**, then an increase in the price of corn causes an increase in the demand for beans; consumers buy more beans, not because the price of beans fell, but because the price of corn increased and consumers choose to substitute beans for corn. **Complements** are two items used together, such as hotdogs and hotdog buns. Remember that a change in the price of hotdogs does <u>not</u> cause a change in the demand for hotdogs, only a movement along the demand function; however, the demand for hotdog buns increases (shifts to the right) when the price of a complementary item (hotdogs) falls.

Demand may change if the **number of buyers** in a market changes. A market demand curve is derived by adding the quantity demanded (Q_D) of each buyer at each price. For example, if the market consists of two consumers, Lara and Jesse, market demand is obtained by adding, at each price, the amount demanded by both buyers.

Price	Lara's Q_D	Jesse's Q_D	Total Q_D
$3.00	10	15	25
$2.00	14	22	36

The market demand curve can be drawn by plotting total Q_D at each price. Graphically, a market demand curve is derived by **horizontally** adding the individual demand curves of the consumers in the market, as shown below.

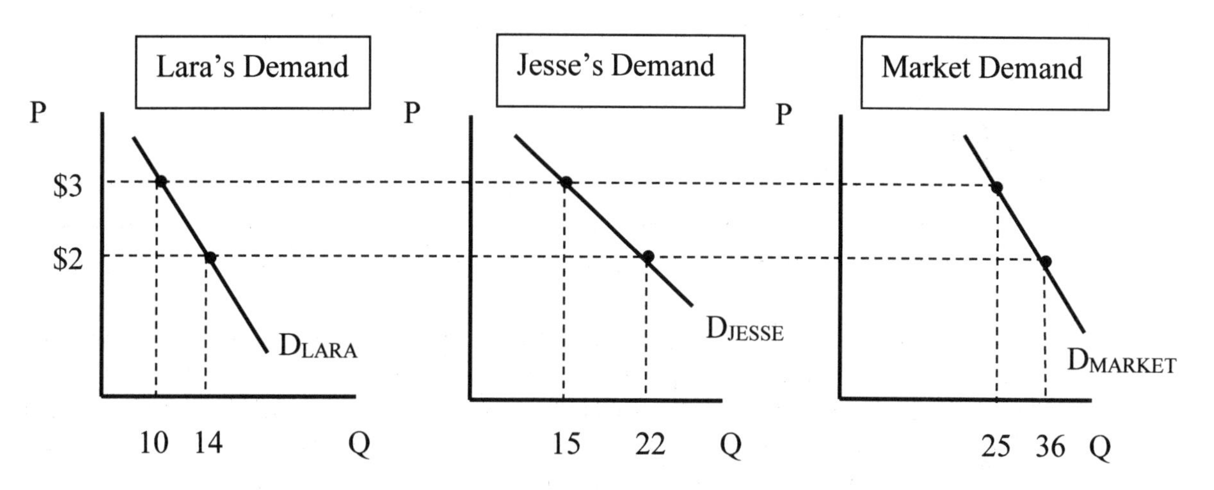

If another consumer is added to this market (assuming the third consumer has a positive Q_D at prices of $2.00 and $3.00), total Q_D will be larger at each price. Graphing market demand with three consumers gives a market demand curve that is to the right of the market demand curve generated assuming two consumers, and so on. Therefore, each time another consumer is added to the market, the market demand curve will typically shift rightward, or increase.

Expectations can influence buying decisions in different ways. For example, a consumer's demand for normal goods would likely fall today if the consumer expects a drop in income or wealth in the near future. Similarly, the expectation of higher product prices in the future can motivate consumers to buy now, causing the demand for those products to increase and shift to the right.

Once you learn the distinction between a shift and a movement along demand, you can rely on your common sense to help you determine the direction of a shift when you are asked to analyze a specific event. Remember, only a change in the price of X will cause a movement along the demand curve for X, so do not confuse movements along demand (changes in quantity demanded) with changes in demand (shifts).

Factors that Shift Supply

The law of supply specifies a direct relationship between price and quantity supplied, ceteris paribus, and a supply curve shows this relationship. The supply curve on the left (below) shows that the quantity supplied is Q_1 when the price is P_1 and that the quantity supplied increases to Q_2 when the price increases to P_2. The change in price causes a **movement along** the supply curve from point A to point B. The only factor that causes a movement along supply is a change in the price of the product. Furthermore, a change in the price of this product does not cause the supply of this product to change or shift.

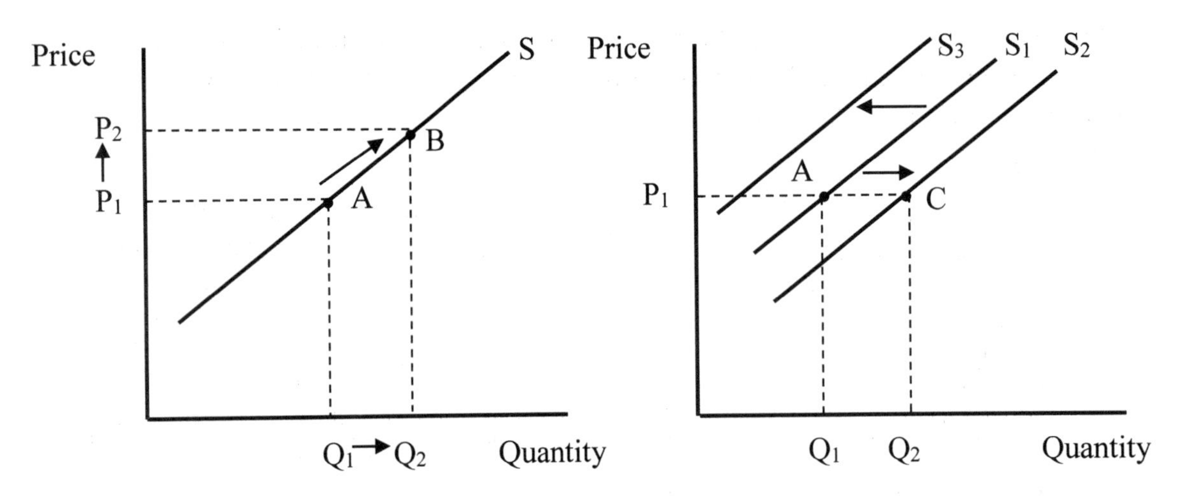

Sellers may change the quantity offered for sale at every price when a non-price influence on supply changes. A change in supply is graphed as a shift of the supply curve. An **increase in supply** is represented by a rightward shift of the supply curve, such as the shift from S_1 to S_2 in the graph on the right. As supply increases, or shifts to the right, firms are willing and able to sell more of this product at every price. For example, if the price is P_1, firms want to sell Q_2 units rather than Q_1. A **decrease in supply** is illustrated by a leftward shift of the supply curve, such as the shift from S_1 to S_3 in the graph on the right. There are many events that can cause supply to shift. Some events cause supply to increase and shift to the right. Other events cause supply to decrease and shift to the left.

Generally, a market supply curve shifts as a result of a change in:

- Quantity or cost of inputs
- Production technology
- The price of other producible goods
- The number of sellers
- Expectations (of sellers)
- Taxes and Subsidies
- Acts of nature

Changes in **costs of production** affect supply decisions. When suppliers can produce their product at a lower cost, the result is an increase in supply. Holding product price the same, lower production costs mean higher profits, and higher profits motivate firms to sell more at each price. Cheaper raw materials or lower wage rates cause costs of production to fall and supply to increase and shift to the right, while more expensive inputs cause supply to decrease, or shift to the left.

Improved **production technology** causes supply to increase, or shift to the right. Technological advance has the effect of making it cheaper to produce, or provide, a good or service. For example, advances in telecommunications have made it cheaper to provide cellular service, and the development of microchips made personal computers smaller and cheaper to produce. If a given technology made it more expensive to produce the same product, a firm would not adopt it, so decreases in technology are not considered to be relevant.

Changes in the **price of other producible goods** can also shift the supply curve. If there is more than one possible product that the seller can make with available resources, then a change in one product price can affect the supply of the other product. For example, if the price of wheat increases, the supply of corn can fall as farmers plant wheat instead of corn. The change in the price of wheat will cause a movement along the supply curve of wheat and a shift of the supply curve of corn.

Just as a market demand curve is derived by adding the quantity demanded of each consumer at different possible prices, a market supply curve is derived by adding the quantity supplied of each seller at different possible prices. An increase in **the number of sellers** causes the market supply curve to increase, or shift to the right, while a decrease in the number of sellers causes the market supply curve to decrease, or shift to the left.

If **sellers' expectations** change, the supply curve may shift as a result. For example, if sellers expect the price of their product to rise in the future, they may hoard the product, hoping to sell it later at a higher price. This behavior causes supply to decrease in the present period.

Supply functions may change in response to changes in **taxes or subsidies**. Taxes effectively make selling a product more expensive if it is the seller's duty to collect taxes on each sale and then send the money to the government, which is typical. A subsidy is the opposite of a tax, with the government paying the seller and making it cheaper for sellers to provide the product. Thus, a tax, or an increase in a tax, causes supply to decrease and shift to the left, while a subsidy, or an increase in a subsidy, causes supply to increase and shift to the right.

Acts of nature may also be responsible for supply shifts in some cases, especially in agricultural markets. Floods or droughts can reduce supply by destroying crops. Unusually good weather can cause a bumper crop, resulting in increased supply.

Once again, common sense is the best guide when analyzing events to determine whether supply shifts or demand shifts, and the direction of the shifts. This allows you to move from a real-world event to a prediction about how that event will likely affect product prices, production levels (quantity supplied), and consumption levels (quantity demanded). This final step, presented in the next section, reveals the purpose and value of demand and supply analysis to anyone who has ever asked a question like "why is the price of gasoline so high?" or "why are cell phones so cheap?"

Changes in Equilibrium Price and Quantity: Shifts in Demand and Supply

To analyze a single event, such as a change in income or a change in production technology, first determine whether the event shifts demand or supply, and then determine the direction of the shift. A shift of either demand or supply will generate a new intersection point of the demand and supply curves and a new equilibrium price and quantity in the market. The best way to predict how equilibrium price and quantity change, given a demand shift or a supply shift, is to sketch the graph. The four graphs below show the four possible single shifts. In each case, the initial equilibrium is given by point A, and the new equilibrium (after the shift) is given by point B; the effect of the shift on equilibrium price and quantity is indicted by the arrows.

Increase in Demand

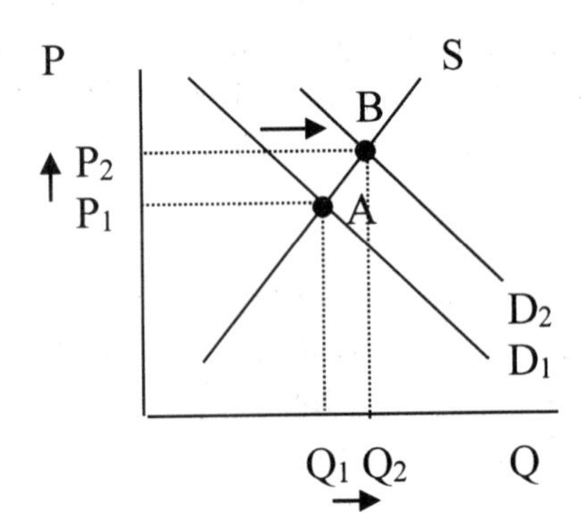

An increase in demand leads to an increase in both equilibrium price and quantity.

Decrease in Demand

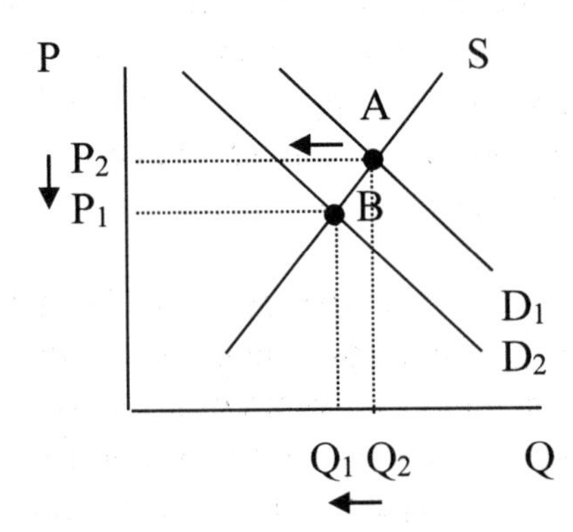

A decrease in demand leads to a decrease in both equilibrium price and quantity.

Increase in Supply

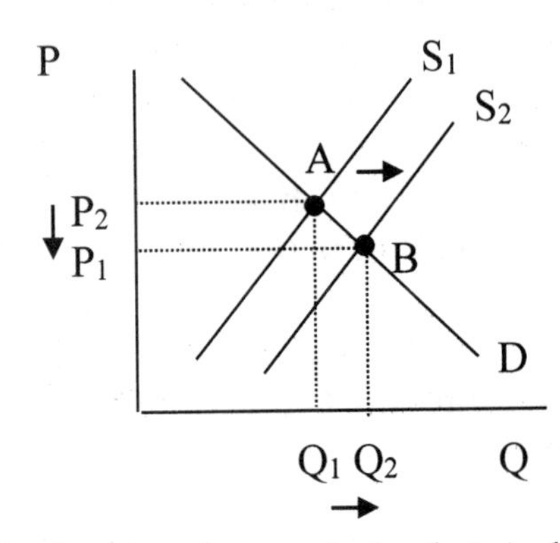

An increase in supply leads to a decrease in equilibrium price and an increase in equilibrium quantity.

Decrease in Supply

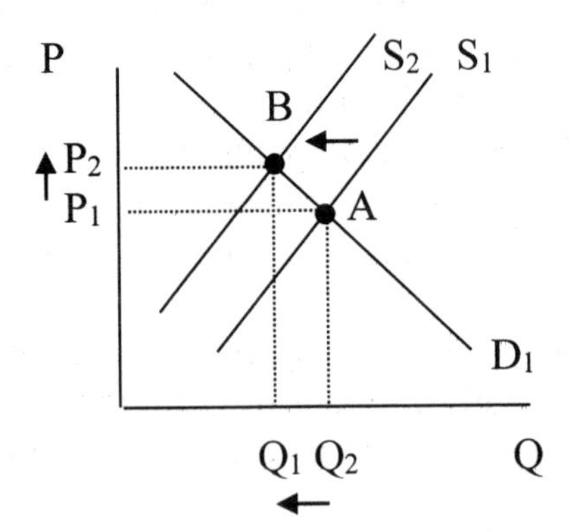

A decrease in supply leads to an increase in equilibrium price and a decrease in equilibrium quantity.

The four graphs above show what happens when one curve shifts and the other stays the same. In reality, there may be several factors changing at once in a particular market and the analysis becomes more complicated.

The impact of a double shift depends on the magnitude of each shift. For example, what happens if production technology improves, causing supply to increase, and at the same time, a change in consumer preferences causes an increase in demand? Both changes cause equilibrium quantity to increase, as shown in the graphs on the previous page. However, the increase in demand causes equilibrium price to go up, while the increase in supply causes equilibrium price to go down. Which direction price moves depends on which shift is bigger.

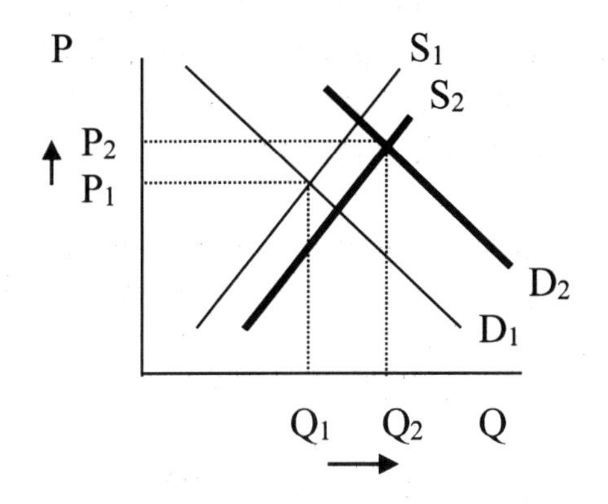

When demand and supply are both shifting to the right, the effect on equilibrium price depends on the size of the two shifts.

If the demand shift is larger, as shown to the left, then equilibrium price rises.

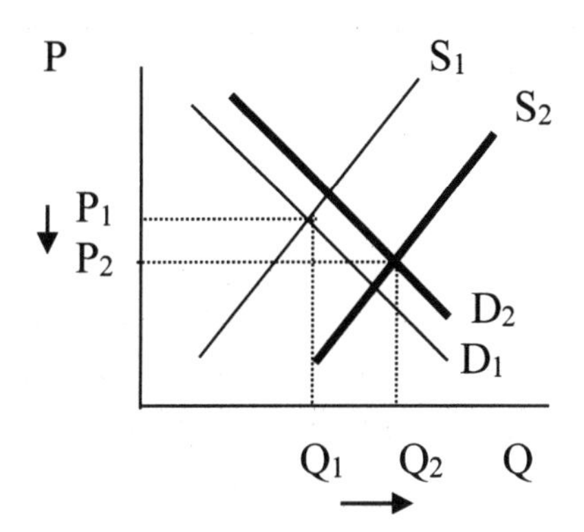

If the supply shift is larger, as shown to the left, then equilibrium price falls.

In either case, equilibrium quantity rises because both shifts cause an increase in quantity.

When demand and supply shift simultaneously, it may be best to draw two graphs: one with demand shifting and another with supply shifting. The direction of the change in P and Q in each graph can then be compared.

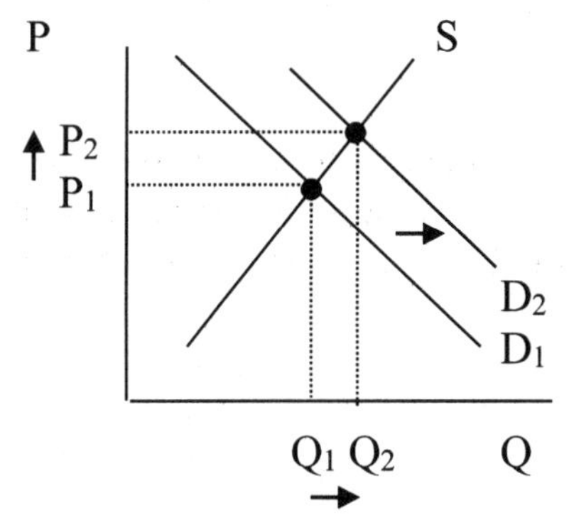

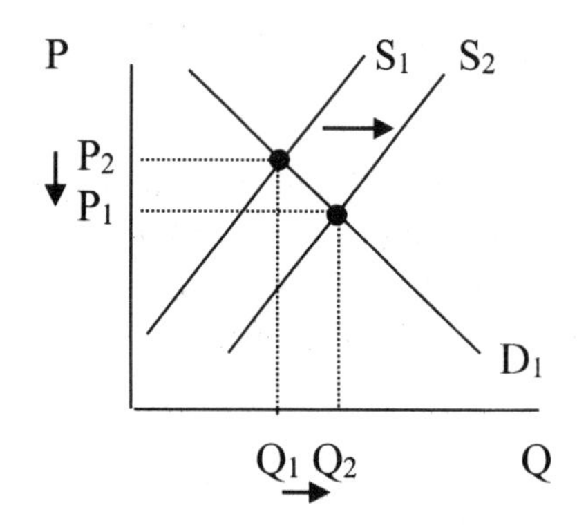

If both demand and supply increase, demand and supply analysis leads to the prediction that equilibrium quantity will increase, but equilibrium price could increase, decrease, or stay the same; additional information about the size of the two shifts is needed to predict whether equilibrium price rises or falls.

There are four possible combinations of simultaneous shifts in demand and supply. Each combination can be analyzed graphically, as in the previous example, or by recalling what happens to equilibrium price and quantity when there is a shift in supply and demand and combining the two outcomes. The four different combinations are summarized below without using the graphs, but you are encouraged to sketch graphs to verify these results.

- Both supply and demand increase (shift to the right): equilibrium quantity increases, but the change in equilibrium price cannot be predicted unless we know the magnitude of the two shifts. It would also be correct to say that the equilibrium price may rise, fall, or stay the same, or to say that the change in equilibrium price is indeterminate.

- Both supply and demand decrease (shift to the left): equilibrium quantity decreases, but the change in equilibrium price cannot be predicted unless we know the magnitude of the two shifts. It would also be correct to say that the equilibrium price may rise, fall, or stay the same, or to say that the change in equilibrium price is indeterminate.

- Supply decreases (shifts to the left) and demand increases (shifts to the right): equilibrium price increases, but the change in equilibrium quantity cannot be predicted unless we know the magnitude of the two shifts. It would also be correct to say that the equilibrium quantity may rise, fall, or stay the same, or to say that the change in equilibrium quantity is indeterminate.

- Supply increases (shifts to the right) and demand decreases (shifts to the left): equilibrium price decreases, but the change in equilibrium quantity cannot be predicted unless we know the magnitude of the two shifts. It would also be correct to say that the equilibrium quantity may rise, fall, or stay the same, or to say that the change in equilibrium quantity is indeterminate.

Remember that the circular flow model of chapter 1 distinguished between product markets and resource markets. The analysis in this chapter has focused on product markets, but the supply and demand model can also be used to analyze resource markets, like the market for labor services, where households make supply decisions and business firms make demand decisions.

Microeconomic theory is primarily related to either demand (consumer behavior theory) or supply (theory of the firm). The appendix to this chapter provides a more in-depth analysis of consumer behavior theory, and some of the later chapters in the book provide a more in-depth analysis of the theory of the firm.

NAME Drew Doller SECTION#

PRINT LAST NAME, FIRST NAME

DEMAND AND SUPPLY

1. The law of demand states that:
   a. price is the only variable that can cause consumers to purchase more or less.
   b. consumers do not buy more or less when price changes.
   c. price and quantity demanded are directly (positively) related, ceteris paribus.
   d. price and quantity demanded are inversely (negatively) related, ceteris paribus.

D

Use the graph below to answer questions 2 through 4.

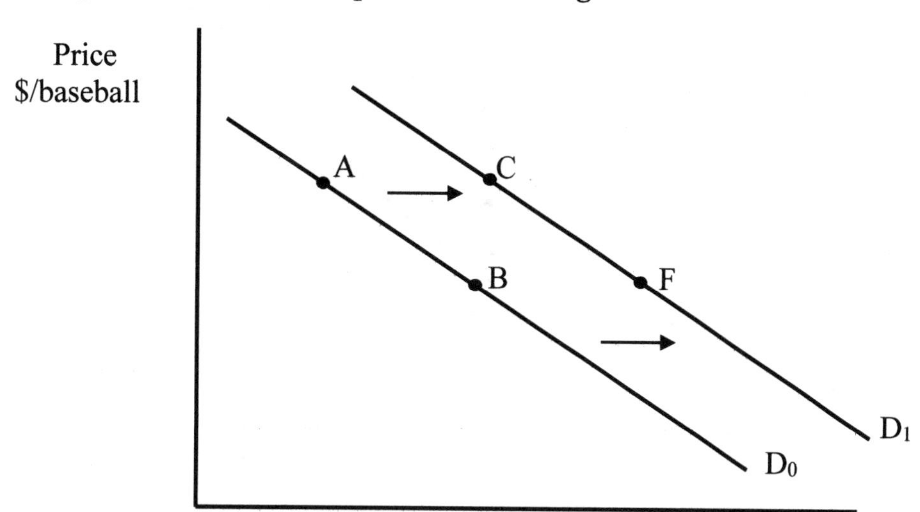

2. The movement from point A to point ___ is caused by a lower price, while the shift from point A to point ___ could be caused by an increase in the number of consumers.
   a. C; B b. B; C c. F; B d. C; F

B

3. The movement from point A to point B represents the ______ in the quantity demanded of baseballs resulting from ____________.
   a. decrease; an increase in the price of a baseball
   b. decrease; a decrease in the price of a baseball
   c. increase; an increase in the price of a baseball
   d. increase; a decrease in the price of a baseball

D

4. An increase in the demand for baseballs is shown by a:
   a. movement from point A to point B.
   b. movement from point B to point A.
   c. shift from D_0 to D_1.
   d. shift from D_1 to D_0.

C

5. If price and quantity demanded are inversely related, then:
   a. an increase in price causes demand to decrease or shift to the left.
   b. a decrease in price causes demand to increase or shift to the right.
   c. the demand function is downward-sloping.
   d. the demand function is upward-sloping.

C

NAME____SECTION#________________

PRINT LAST NAME, FIRST NAME

6. The law of supply states that:
   a. price and quantity supplied are inversely related, ceteris paribus.
   b. price and quantity supplied are directly related, ceteris paribus.
   c. price and quantity supplied are unrelated.
   d. quantity demanded and quantity supplied are directly related.

Use the graph below to answer questions 7 through 9.

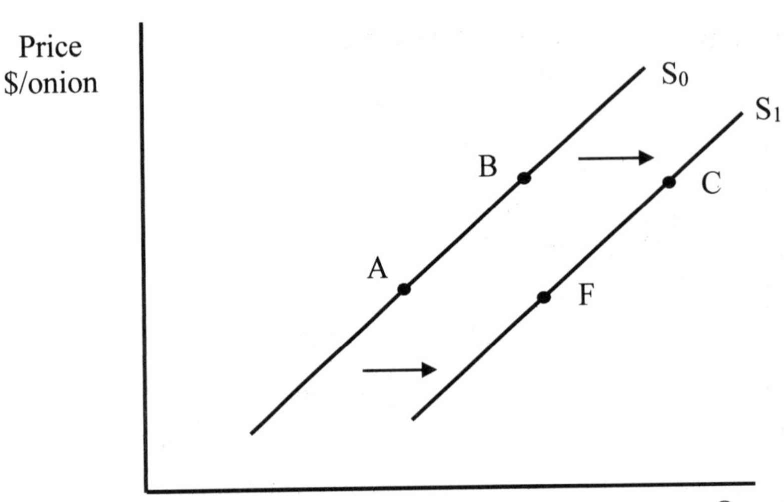

7. The movement from point B to point ___ is caused by a lower price, while the shift from point B to point ___ is caused by an increase in the number of sellers in the market.
   a. C; A b. A; C c. C; F d. F; A

8. The effect of a decrease in the price of onions is shown by a movement from point:
   a. A to point B. c. B to point C.
   b. B to point A. d. F to point A.

9. The effect of a decrease in the cost of growing onions is shown by a:
   a. movement from point A to point B. c. shift from S_0 to S_1.
   b. movement from point B to point A. d. shift from S_1 to S_0.

10. Ceteris paribus, a decrease in the number of firms selling calculators will result in:
    a. a decrease in the supply of calculators.
    b. a decrease in the demand for calculators.
    c. an increase in the supply of calculators.
    d. an increase in the demand for calculators.

NAME____SECTION#________________
PRINT LAST NAME, FIRST NAME

MARKET EQUILIBRIUM

Use the graph below to answer questions 1 through 10.

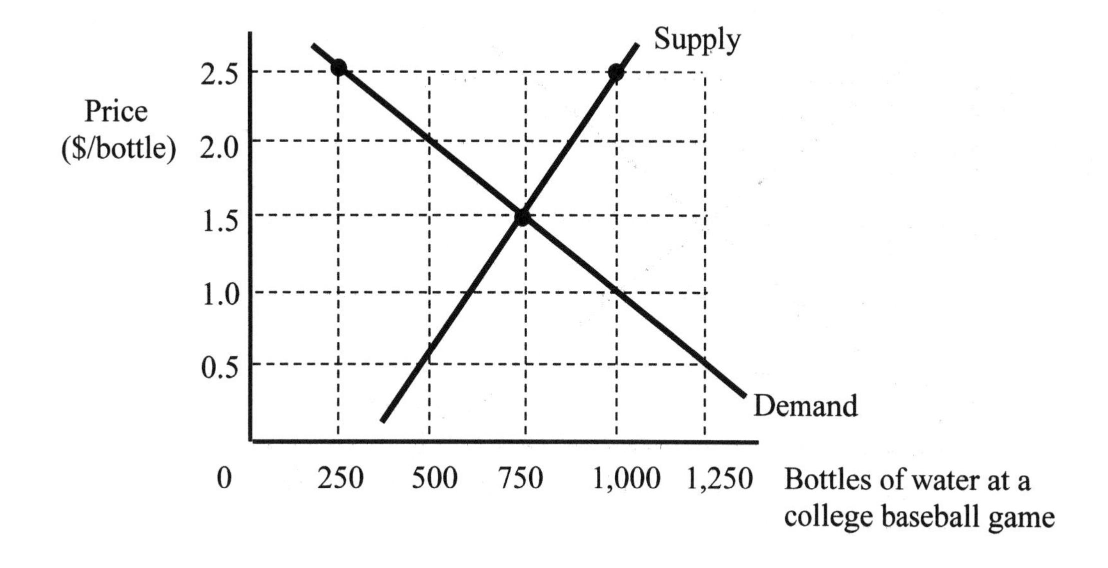

If price is $2.50, quantity demanded is 1) __________ and quantity supplied is 2) __________;

therefore, there would be a market 3) _______________ equal to 4) __________ bottles.
shortage/surplus

If price is $0.5, quantity demanded is 5) __________ and quantity supplied is 6) __________;

therefore, there would be a market 7) _______________ equal to 8) _________ bottles.
shortage/surplus

Equilibrium price is 9) $__________ and equilibrium quantity is 10) __________ bottles

of water.

NAME____SECTION#________________
PRINT LAST NAME, FIRST NAME

MARKET EQUILIBRIUM

Use the graph below to answer questions 1 through 10.

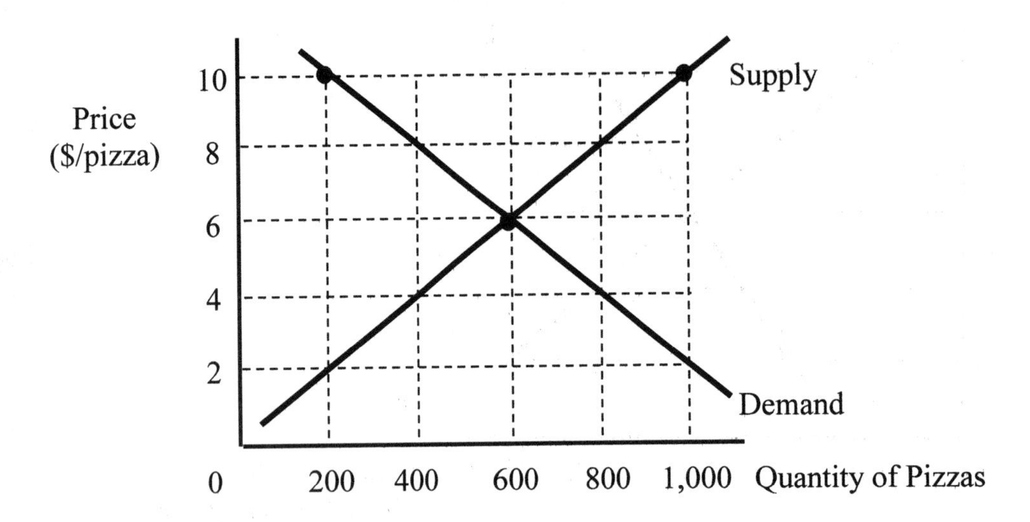

If price is $4, quantity demanded is 1) __________ and quantity supplied is 2) __________;

therefore, there would be a market 3) _______________ equal to 4) __________ pizzas.
shortage/surplus

If price is $10, quantity demanded is 5) __________ and quantity supplied is 6) __________;

therefore, there would be a market 7) _______________ equal to 8) __________ pizzas.
shortage/surplus

Equilibrium price is 9) $__________ and equilibrium quantity is 10) __________ pizzas.

NAME____SECTION#______________

PRINT LAST NAME, FIRST NAME

DEMAND AND SUPPLY

1. According to the law of demand, an increase in the price of coffee leads to:
   a. a decrease in the quantity demanded of coffee, ceteris paribus.
   b. a decrease in the demand for coffee, shown as a leftward shift.
   c. an increase in the quantity demanded of coffee, ceteris paribus.
   d. an increase in the demand for coffee, shown as a rightward shift.

2. According to the law of supply, an increase in the price of apples leads to:
   a. an increase in the quantity supplied of apples, ceteris paribus.
   b. an increase in the supply for apples, shown as a rightward shift.
   c. a decrease in the quantity supplied of apples, ceteris paribus.
   d. a decrease in the supply for apples, shown as a leftward shift.

3. A market is in equilibrium when:
   a. quantity supplied is equal to quantity demanded.
   b. quantity supplied is greater than quantity demanded.
   c. quantity demanded is greater than quantity supplied.
   d. supply is equal to demand.

4. Prices above equilibrium lead to ______________, while prices below equilibrium lead to ______________.
   a. market surpluses and increases in price; market shortages and decreases in price.
   b. market surpluses and decreases in price; market shortages and increases in price.
   c. market shortages and increases in price; market surpluses and decreases in price.
   d. market shortages and decreases in price; market surpluses and increases in price.

5. If quantity supplied exceeds quantity demanded, the resulting market _____ motivates firms to _____ product price.
   a. surplus; raise
   b. surplus; lower
   c. shortage; raise
   d. shortage; lower

6. Markets tend to move toward equilibrium:
   a. if government does an effective job of setting price limits.
   b. if prices are able to change to clear surpluses and shortages.
   c. when output can be restricted to offset falling prices.
   d. when consumer demand can be manipulated to ensure low prices.

7. Which of the following will lead to a decrease in the demand for water skis?
   a. A decrease in the price of motor boats (a complementary good)
   b. A decrease in the price of knee boards (a substitute good)
   c. An increase in the price of water skis
   d. A decrease in the price of water skis

NAME____SECTION#______________

PRINT LAST NAME, FIRST NAME

Use the graph below to answer questions 8 through 10.

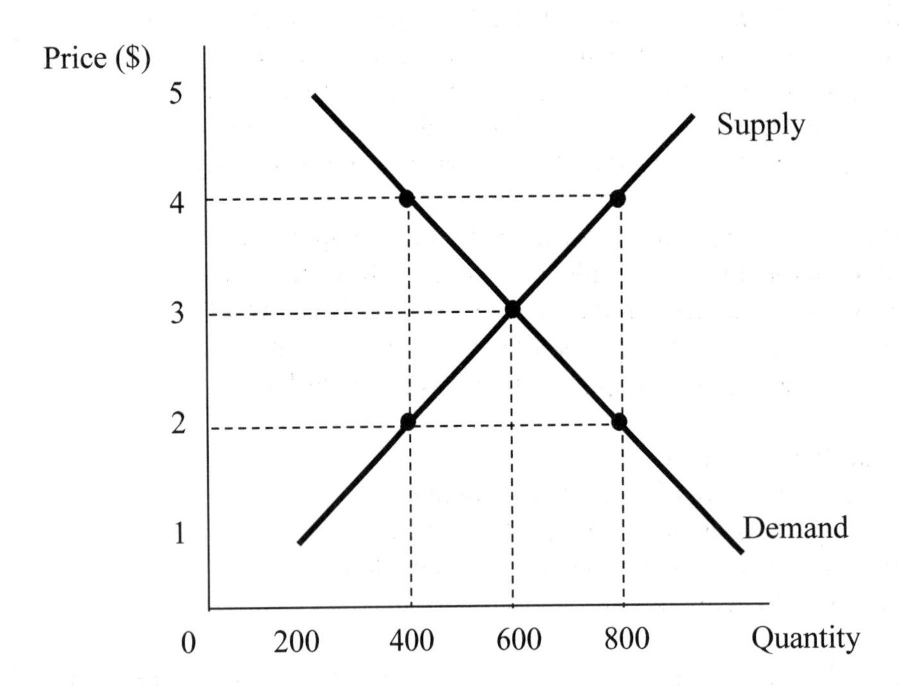

8. When the price is equal to $3, quantity demanded equals _____ units and quantity supplied equals _____ units.
   a. 400; 400 b. 600; 600 c. 400; 800 d. 800; 400

9. When the price is equal to $2, quantity demanded equals _____ units and quantity supplied equals _____ units.
   a. 400; 400 b. 600; 600 c. 400; 800 d. 800; 400

10. When the price is equal to $4, quantity demanded equals _____ units and quantity supplied equals _____ units.
   a. 400; 400 b. 600; 600 c. 400; 800 d. 800; 400

NAME____ SECTION#______________
PRINT LAST NAME, FIRST NAME

DEMAND AND SUPPLY SHIFTS

Match the graph showing a demand or supply shift with the event that would cause the shift.

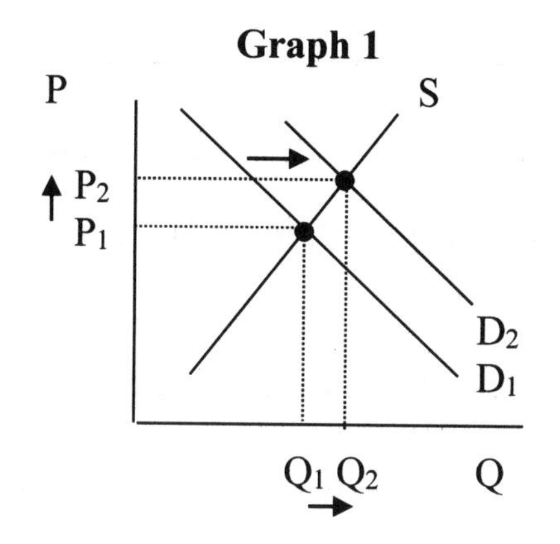

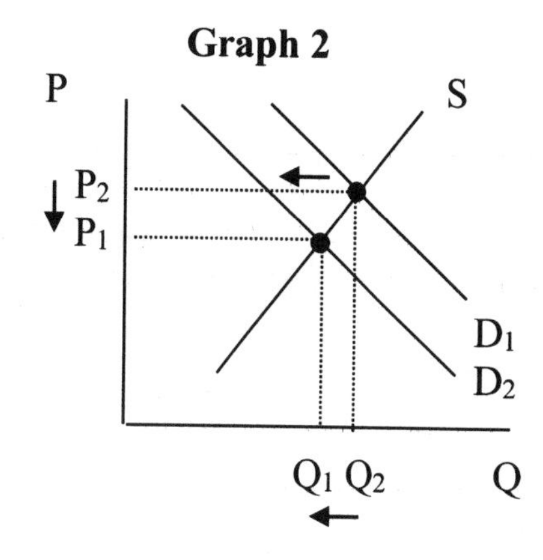

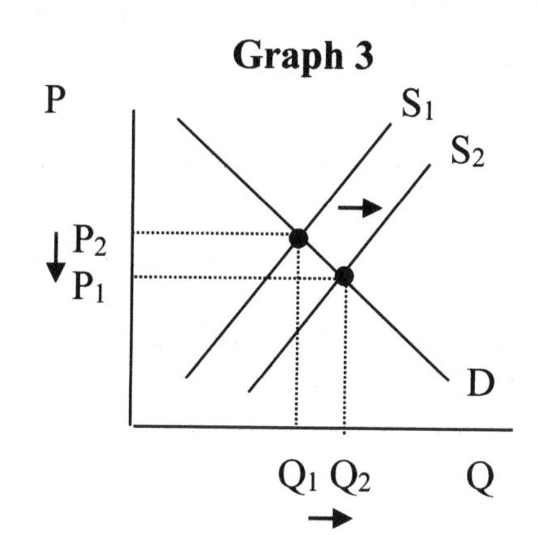

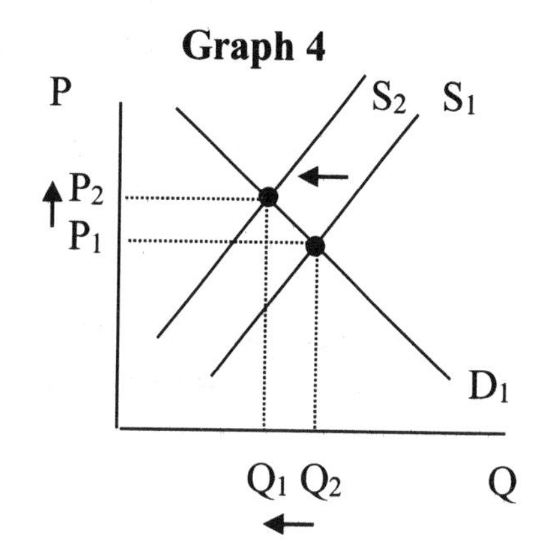

Graph # Events:

_____ 1. A decrease in the price of a good considered a substitute by consumers

_____ 2. An increase in the price of a good considered a substitute by consumers

_____ 3. An increase in the costs of production

_____ 4. A decrease in the costs of production

_____ 5. A decrease in the price of a good considered a complement by consumers

_____ 6. An increase in the price of a good considered a complement by consumers

_____ 7. Improved production technology

_____ 8. A decrease in consumer income, assuming the product is a normal good

_____ 9. A decrease in consumer income, assuming the product is an inferior good

_____ 10. An increase in consumer income, assuming the product is a normal good

NAME____SECTION#________________

PRINT LAST NAME, FIRST NAME

DEMAND AND SUPPLY

Assume there is an increase in the price of a cereal. According to the law of demand, what happens in the market for cereal when the price of a cereal increases, ceteris paribus?

____

____

Now assume cereal and milk are complements. What happens in the market for milk when the price of cereal increases, ceteris paribus?

____

____

Starting from equilibrium in the market for milk, explain how an increase in the price of cereal affects equilibrium price and quantity in the market for milk, ceteris paribus.

____

____

Draw a graph of the market for milk, labeling both axes and the demand and supply curves. Show any shift(s) that occurred as a result of the increase in the price of cereal.

NAME____SECTION#____________
PRINT LAST NAME, FIRST NAME

DEMAND AND SUPPLY

Use the graph below to answer questions 1 through 4.

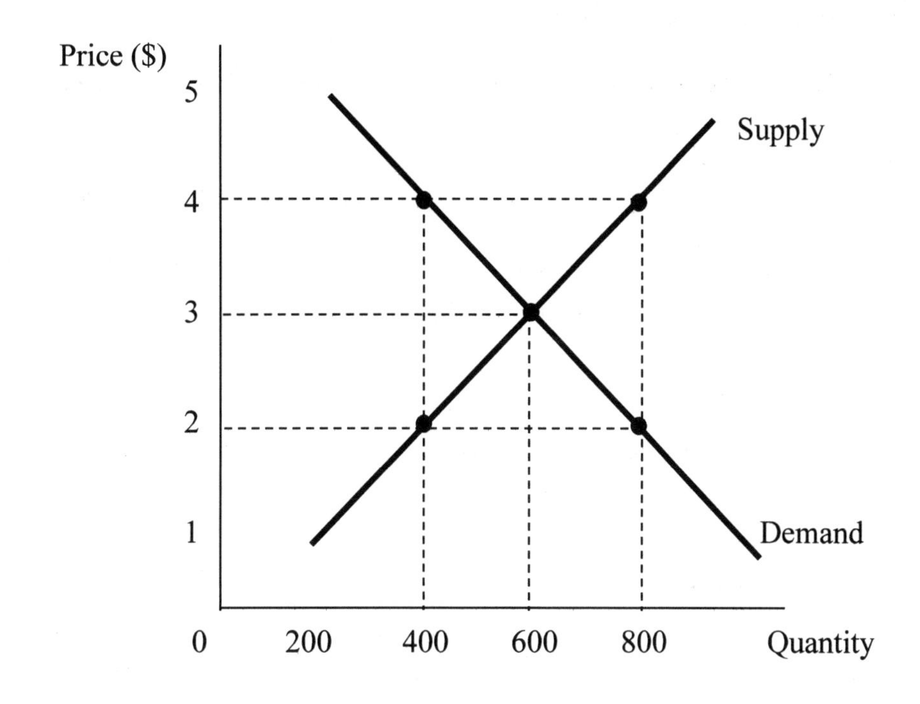

1. Quantity demanded and quantity supplied are equal when the price is equal to:
   a. $1. b. $2. c. $3. d. $4.

2. If the price in this market is set at $2, a __________ of __________ units will result.
   a. shortage; 200
   b. shortage; 400
   c. surplus; 200
   d. surplus; 400

3. If the price in this market is set at $4, a __________ of __________ units will result.
   a. shortage; 200
   b. shortage; 400
   c. surplus; 200
   d. surplus; 400

4. If, at the current price, quantity demanded is equal to 400 units and quantity supplied is equal to 800 units, then price will:
   a. increase, causing quantity demanded to fall and quantity supplied to rise.
   b. increase, causing quantity demanded to rise and quantity supplied to fall.
   c. decrease, causing quantity demanded to fall and quantity supplied to rise.
   d. decrease, causing quantity demanded to rise and quantity supplied to fall.

NAME____SECTION#______________

PRINT LAST NAME, FIRST NAME

5. Which of the following would be expected to decrease the demand for textbooks?
   a. An increase in the price of textbooks
   b. A decrease in college enrollment
   c. An increase in financial assistance to college students
   d. A decrease in the tuition per college class

6. Ceteris paribus, an increase in the supply of tortillas causes the equilibrium price of tortillas to __________ and the equilibrium quantity of tortillas to __________.
   a. increase; increase
   b. increase; decrease
   c. decrease; increase
   d. decrease; decrease

7. Assuming tomato juice is a normal good, an increase in consumer income will cause an increase in the ___________ tomato juice and a(n) ________ in the price of tomato juice.
   a. demand for; increase
   b. supply of; increase
   c. demand for; decrease
   d. supply of; decrease

8. Ceteris paribus, an increase in the demand for tortillas causes the equilibrium price of tortillas to __________ and the equilibrium quantity of tortillas to __________.
   a. increase; increase
   b. increase; decrease
   c. decrease; increase
   d. decrease; decrease

9. Assume teenagers in a town can either babysit or rake leaves to earn money on the weekends. Ceteris paribus, if the price paid for an hour of babysitting increases relative to the price paid for an hour of leaf raking, then:
   a. the supply of teens available to rake leaves is likely to decrease.
   b. the supply of teens available to baby sit is likely to decrease.
   c. the demand for baby sitting is likely to increase.
   d. the demand for leaf raking is likely to decrease.

10. Technological improvements that reduce the cost of manufacturing smaller personal computers combined with an increase in the demand for smaller personal computers results in an increase in equilibrium:
   a. quantity, but no change in equilibrium price.
   b. price, but no change in equilibrium quantity.
   c. quantity, but the change in equilibrium price depends on the size of the shifts.
   d. price, but the change in equilibrium quantity depends on the size of the shifts.

NAME____SECTION#________________

PRINT LAST NAME, FIRST NAME

DEMAND AND SUPPLY

1. Which of the following would be expected to increase the supply of copy machines?
   a. A decrease in the number of firms manufacturing copy machines
   b. A decrease in the price of copy machines
   c. A decrease in the price of copy paper
   d. A decrease in the cost of manufacturing copy machines

2. A decrease in the demand for oranges with no change in supply will result in a(n) __________ in the equilibrium price and a(n) __________ in the equilibrium quantity.
   a. increase; increase
   b. increase; decrease
   c. decrease; increase
   d. decrease; decrease

3. If the demand for RC Cola increases following a decrease in income, then:
   a. the law of demand does not apply to RC Cola.
   b. RC Cola is an example of a normal good.
   c. RC Cola is an example of an inferior good.
   d. RC Cola and Pepsi are complementary goods.

4. According to the model of demand and supply, a decrease in the supply of cell phones is most likely to have been caused by:
   a. an increase in the price of a cell phone.
   b. a decrease in the price of a cell phone.
   c. an improvement in the technology used to produce cell phones.
   d. an increase in the cost of manufacturing cell phones.

5. Which of the following would ***best*** explain an increase in the demand for jeans?
   a. A decrease in income, assuming jeans are normal goods
   b. A decrease in the popularity of jeans
   c. An increase in the number of schools that allow students to wear jeans
   d. A decrease in the price of jeans

6. Ceteris paribus, a decrease in the supply of grape juice combined with an increase in the demand for grape juice causes the equilibrium price of grape juice to:
   a. fall, but the effect on equilibrium quantity cannot be determined from the information given.
   b. fall with no change in the equilibrium quantity.
   c. rise, but the effect on equilibrium quantity cannot be determined from the information given.
   d. rise with no change in the equilibrium quantity.

NAME____SECTION#______________

PRINT LAST NAME, FIRST NAME

7. Ceteris paribus, if demand and supply both increase at the same time, equilibrium price ________ and equilibrium quantity ________.
   a. increases; may rise, fall, or stay the same, depending on the size of the two shifts.
   b. decreases; may rise, fall, or stay the same, depending on the size of the two shifts.
   c. may rise, fall, or stay the same, depending on the size of the two shifts; increases
   d. may rise, fall, or stay the same, depending on the size of the two shifts; decreases

Use the graph below to answer questions 8 through 10.

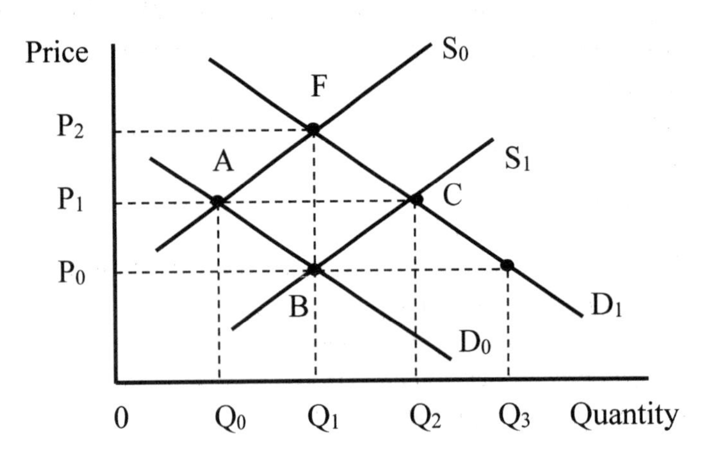

8. Assume this market is initially in equilibrium at point F. A decrease in the number of buyers in this market combined with improved production technology would most likely change equilibrium to point:
   a. A b. B c. C d. F

9. Assume this market is initially in equilibrium at point A. An increase in the number of buyers and sellers in this market would most likely change equilibrium to point:
   a. A b. B c. C d. F

10. If demand is represented by D_1 and supply is represented by S_1, at a price of P_1:
   a. quantity supplied is equal to Q_2.
   b. quantity demanded is equal to Q_2.
   c. the market is in equilibrium.
   d. All of the above statements are true.

Appendix: Consumer Behavior

Economic theory is based on the assumption that people make rational decisions that are in their own best interests. Consumers make decisions about which goods and services to purchase on a daily basis, and these decisions are very important to consumer well-being. There are many different ways to spend a given amount of money, but a rational consumer will spend the amount in a way that maximizes the consumer's satisfaction or sense of happiness.

It is unfortunately not possible to observe or measure consumer well-being, so consumer behavior theory might seem a little abstract. Economists use the concept of **utility** to refer to consumer satisfaction, and have developed a measurement called **utils** to describe how much satisfaction or pleasure a consumer enjoys. The assumed goal of consumers is to *maximize total utility, given the limitations created by the consumer's budget.*

Even though it is impossible to actually observe how much utility a consumer enjoys after making a purchase, there is a specific pattern that seems logical. This pattern relates to **marginal utility**, or the additional satisfaction gained when one additional unit of a good or service is consumed. As consumers, we can all relate to the idea that eating one slice of pizza might be pleasant, but eating a tenth slice would probably be awful.

The **law of diminishing marginal utility** states that as more of one good is consumed relative to other goods, the *additional* (or marginal) satisfaction gained from consuming another unit of that good eventually declines.

As a simple example, if a consumer has just eaten one apple and gained 20 utils as a result, the theory predicts that the consumer will probably gain *less* than 20 utils from a second apple. A reasonable (but hypothetical) utility function might be:

Quantity of Apples	Total Utility	Marginal Utility
0	0	
1	20	20
2	35	15
3	45	10
4	50	5

Marginal utility is calculated as the change in total utility divided by the change in quantity consumed ($\Delta TU/\Delta Q$). In special cases, marginal utility may initially rise, but will always begin to diminish at some point according to the law of diminishing marginal utility.

Although the exact amount of utility a consumer receives from each additional unit consumed cannot be measured, the value of something to a consumer can be estimated by the maximum amount of money the consumer is willing to pay to acquire it. **Marginal benefit** (MB) is a measure of the value of each additional unit to the consumer in terms of how much money each additional unit is worth to the consumer, or the maximum amount the consumer would pay for each additional unit. *The law of diminishing marginal utility suggests that marginal benefit falls as the quantity consumed rises.*

Cardinal versus Ordinal Utility

Economists have developed two approaches to the study of consumer utility, the cardinal approach and the ordinal approach. The **cardinal** approach is based on the assumption that the amount of **utility**, or satisfaction, which a consumer receives from a product can be measured consistently, using a unit of measure called a *util*. For example, suppose that consuming an apple gives the consumer 20 utils of satisfaction and consuming an orange gives 40 utils of satisfaction; then, the measure is consistent if the consumer enjoys the orange exactly twice as much as the apple. The cardinal approach requires a precise measurement of consumer satisfaction that is not available, but economists have confirmed consumer theories using an ordinal approach.

The **ordinal** approach requires only that consumers can rank their preferences by indicating whether they prefer an apple to an orange, prefer an orange to an apple, or are indifferent between the two choices, as an example. Students who plan to continue their studies beyond the introductory classes should learn about both the cardinal and ordinal utility approaches.

In choosing between two goods, such as apples and oranges, a consumer will take into account the utility gained from eating apples and oranges as well as the respective prices. One way to model this is to work with a hypothetical example with known values for utility. The numbers in the table include total utility (TU), marginal utility (MU), and marginal utility per dollar spent (MU/Price) for both apples and oranges, assuming the price per apple is $1 and the price per orange is $2.

Apples

Quantity	TU	MU	MU/Price
0			
1	20	20	20
2	35	15	15
3	45	10	10
4	50	5	5

Oranges

Quantity	TU	MU	MU/Price
0			
1	40	40	20
2	76	36	18
3	100	24	12
4	112	12	6

Suppose a consumer has $8 to spend. There are different combinations of apples and oranges from which the consumer can choose, all of which are affordable. However, there is one unique combination of apples and oranges that maximizes total utility, subject to the $8 spending limit or budget. The combination associated with the greatest total utility, that is also affordable, is the combination the consumer will choose according to the model.

One way to identify the optimal combination is to consider the MU/Price numbers and proceed one step at a time. Suppose the consumer first purchases an apple and an orange, spending $3 for a total of 60 utils. The consumer has $5 remaining. The next purchase should be an orange, because the second orange provides 18 utils per dollar while the second apple provides only 15. With $3 remaining, the consumer will next choose the second apple, followed by a third orange.

Notice that each purchase is made by choosing the highest value for MU/Price or by keeping the MU/Price of apples balanced with the MU/Price of oranges. The optimal combination is 2 apples and 3 oranges, given the $8 budget and the two prices. This optimal combination provides total utility of 135, whereas a sub-optimal combination (like 4 oranges) provides less utility (112 utils for 4 oranges) even though it would cost the same amount as the optimal combination.

Assuming that utility functions are continuous (that is, the utility associated with every possible quantity, including all fractions of apples and oranges, is known), the consumer's tendency to maintain a balance between the MU/Price of apples and the MU/Price of oranges can be converted into a mathematical rule for identifying the optimal combination of apples and oranges.

$$\frac{MU_{apples}}{P_{apples}} = \frac{MU_{oranges}}{P_{oranges}}$$

This is the same rule that is identified using the ordinal approach, as shown below.

Assume there are only two goods available to the consumer, X and Y. The household's budget constraint is given by $P_X X + P_Y Y = B$, where X denotes the quantity of good X consumed, Y denotes the quantity of good Y consumed, P_X and P_Y denote prices, and B measures the consumer's available budget, which is assumed to be entirely spent on some combination of X and Y. The slope of the budget line is equal to $-P_X/P_Y$.

As an example, suppose the consumer has $50 to spend, each unit of X costs $5 and each unit of Y costs $10. This budget line has a slope of –1/2.

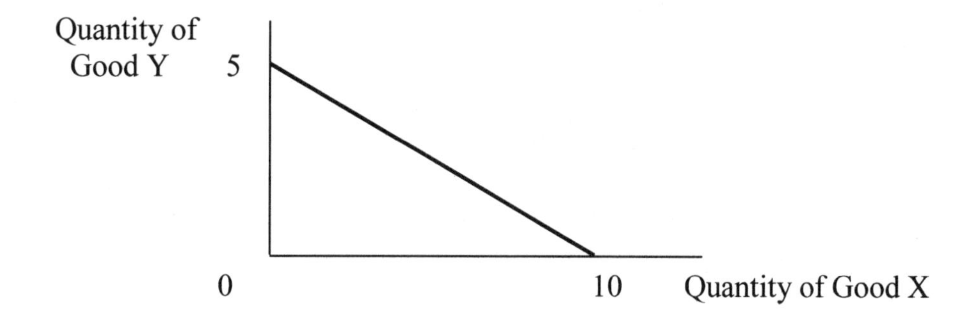

Although any point on the budget line is affordable and costs the same amount ($B), the consumer will prefer some of these affordable combinations to others. Consumer equilibrium is the point on the budget line that yields the greatest possible amount of **utility** to the consumer.

A consumer's preferences may be represented graphically with **indifference curves**. Each indifference curve shows all the bundles of two goods, X and Y, that yield a fixed amount of utility for the consumer.

The slope of an indifference curve is equal to the **marginal rate of substitution (MRS)**, which measures how many units of good Y the consumer would be willing to give up in exchange for one additional unit of good X while keeping total utility unchanged. The slope of an indifference curve is equal to $-MU_X/MU_Y$. The MRS falls as the consumer moves downward along a given indifference curve, since the more X the consumer already has, the less extra utility the consumer will gain from an additional unit of X (this follows from the **law of diminishing marginal utility**).

Because MRS decreases as a consumer moves downward along a given indifference curve, the curve will be convex to the origin or bowed-inward. Indifference curves are graphed with the quantity of X on the horizontal axis and the quantity of Y on the vertical axis. Two hypothetical indifference curves are shown below.

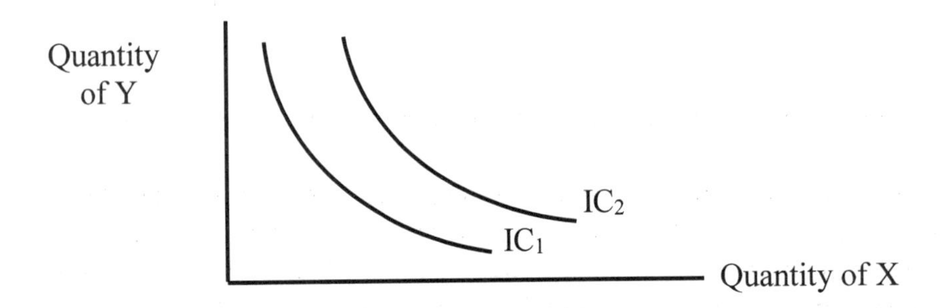

Indifference curves are downward-sloping, non-intersecting, and convex, reflecting three basic assumptions about a rational consumer's preferences: 1) more is preferred to less, 2) preferences are consistent (if bundle A is preferred to bundle B, and bundle B is preferred to bundle C, then bundle A is preferred to bundle C), and 3) diminishing marginal utility (which implies diminishing MRS). Since consumers are assumed to prefer more to less, any point on IC_2 is preferred to any point on IC_1.

Combining budget constraint lines and indifference curves in the same graph, consumer equilibrium occurs at the point where the indifference curve is tangent to the budget constraint line, because this indicates that the consumer is on the highest attainable indifference curve. At the point of tangency, the slope of the indifference curve is equal to the slope of the budget line, so $MU_X/MU_Y = P_X/P_Y$, or

$$\frac{MU_X}{P_X} = \frac{MU_Y}{P_Y}$$

which is the same equilibrium condition obtained using the cardinal approach.

Changes in the consumer's budget or product prices cause the budget line to shift, resulting in changes in the point of consumer equilibrium. This model provides a means of deriving demand curves (by letting the price of one good change, holding all else constant, and observing the effect on the quantity demanded of that good) as well as demand shifts (by letting income change or by letting the price of Y change and observing the effect on the quantity demanded of X).

As an example, assume the following information:

- Initially, budget = $200, price of coffee = $5, and price of tea = $2
- Due to favorable weather conditions, the price of coffee falls from $5 to $4, but there is no change in the consumer's budget or the price of tea

The decrease in the price of coffee causes the budget line to rotate outward, leading to a movement along the demand for coffee curve.

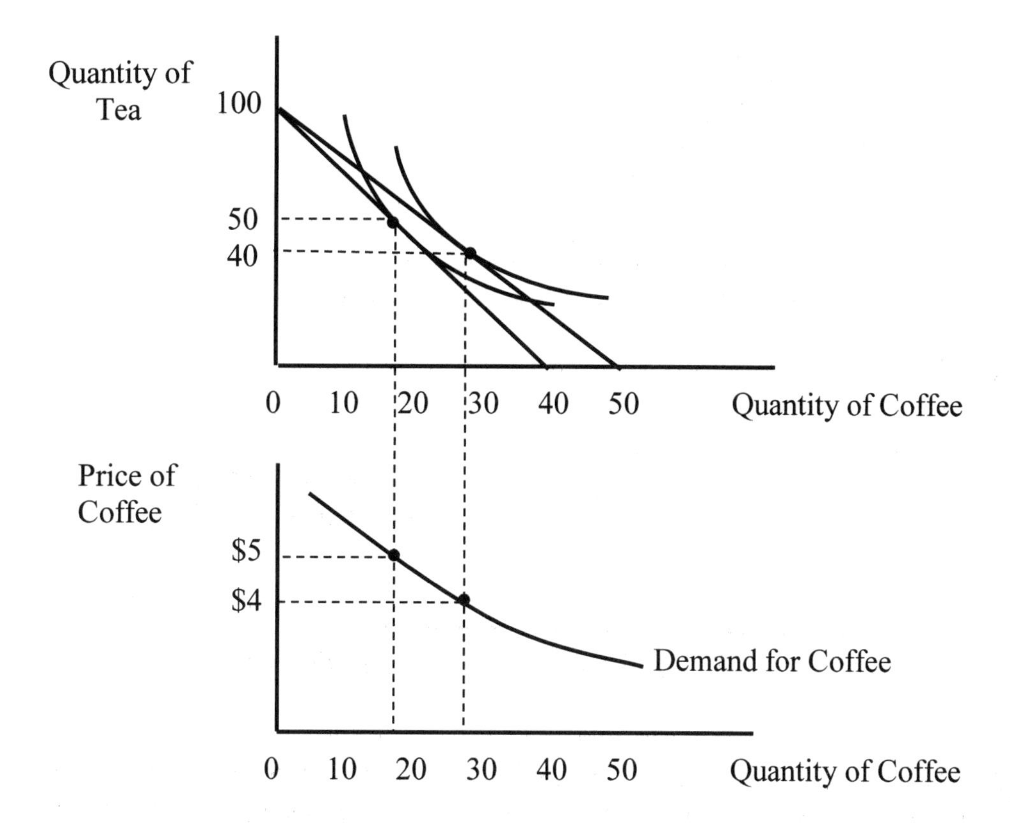

The quantity of coffee demanded when the price is $5 is 20 because the consumer's indifference curve is tangent to the first budget line at a quantity of 20. When the price of coffee falls, the budget line rotates outward, allowing the consumer to reach a higher indifference curve. The graphs above indicate that the quantity of coffee demanded is 30 when the price falls to $4. These two points can be connected to derive a downward-sloping demand curve.

Other changes can occur which would cause the demand for coffee to shift, such as a change in the available budget, a change in the price of a related good (tea), or a change in the consumer's preference structure.

As another example, assume the following information:

- Initially, budget = $200, price of coffee = $5, and price of tea = $2
- Due to a report about the positive heath effects of drinking tea, the demand for tea has increased, causing the price of tea to increase to $4.

The increase in the price of tea causes the budget line to rotate inward so the consumer is forced to move to a new equilibrium point on a lower Indifference Curve.

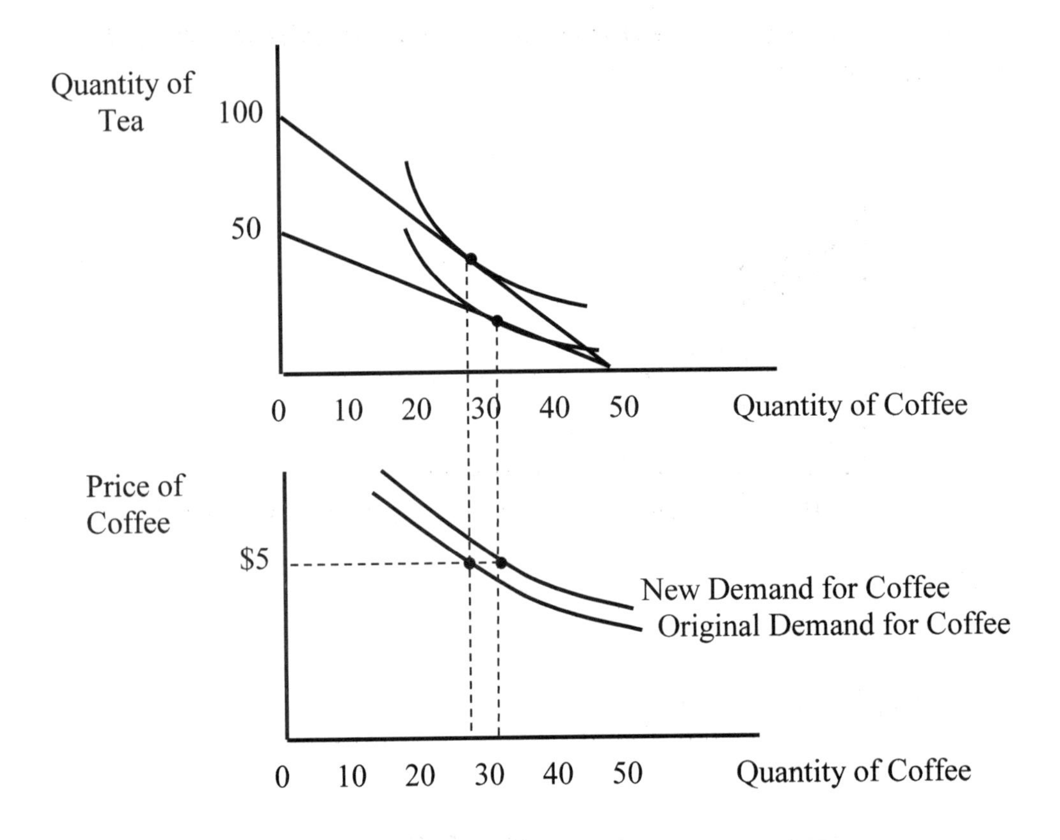

Typically, the demand for a product like coffee will increase, or shift to the right, when the price of a substitute product like tea increases. There are other changes that the model can be used to illustrate, and this tool of analysis is important in higher-level classes, but is not always presented in introductory classes.

NAME______________________________SECTION#__________
PRINT LAST NAME, FIRST NAME

CONSUMER BEHAVIOR

1. The law of diminishing marginal utility says that as consumption of one good increases relative to other goods, the additional satisfaction (marginal utility) gained from consuming yet another unit of that good:
   a. continues to increase as long as income is diminishing.
   b. eventually becomes zero, but never decreases.
   c. may decrease initially, but will eventually increase.
   d. may increase initially, but will eventually decrease.

2. Which of the following best illustrates the concept of diminishing marginal utility?
   a. Paying $24 for a concert ticket when you are willing and able to pay $40 for it
   b. Receiving less enjoyment from the second slice of pizza than from the first
   c. Receiving more utility from two slices of pizza than from one slice of pizza
   d. Liking a song better the fourth time you heard it than the first time you heard it

3. Economic models assume that consumers are:
   a. rational utility-maximizers with limited income.
   b. rational utility-maximizers with unlimited income.
   c. irrational decision-makers who do not know their own preferences.
   d. rational decision-makers who do not know how much income they can spend.

4. The cardinal approach to the study of consumer utility is based on the assumption that:
   a. the amount of utility, or satisfaction, which a consumer receives from a product can be measured.
   b. consumers can rank preferences, but cannot precisely measure utility.
   c. consumers base their decisions on what they can afford, not on what they prefer.
   d. consumers base their decisions on what they prefer, not on what they can afford.

5. The ordinal approach to the study of consumer utility requires that:
   a. the amount of utility, or satisfaction, which a consumer receives from a product can be measured.
   b. consumers can rank preferences, but cannot precisely measure utility.
   c. consumers base their decisions on what they can afford, not on what they prefer.
   d. consumers base their decisions on what they prefer, not on what they can afford.

6. Assume Emma's total utility is equal to 25 after eating an apple and rises to 40 after eating a second apple. These numbers indicate that:
   a. the law of diminishing marginal utility does not hold for Emma.
   b. the marginal utility of the second apple is greater than the marginal utility of the first apple.
   c. the marginal utility of the first apple is 25, and the marginal utility of the second apple is 15.
   d. the marginal utility of the first apple is 25, and the marginal utility of the second apple is 40.

NAME____SECTION#________________

PRINT LAST NAME, FIRST NAME

Use the table below to answer questions 7 through 10.

Quantity of Lattes	Total Utility	Marginal Utility
0	0	
		50
1	50	
		______
2	90	
		30
3	______	
		______
4	______	

7. The marginal utility of the second latte is equal to:
   a. 10.
   b. 20.
   c. 30.
   d. 40.

8. The total utility of three lattes is equal to:
   a. 50.
   b. 90.
   c. 120.
   d. 150.

9. Assuming diminishing marginal utility, the marginal utility of the fourth latte is:
   a. more than 120.
   b. between 90 and 120.
   c. between 30 and 90.
   d. less than 30.

10. Assuming diminishing marginal utility, the total utility of four lattes is:
    a. more than 150.
    b. between 120 and 150.
    c. between 30 and 90.
    d. less than 30.

NAME______________________________________SECTION#______________
PRINT LAST NAME, FIRST NAME

UTILITY

Use the table below to fill in the blanks.

Pizzas			Hamburgers		
Quantity	Total Utility	Marginal Utility	Quantity	Total Utility	Marginal Utility
0	0		0	0	
1	60	60	1	25	25
2	100	1) _____	2	4) _____	15
3	125	2) _____	3	5) _____	10
4	135	3) _____	4	6) _____	5

Assume the price per pizza is $10, while the price per hamburger is $5.

If the consumer has a budget of $25, what is the utility-maximizing combination of pizzas and hamburgers?

7) _________ pizzas and 8) _________ hamburgers

If the consumer has a budget of $40, what is the utility-maximizing combination of pizzas and hamburgers?

9) _________ pizzas and 10) _________ hamburgers

NAME____SECTION#______________

PRINT LAST NAME, FIRST NAME

DERIVING A DEMAND CURVE

Graph two budget lines assuming:

(1) price of X = $5, price of Y = $10, and the consumer's budget is $200; and
(2) price of X = $4, price of Y = $10, and the consumer's budget = $200.

Sketch an indifference curve for each budget line to show consumer equilibrium (you are free to decide where the equilibrium points should be). Use the equilibrium values shown in your graph to plot two points on the demand for X curve. Label all relevant values in your graphs.

Budget Lines and Indifference Curves:

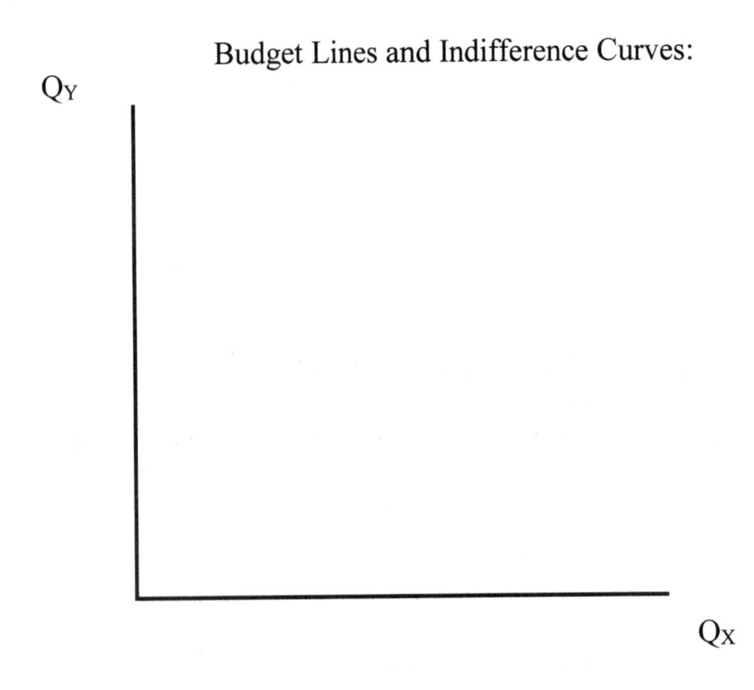

Demand Function:

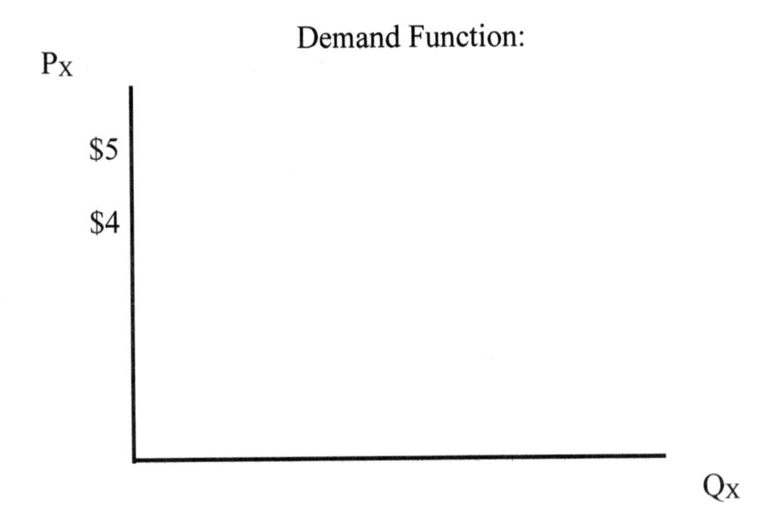

NAME____SECTION#______________

PRINT LAST NAME, FIRST NAME

BUDGET LINES AND INDIFFERENCE CURVES

1. As a consumer moves down along a given budget line:
   a. total utility is increasing.
   b. total utility remains unchanged.
   c. total expenditure is increasing.
   d. total expenditure remains unchanged.

2. As a consumer moves upward along a given indifference curve, total utility:
   a. first decreases, then increases.
   b. first increases, then decreases.
   c. remains constant.
   d. increases.

3. As a consumer moves downward along a given indifference curve, giving up some of good Y to get more of good X, the marginal rate of substitution of X for Y:
   a. decreases.
   b. increases.
   c. goes from positive to negative.
   d. goes from negative to positive.

4. A diminishing marginal rate of substitution:
   a. causes the indifference curve to bow inward.
   b. makes it impossible to identify a unique consumer equilibrium.
   c. implies that consumers will give up more Y to obtain an additional X when they have a larger amount of X.
   d. implies that consumers do not like to consume X and Y at the same time.

5. The theory of utility assumes that a consumer will attempt to:
   a. remain on the same indifference curve when income changes.
   b. remain on the same indifference curve when prices change.
   c. reach the highest possible indifference curve.
   d. reach the lowest possible budget line.

6. Indifference curve analysis indicates that consumer equilibrium exists:
   a. where the budget line is tangent to the indifference curve.
   b. at any point where the budget line intersects the indifference curve.
   c. where any two indifference curves intersect.
   d. where the slope of the indifference curve is equal to one.

NAME____SECTION#______________

PRINT LAST NAME, FIRST NAME

Use the graph below to answer questions 7 – 10.

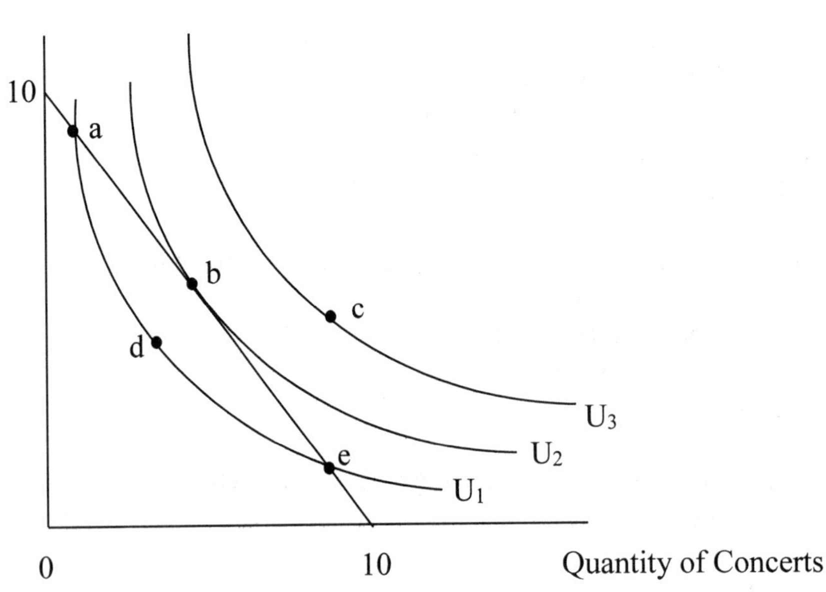

7. Consumer equilibrium is represented by point:
   a. a.
   b. b.
   c. c.
   d. d.

8. Points a, d, and e:
   a. are all equilibrium points.
   b. all cost the same.
   c. all give the consumer the same amount of utility.
   d. are all outside of the consumer's budget.

9. Points a, b, and e:
   a. are all equilibrium points.
   b. all cost the same.
   c. all give the consumer the same amount of utility.
   d. are all outside of the consumer's budget.

10. Which statement is ***false***?
    a. The consumer prefers combination d to combination e.
    b. If baseball game tickets cost $20 each, then the consumer has a budget of $200.
    c. An increase in income may allow this consumer to purchase combination c.
    d. Combinations d and e provide the same level of utility to the consumer.

CHAPTER 5 Elasticity

Elasticity measures the responsiveness of one variable to a change in another variable and is one of the most widely applied concepts in microeconomics. This chapter looks at several elasticity measures, starting with price elasticity of demand.

Price Elasticity of Demand

The Law of Demand indicates that price and quantity demanded are inversely related, ceteris paribus. Based on this relationship, sellers can predict that increasing the price of a product will lead to a decrease in the quantity demanded by buyers, assuming nothing changes except the price of the product. Similarly, decreasing the price of a product will lead to an increase in quantity demanded by buyers, ceteris paribus.

The **price elasticity of demand** measures the responsiveness of quantity demanded to a given change in the price of the product in percentage terms. This measure will always be negative as long as the relationship between price and quantity demanded is inverse, as implied by the Law of Demand.

Most analysts drop the negative sign and focus on the **absolute value** of the ratio to interpret price elasticity of demand coefficients, and this approach is taken here. When a value is written with bars (vertical lines) on both sides, this represents absolute value, which is always a positive number. For example, $|-2| = |2| = 2$. The symbol delta, Δ, is used to denote "change in."

Price elasticity of demand (E_D) is calculated using the formula:

$$E_D = \left| \frac{\%\Delta Q_D}{\%\Delta P} \right|$$

For example, if the price of a product increases by 5 percent and, as a result, quantity demanded falls by 10 percent, then the price elasticity of demand coefficient is:

$$E_D = |\%\Delta Q_D/\%\Delta P|$$

$$E_D = |-10\%/5\%|$$

$$E_D = 10/5$$

$$E_D = 2$$

Price elasticity of demand is a unit-less measure which can be greater than one, equal to one, or less than one. Depending on the value of price elasticity of demand, a response is classified as elastic ($E_D > 1$), unit elastic ($E_D = 1$) or inelastic ($E_D < 1$).

1) Elastic Demand: if price elasticity is **greater than one**, demand is **elastic** because the given price change causes a relatively large change in quantity demanded ($\%\Delta Q_D > \%\Delta P$). This means buyers ARE responsive to a change in price over the given price range.

Applying the formula for price elasticity of demand, there is no upper limit on price elasticity of demand, since $E_D = |\%\Delta Q_D/\%\Delta P|$ approaches infinity as $\%\Delta P$ approaches zero. The graph below illustrates **perfectly elastic demand**. Notice that this graph looks a little like the letter "E" and the word elastic begins with the letter "E", so it is easy to remember that a horizontal demand line is perfectly elastic.

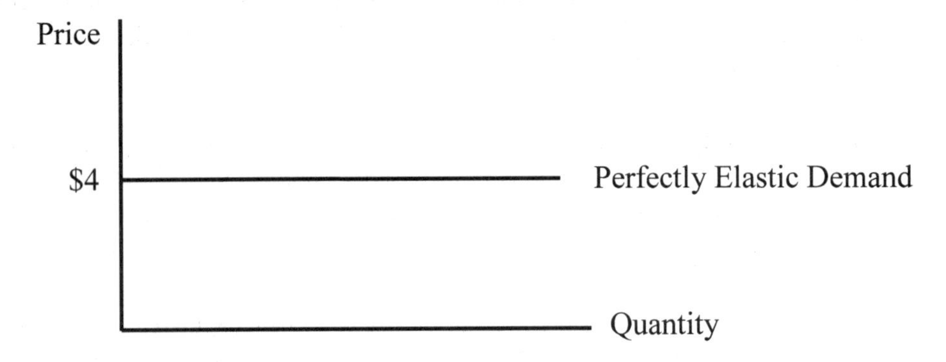

2) Unit Elastic Demand: if price elasticity is **equal to one**, demand is **unit elastic** because a given percentage change in price causes quantity demanded to change by the same percentage.

3) Inelastic Demand: if price elasticity is **less than one**, demand is **inelastic** because the given price change causes a relatively small change in quantity demanded ($\%\Delta Q_D < \%\Delta P$). This means buyers ARE NOT responsive to a change in price over the given price range.

If demand is perfectly inelastic, $E_D = |\%\Delta Q_D/\%\Delta P| = 0$ because $\%\Delta Q_D = 0$, so the lower limit on price elasticity of demand is zero. The graph below illustrates **perfectly inelastic demand**. Notice that this graph looks like the letter "I" and the word inelastic begins with the letter "I", so it is easy to remember that a vertical demand line is perfectly inelastic.

The diagram below summarizes the ranges of price elasticity of demand.

Perfectly Inelastic	Unit Elastic	Perfectly Elastic
0	1	approaching infinity
Relatively Inelastic	Relatively Elastic	

There are several factors that help predict whether the demand for a particular good or service is likely to be elastic or inelastic. The **determinants** of price elasticity of demand are:

1) **Luxury or Necessity**: a product that is a luxury will have a more elastic demand than a product deemed a necessity.

2) **The share of total budget**: the larger the proportion of a budget the good constitutes, the more elastic the demand and the greater the value of price elasticity.

3) **Availability of substitutes**: the greater the number of substitutes, the more elastic the demand and the greater the value of price elasticity.

4) **Time allowed for adjustment**: the more time consumers are given to adjust to a price change, the more elastic the demand and the greater the value of price elasticity.

A **luxury** is a product that consumers can easily do without and a **necessity** is a product that consumers cannot easily do without. This distinction can cause confusion if luxuries are assumed to be items purchased by wealthy people, since wealthy people generally do not pay as much attention to product prices as people on a budget. If an item is a luxury, demand is elastic because consumers can do without the item if the price goes up. If an item is a necessity, demand is inelastic because consumers still need to buy the item regardless of price.

The price of a particular product is a smaller **share of the budget** for someone with high income, so a rich person's demand for that product will likely be less elastic than a poor person's, ceteris paribus. The demand for items with a low price (like chewing gum) tends to be inelastic because these items are a small share of the total budget for most consumers. The demand for items with a high price (like automobiles) tends to be elastic because these items are a large share of the budget for most consumers.

The greater the **availability of substitutes**, the more elastic the demand. Demand is perfectly elastic if there are perfect substitutes. However, even if there are no perfect substitutes, demand will only be perfectly inelastic up to a relatively high price. There will be some maximum price beyond which people cannot or will not pay.

With respect to the **time** allowed for adjustment, the consumer's initial reaction to a price increase may be a relatively small decline in quantity demanded, but given time, consumers will likely find substitutes or ways to conserve, resulting in a greater decline in quantity demanded.

Consider the effect of an increase in the price of gasoline. The graph indicates that an increase in the price per gallon from $1.99 to $2.29 caused quantity demanded to fall from 10,000 gallons to 9,000 gallons.

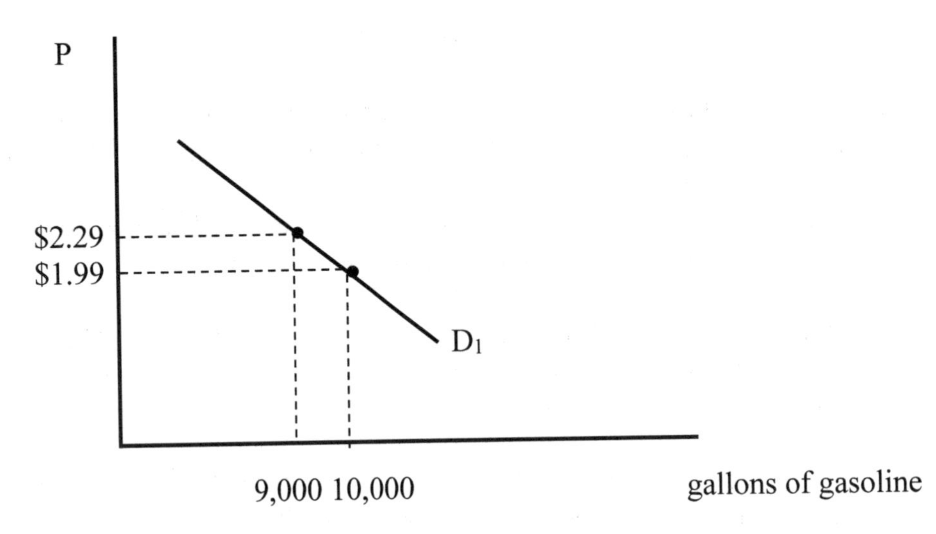

As more time passes and the price remains at $2.29 per gallon, consumers are likely to make some adjustments, like buying a more fuel-efficient car, relying more on public transportation, carpooling, or even moving to be closer to work. As a result of these adjustments, quantity demanded falls even further to 8,000, as shown in the graph below.

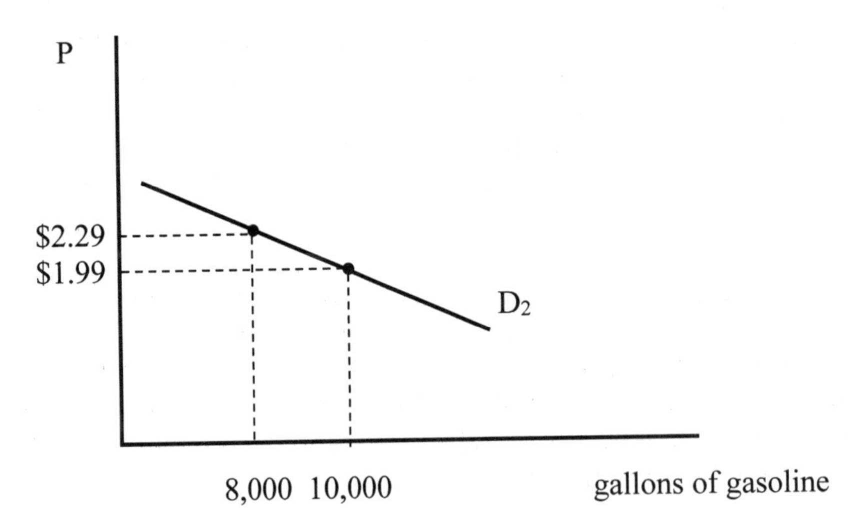

D_2 is more elastic than D_1 because the quantity change is larger and the price change is the same. Generally, demand becomes more elastic when consumers have more time to adjust to a change in price.

The percentage change in some variable, x, is normally calculated using the formula:

$$\%\Delta x = (x_2 - x_1)/x_1$$

For example, if your salary rose from $20,000 to $30,000, you could calculate the percentage change in your salary using this formula:

$$\frac{\$30{,}000 - \$20{,}000}{\$20{,}000} = \frac{\$10{,}000}{\$20{,}000} = 0.5 = 50\%$$

Calculating a percentage change in any variable is straightforward, but notice that if you apply the same approach but assume that your salary fell from $30,000 to $20,000, instead of increasing from $20,000 to $30,000, you would get a different answer.

$$\frac{\$20{,}000 - \$30{,}000}{\$\ 30{,}000} = \frac{-\$10{,}000}{\$30{,}000} = -0.33 = -33\%$$

Not only is the answer different in sign (negative rather than positive), but the numerical value is also different.

Using the **midpoint formula** to calculate percentage changes when measuring elasticities eliminates the problem of getting a different answer when price increases compared to when price decreases. This formula places the midpoint (or average) value in the denominator rather than the original value.

$$\%\Delta x = \frac{x_2 - x_1}{(x_1 + x_2)/2} = \frac{\text{change}}{\text{midpoint or average}}$$

Applying the midpoint formula to calculate the percentage change in salary:

$$\frac{\$30{,}000 - \$20{,}000}{\$25{,}000} = \frac{\$10{,}000}{\$25{,}000} = 0.4 = 40\%$$

$$\frac{\$20{,}000 - \$30{,}000}{\$25{,}000} = \frac{-\$10{,}000}{\$25{,}000} = -0.4 = -40\%$$

The midpoint formula yields the same value, a 40 percent change, whether salary rises from $20,000 to $30,000 or falls from $30,000 to $20,000. The same format is applied to price and quantity changes for elasticity calculations.

Applying the midpoint formula to calculate both the percentage change in quantity and the percentage change in price yields the formula for price elasticity of demand shown below.

$$E_D = \left| \frac{\dfrac{Q_2 - Q_1}{\left[\dfrac{Q_1 + Q_2}{2}\right]}}{\dfrac{P_2 - P_1}{\left[\dfrac{P_1 + P_2}{2}\right]}} \right|$$

In this equation, Q_1 is the initial quantity and Q_2 is the new quantity. The numerator represents the percentage change in quantity demanded, or $\%\Delta Q_D$. P_1 is the initial price and P_2 is the new price. The denominator represents the percentage change in price, or $\%\Delta P$. In order to calculate the price elasticity of demand coefficient, the midpoint formula applies the average percentage change formula twice, once to quantity data and again to price data.

The graph below shows a hypothetical demand curve and assumes a linear relationship between price and quantity demanded.

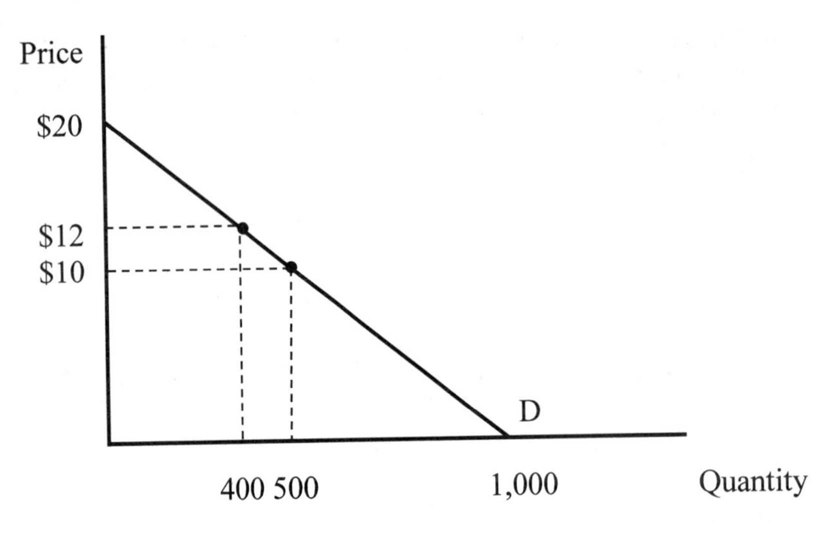

Plugging in the data, with $P_1 = \$12$, $Q_1 = 400$, $P_2 = \$10$, and $Q_2 = 500$, price elasticity is

$$E_D = \left| \frac{\dfrac{500 - 400}{\left[\dfrac{400 + 500}{2}\right]}}{\dfrac{10 - 12}{\left[\dfrac{12 + 10}{2}\right]}} \right| = \frac{\dfrac{100}{450}}{\dfrac{2}{11}} = \frac{0.22222}{0.18181} = 1.222$$

Below are examples to illustrate some of the results obtained thus far.

Example 1: Suppose consumers decrease the amount of specialty breads they buy at the grocery store by 20% when the price of these breads increases by 10%. The 10% increase in price results in a 20% decrease in quantity demanded; 20%/10% is 2, indicating that consumers are relatively responsive to a price change and that the demand for specialty breads is **elastic**.

Example 2: When the price of a can of Name Brand Hairspray is $2, quantity demanded is 1,000 cans. When the price of Name Brand Hairspray falls to $1.50, quantity demanded increases to 1,200 cans. Using the midpoint formula to calculate percentage changes, the price elasticity of demand for Name Brand Hairspray is 0.636 (you should verify this). Since price elasticity is less than one, consumers are not very responsive to the price change and the demand for Name Brand Hairspray is **inelastic**.

Example 3: If the quantity demanded of an output increases by 10% when the price of the output decreases by 10%, the percentage change in quantity demanded is equal to the percentage change in price. The price elasticity coefficient is equal to one, and demand is **unit elastic**.

Although slope is constant when demand is linear, price elasticity changes, as shown in the graph below.

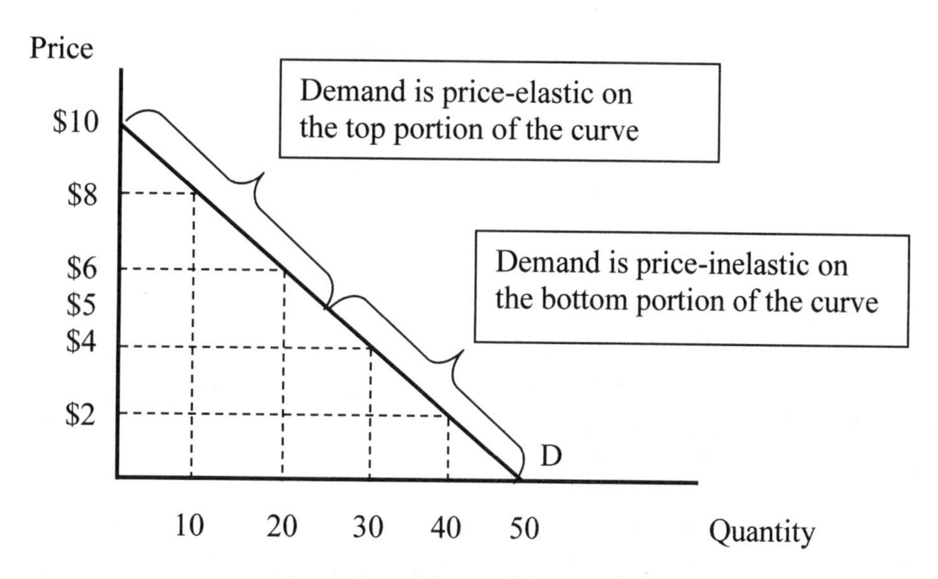

As price falls from $8 to $6, for example, quantity demanded increases from 10 to 20. Using the midpoint formula, the percentage change in quantity demanded is 10/15 = 67 percent, and the percentage change in price is 2/7 = 29 percent (approximately). The price elasticity of demand is therefore 67/29 = 2.3, which is greater than one so demand is elastic on this portion of the curve.

If price falls from $4 to $2, and quantity demanded increases from 30 to 40 units, price elasticity of demand is equal to 29/67 = 0.43 (approximately), which is less than one, so demand is inelastic on this portion of the curve.

Information about a product's price elasticity of demand can help a firm predict the impact of a price change on the firm's total revenue. Total revenue is the term used for what the firm receives from the sale of output and is found by multiplying the price of each unit (price = P) by the quantity of output sold (quantity = Q). Total revenue is price times quantity, or

Total Revenue = Price x Quantity = P x Q

The relationship between price elasticity of demand and total revenue can be illustrated using a demand schedule and the demand curve drawn using the data in the demand schedule. The following table is the demand schedule that corresponds to the demand curve that was used on the previous page to show how price elasticity varies along a linear demand curve.

Price	Quantity Demanded	P*Q = Total Revenue
$10	0	$ 0
9	5	45
8	10	80
7	15	105
6	20	120
5	25	125
4	30	120
3	35	105
2	40	80
1	45	45
0	50	0

When price is $8, quantity demanded is 10 and total revenue is $8 x 10 = $80. When price is $6, quantity demanded is 20 and total revenue is $6 x 20 = $120. Lowering price from $8 to $6 causes total revenue to increase from $80 to $120. Recall from the previous page that price elasticity of demand is approximately 2.3 on this portion of demand, so demand is elastic since 2.3 > 1. *Lowering price when demand is elastic leads to an increase in total revenue.*

When price is $4, total revenue is $4 x 30 = $120; when price is $2, total revenue is $2 x 40 = $80. Lowering price from $4 to $2 causes total revenue to decrease from $120 to $80. Recall from the previous page that price elasticity of demand is approximately 0.43 on this portion of demand, so demand is inelastic since 0.43 < 1. *Lowering price when demand is inelastic leads to a decrease in total revenue.*

Further investigation reveals that total revenue is at a maximum at the midpoint on the demand curve, where price is $5; at P = $5, quantity is 25 and total revenue is $5 x 25 = $125. The midpoint of the demand curve is also where demand is unit elastic.

The ranges of elasticity and the impact of a price decrease are summarized below.

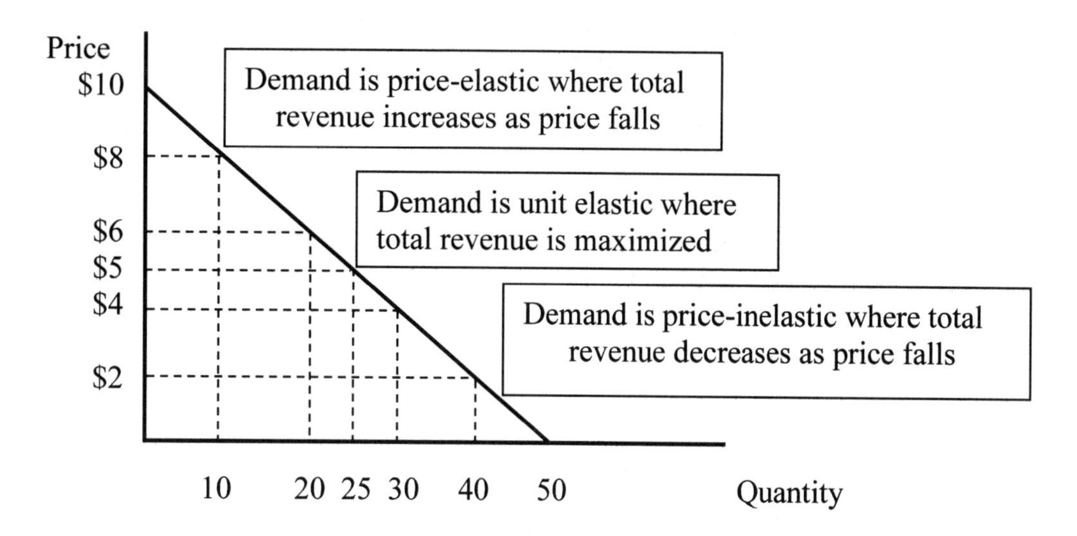

The total revenue function below shows the relationship between quantity demanded and total revenue, plotting data from the chart on the previous page.

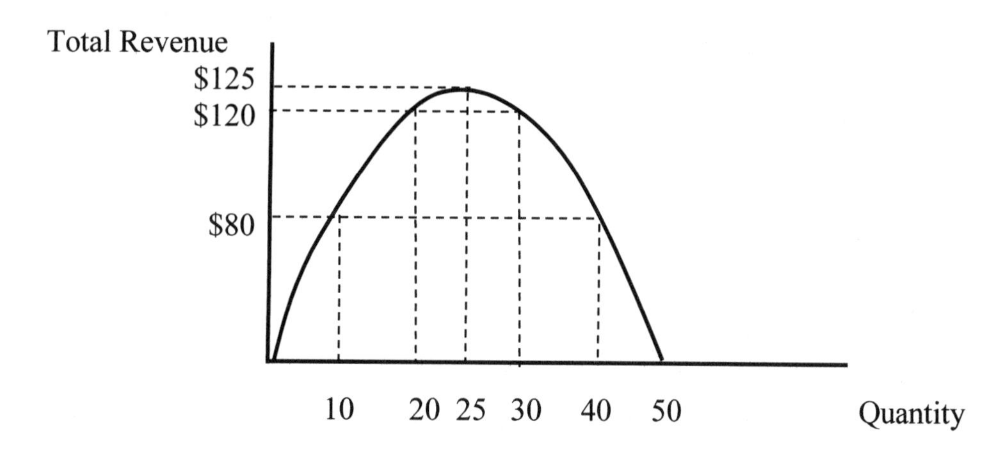

Total revenue initially increases as price is lowered because demand is elastic on the top portion of the demand curve. The point where the total revenue function is maximized (Q = 25 and TR = $125) corresponds to the point where price elasticity of demand is equal to one and demand is unit elastic. In the inelastic range of the demand curve, total revenue falls as price falls.

The concept of elasticity and understanding the relationship between price elasticity of demand and total revenue is important for firms with price-setting ability. Knowing whether or not demand is elastic or inelastic can help a firm when it is considering price changes for its product. For example, suppose a health club has estimated price elasticity to be 1.8, which implies that demand is elastic. If demand is elastic, total revenue increases when price is reduced. Specifically, the price elasticity of demand indicates that a 10% price cut will generate an 18% increase in memberships, resulting in higher revenue for the club.

Elastic Demand: When demand is elastic, raising price (P) will cause total revenue (P x Q) to fall and lowering price will cause total revenue to rise.

For elastic demand, a given change in price results in a relatively large change in quantity demanded.

↓P → ↑Q_D → ↑TR

In the case of a price decrease, the positive effect on revenue of higher quantity demanded is more than enough to compensate for the lower price received on each unit sold, so the price cut leads to an increase in total revenue.

↑P → ↓Q_D → ↓TR

In the case of a price increase, the positive effect of a higher price is small compared to the negative effect of reduced quantity demanded, so the price increase causes total revenue to fall.

Inelastic Demand: When demand is inelastic, raising price (P) will cause total revenue (P x Q) to rise and lowering price will cause total revenue to fall.

For inelastic demand, a given change in price results in a relatively small change in quantity demanded.

↓P → ↑Q_D → ↓TR

In the case of a price decrease, the negative effect on revenue of a lower price per unit dominates the positive effect of higher quantity demanded, so the price cut reduces total revenue.

↑P → ↓Q_D → ↑TR

In the case of a price increase, the positive effect of a higher price dominates the negative effect of lower quantity demanded, so the price hike causes total revenue to increase.

Unit-Elastic Demand: If demand is unit-elastic, then the two effects offset each other. For demand to be unit elastic, the product price would have to already be in the midpoint of the demand function. If this is the case, the firm is already maximizing revenue so it is not possible to increase total revenue by either raising or lowering price.

Complete the example below to practice some of the calculations presented so far. First, calculate total revenue (P x Q) at each point assuming the quantity sold by the firm is equal to the quantity demanded.

	Price	Quantity Demanded	Total Revenue
Point A	$36	10	$________
Point B	$28	30	$________
Point C	$20	50	$________
Point D	$12	70	$________
Point E	$4	90	$________

Verify that total revenue increases from $360 at point A to $840 at point B and $1,000 at point C, then falls back to $840 at point D and $360 at point E.

Next, calculate price elasticity of demand (E^D) for each segment of the demand curve using the midpoint formula.

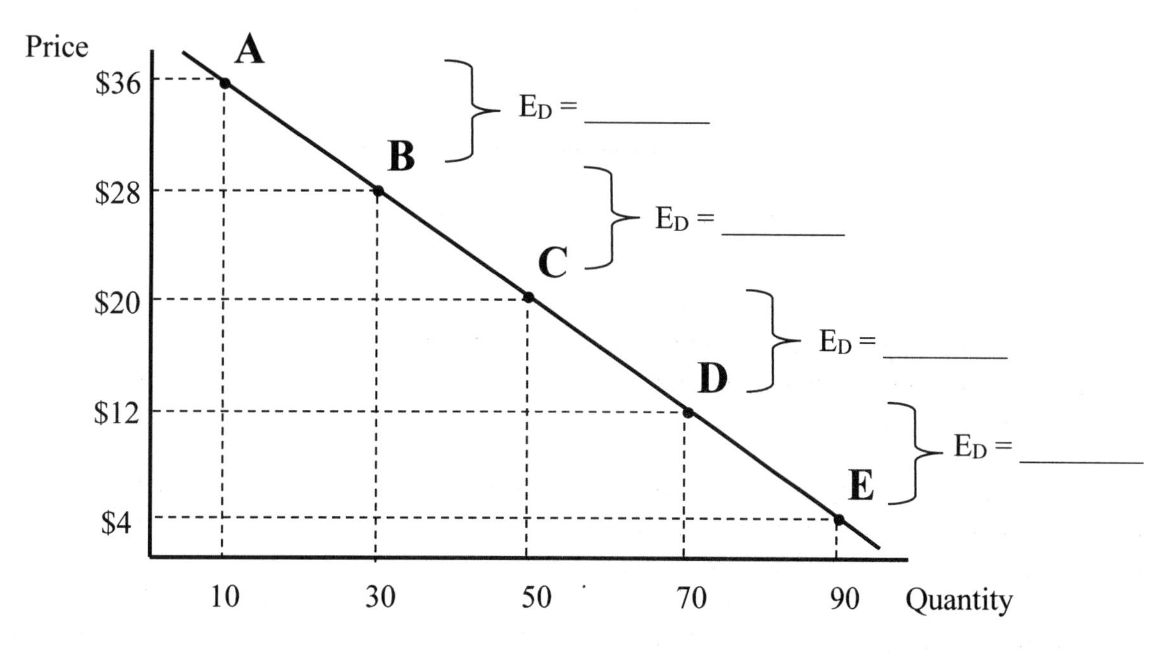

Verify that price elasticity of demand is equal to 4 along segment AB, but falls to 1.5 along segment BC. On the bottom portion of this demand curve, price elasticity changes from approximately 0.67 along segment CD to 0.25 along segment DE.

These calculations support the conclusions reached in the discussion: when demand is elastic (on the top portion), lowering price causes total revenue to increase; when demand is inelastic (on the bottom portion), lowering price causes total revenue to fall.

Income Elasticity

An important determinant of demand is income. The responsiveness of quantity demanded to a change in income is **income elasticity of demand**, which is calculated using the equation below. Do not take the absolute value when calculating income elasticity.

$$E_I = \frac{\%\Delta Q_D}{\%\Delta \text{Income}}$$

When income changes, the demand curve shifts, so there is both a change in demand and a change in quantity demanded at every price, as shown in the graph below.

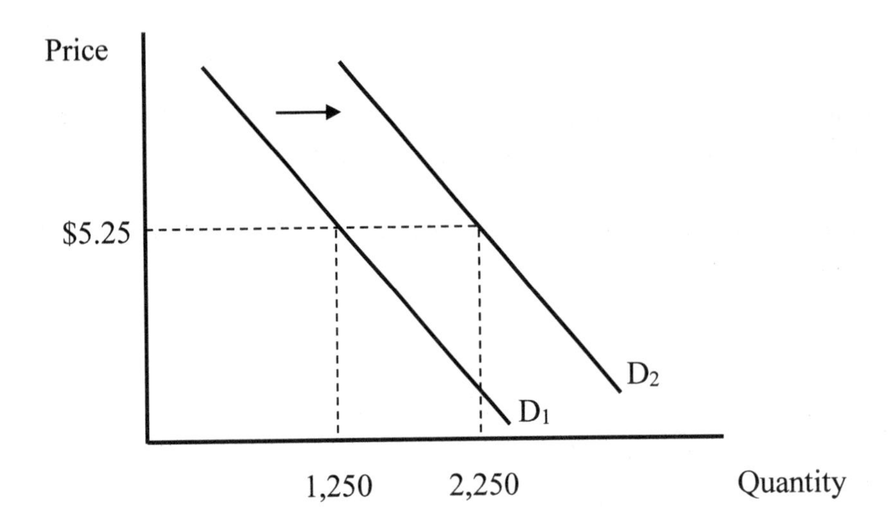

The graph indicates that consumers choose to buy more of this product, not because price has fallen, but because income has increased. Before relating an increase or decrease in income to an increase or decrease in demand, review the terms 'normal good' and 'inferior good' from the chapter on supply and demand.

For **normal goods**, an increase in income leads to an increase in the demand for the product. Income elasticity measures the size of the increase in the amount purchased relative to the change in income that led to this increase in demand. For normal goods, income elasticity is a positive number, because an increase in income causes the demand for normal goods to increase, and a decrease in income causes the demand for normal goods to decrease. If a 10% increase in income causes consumers to increase their spending on health care by 5%, income elasticity for health care is equal to 0.5.

If the income elasticity coefficient is negative, indicating that consumers buy less of this product when income rises, and more of this product when income falls, the product is an **inferior good**. If a 10% increase in income causes consumers to decrease their spending on generic canned goods by 2%, income elasticity is equal to -0.2.

Cross Elasticity

The demand for a product may change in response to a change in the price of a related product. Remember that when two products are **substitutes** for one another, an increase in the price of one causes an increase in the demand for the other, and vice versa. For example, a consumer might respond to an increase in the price of hot dogs by purchasing more hamburgers, implying that hamburgers are a good substitute for hot dogs.

When two products are **complements**, an increase in the price of one causes a decrease in the demand for the other, and vice versa. For example, a consumer might respond to an increase in the price of peanut butter by purchasing less jelly.

The **cross elasticity of demand** is the percentage change in the quantity demanded of one product (product X) divided by the percentage change in the price of a different product (product Y). It is measured using the formula below. Again, do not take the absolute value because the sign of cross elasticity indicates whether pairs of goods are substitutes or complements.

$$E_X = \frac{\%\Delta Q_D \text{ of } X}{\%\Delta P \text{ of } Y}$$

If the two products, X and Y, are totally unrelated, then cross elasticity is zero. The cross elasticity is used to determine whether two products are substitutes or complements.

- If $E_X > 0$, then X and Y are substitutes
- If $E_X < 0$, then X and Y are complements

In 1956, Du Pont, a manufacturer of cellophane wrapping, was accused of having a monopoly, which is a violation of U.S. law. Du Pont's defense was based on the cross elasticity of demand between cellophane wrapping and other wrapping materials (aluminum foil and wax paper). The cross elasticity between cellophane and other wrapping materials was positive and large enough to convince the court that other wrapping materials were a close substitute for cellophane wrapping, demonstrating that Du Pont was not a monopolist.

Price Elasticity of Supply

The law of supply indicates a direct relationship between price and quantity supplied, ceteris paribus. **Price elasticity of supply** (E_S) is defined as the percentage change in quantity supplied divided by the percentage change in price:

$$E_S = \frac{\%\Delta Q_S}{\%\Delta P}$$

Suppose a 10% increase in the price of a product leads to a 5% increase in the quantity supplied. Then, price elasticity of supply is 5%/10% = 0.5, so supply is inelastic.

- If $E_S = 0$, then $\%\Delta Q_S = 0$, and supply is perfectly inelastic (the supply curve is drawn as a vertical line)
- If $E_S < 1$, then $\%\Delta Q_S < \%\Delta P$, and supply is relatively inelastic
- If $E_S > 1$, then $\%\Delta Q_S > \%\Delta P$, and supply is relatively elastic
- E_S approaches infinity as $\%\Delta P$ approaches zero, so when E_S is infinitely large (or $\%\Delta P = 0$), supply is perfectly elastic (the supply curve is drawn as a horizontal line)

One of the main determinants of price elasticity of supply is the amount of time allowed for adjustment. Producers react to a higher product price by increasing output, but increasing output takes time and may not be possible in a very short period of time. Supply is more elastic when more time is allowed for firms to adjust to a given price change.

As an example, consider the number of parking spaces available on a university campus. An increase in the demand for parking spaces, perhaps caused by increased enrollment at the university, causes an increase in the equilibrium price of parking spaces in the graph below. Supply is assumed to be perfectly inelastic if the university does not have the time, space, or funds to build any additional parking lots.

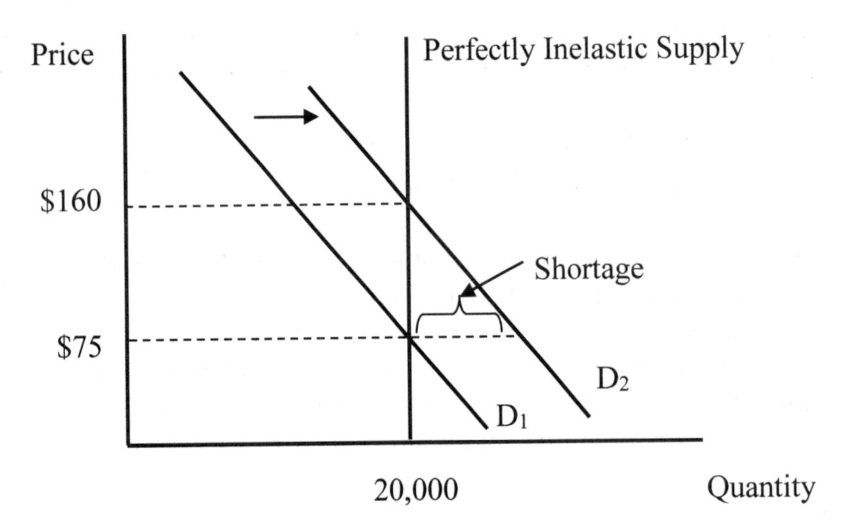

Immediately following the increase in demand, there will be a shortage of parking spaces. If the price is flexible, then a shortage will drive price up from $75 to $160. At the new price of $160, quantity demanded is equal to quantity supplied, so every student who is willing and able to pay $160 for a parking sticker will be able to obtain one. If the university does not adjust the price to $160, then there will be a shortage, and spaces will probably be allocated on the basis of first-come, first-serve, or perhaps using another form of rationing.

As more time passes, the university will likely respond to complaints about expensive parking stickers or a shortage of spaces by building more parking lots or parking garages, so the supply curve would then be upward-sloping to show an increase in the quantity supplied following an increase in the price.

NAME______________________________SECTION#__________
PRINT LAST NAME, FIRST NAME

PRICE ELASTICITY OF DEMAND

1. Price elasticity of demand measures how much, in percentage terms:
   a. demand falls (shifts to the left) when price rises.
   b. demand rises (shifts to the right) when price falls.
   c. quantity demanded falls when price rises.
   d. quantity demanded rises when price rises.

Use the graphs below to answer questions 2 and 3.

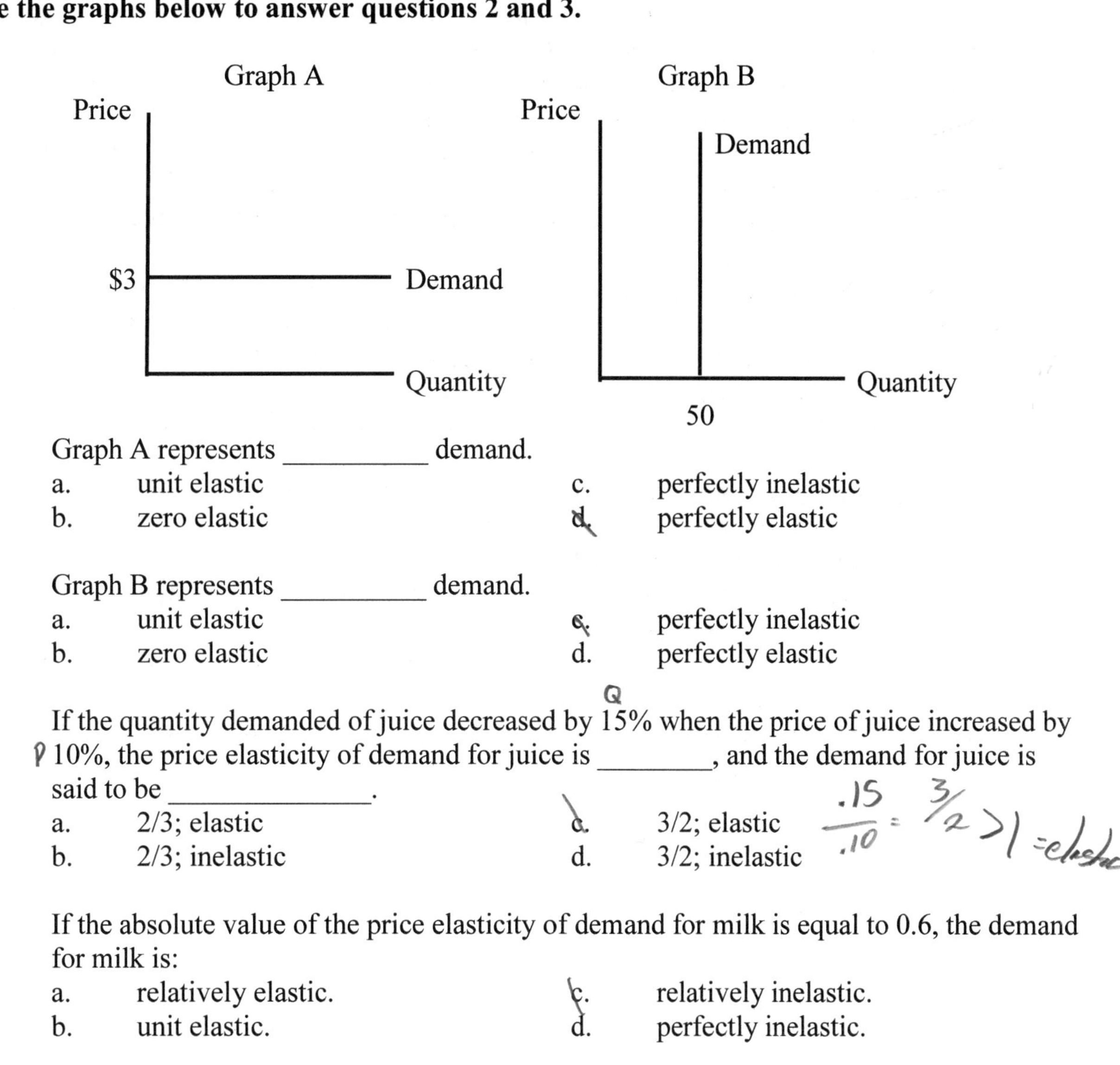

2. Graph A represents __________ demand.
   a. unit elastic
   b. zero elastic
   c. perfectly inelastic
   d. perfectly elastic

3. Graph B represents __________ demand.
   a. unit elastic
   b. zero elastic
   c. perfectly inelastic
   d. perfectly elastic

4. If the quantity demanded of juice decreased by 15% when the price of juice increased by 10%, the price elasticity of demand for juice is ________, and the demand for juice is said to be ______________.
   a. 2/3; elastic
   b. 2/3; inelastic
   c. 3/2; elastic
   d. 3/2; inelastic

5. If the absolute value of the price elasticity of demand for milk is equal to 0.6, the demand for milk is:
   a. relatively elastic.
   b. unit elastic.
   c. relatively inelastic.
   d. perfectly inelastic.

6. Products that are necessities with no close substitutes tend to have _____ demand curves.
   a. perfectly elastic
   b. unit elastic
   c. elastic
   d. inelastic

NAME____SECTION#______________

PRINT LAST NAME, FIRST NAME

7. Ceteris paribus, the demand for a product will be more price-inelastic when:
   a. the product is a necessity.
   b. there are very few close substitutes available.
   c. very little time is allowed for consumers to adjust to a price change.
   d. all of the above result in a more price-inelastic demand.

8. A luxury is defined as a product that:
   a. consumers can more easily do without, compared to a necessity, so the demand for a luxury tends to be more price-inelastic than the demand for a necessity.
   b. consumers can more easily do without, compared to a necessity, so the demand for a luxury tends to be more price-elastic than the demand for a necessity.
   c. is only purchased by wealthy individuals, so the demand for a luxury is always perfectly inelastic since wealthy individuals pay no attention to product prices.
   d. is only purchased by wealthy individuals, so the demand for a luxury is always perfectly elastic since wealthy individuals pay no attention to product prices.

9. If the absolute value of the price elasticity of demand coefficient for movie tickets is 1.2, then the demand for movie tickets is ________, and an increase in the price of movie tickets will lead to a(n) ________ in total revenue for movie theatres.
   a. inelastic; increase
   b. inelastic; decrease
   c. elastic; increase
   d. elastic; decrease

10. If the demand function is linear and downward-sloping, demand is:
   a. inelastic on the top portion, unit elastic in the middle, and elastic on the bottom portion of the demand function.
   b. elastic on the top portion, unit elastic in the middle, and inelastic on the bottom portion of the demand function.
   c. unit elastic on the top portion, elastic in the middle, and inelastic on the bottom portion of the demand function.
   d. elastic at each price if the function is very flat and inelastic at each price if the function is very steep.

NAME________________________________ SECTION#____________

PRINT LAST NAME, FIRST NAME

PRICE ELASTICITY OF DEMAND

1. Price elasticity of demand is calculated as:
   - a. the percentage change in quantity demanded divided by the percentage change in price.
   - b. the percentage change in price divided by the percentage change in quantity demanded.
   - c. the responsiveness of equilibrium price to a shift in the demand curve.
   - d. the responsiveness of equilibrium price to a shift in the supply curve.

2. If the quantity demanded of coffee decreased by 10% when the price of coffee increased by 15%, the price elasticity of demand for coffee is ________, and the demand for coffee is said to be ______________.
   - a. 2/3; elastic
   - b. 2/3; inelastic
   - c. 3/2; elastic
   - d. 3/2; inelastic

3. If the quantity demanded of soda decreased by 15% when the price of soda increased by 15%, the price elasticity of demand for soda is ________, and the demand for soda is said to be ______________.
   - a. 0; unit elastic
   - b. 0; inelastic
   - c. 1; unit elastic
   - d. 1; inelastic

4. If the public transit system raises its fares and experiences an increase in total revenue as a result, the demand for public transportation in this price range is:
   - a. inelastic.
   - b. elastic.
   - c. unit elastic.
   - d. neither elastic nor inelastic.

5. When the price of a hotdog at the ballpark is $2.00, quantity demanded is 1,000. When the price of a hotdog at the ballpark is $2.50, quantity demanded is 850. Using the **midpoint formula**, price elasticity of demand is approximately _______, so an increase in the price of a hotdog ________ total revenue.
   - a. 1.4; increases
   - b. 1.4; decreases
   - c. 0.7; increases
   - d. 0.7; decreases

6. Assume a wireless company has hired you as a consultant to help determine what price to charge for local weekday airtime. You establish that the price elasticity of demand for local weekday airtime is 0.62. If the goal of the company is to increase the revenue generated from the sale of weekday airtime, you should advise the company to:
   - a. raise the price of weekday air time because demand is elastic.
   - b. raise the price of weekday air time because demand is inelastic.
   - c. lower the price of weekday air time because demand is elastic.
   - d. lower the price of weekday air time because demand is inelastic.

NAME____SECTION#______________

PRINT LAST NAME, FIRST NAME

7. An increase in the price of a small town newspaper from $.70 to $.90 results in a decrease in sales from 2,880 to 1,920 per day. The price elasticity of demand coefficient (using the **midpoint formula**) is ________ for this newspaper.
   a. 0.25 b. 0.625 c. 1.4 d. 1.6

8. At a typical store, there are dozens of choices on the breakfast cereal aisle. Therefore, the demand for Cheerios is expected to be:
   a. price-elastic since consumers can switch to corn flakes or shredded wheat if the price of Cheerios increases.
   b. price-inelastic since consumers can switch to corn flakes or shredded wheat if the price of Cheerios increases.
   c. price-elastic since consumers who prefer Cheerios would never consider switching to corn flakes or shredded wheat.
   d. price-inelastic since it would not be possible for the price of corn flakes or shredded wheat to remain the same when the price of Cheerios is increasing.

9. When the price of gasoline goes up, the resulting fall in consumption is likely to be larger after a longer period of time has passed because consumers have found ways to conserve. For this reason, the demand for gasoline is thought to be:
   a. more elastic in the long run than in the short run.
   b. more inelastic in the long run than in the short run.
   c. highly elastic in both the short run and the long run.
   d. highly inelastic in both the short run and the long run.

Use the graph below to answer question 10.

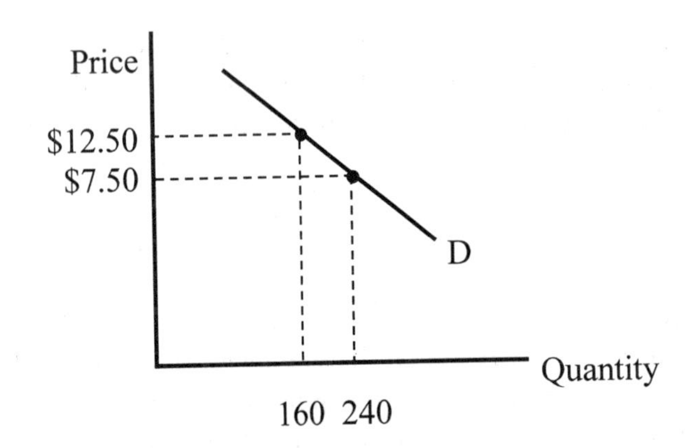

10. As price falls from $12.50 to $7.50 and quantity demanded increases from 160 to 240 units, the price elasticity of demand, calculated using the **midpoint formula**, is equal to:
   a. 50 percent divided by 40 percent, which is 1.25 so demand is elastic.
   b. 50 percent divided by 40 percent, which is 1.25 so demand is inelastic.
   c. 40 percent divided by 50 percent, which is 0.8 so demand is elastic.
   d. 40 percent divided by 50 percent, which is 0.8 so demand is inelastic.

NAME____SECTION#_______________
PRINT LAST NAME, FIRST NAME

PRICE ELASTICITY OF DEMAND

Use the graph below to answer questions 1 through 5:

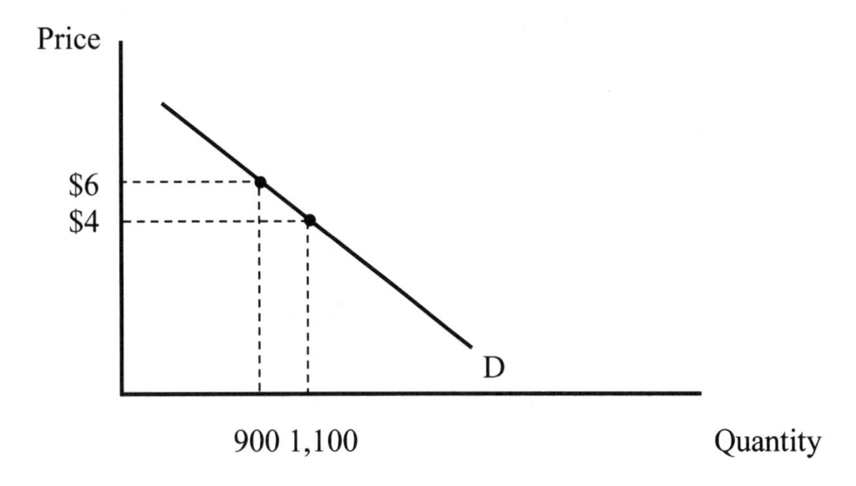

1. If price increases from $4 to $6 or decreases from $6 to $4, the percentage change in price is equal to (show your work, using the midpoint formula):

2. If quantity increases from 900 to 1,100 or decreases from 1,100 to 900, the percentage change in quantity is equal to (show your work, using the midpoint formula):

3. Given the percentage change in quantity and the percentage change in price calculated above, the price elasticity of demand coefficient is equal to (show your work):

4. Based on the price elasticity of demand coefficient calculated above, is demand elastic or inelastic over this price range?

5. If price is $6 and firms are able to sell 900 units, total revenue = $______________

   If price is $4 and firms are able to sell 1,100 units, total revenue = $_____________

NAME____SECTION#____________

PRINT LAST NAME, FIRST NAME

PRICE ELASTICITY OF DEMAND AND TOTAL REVENUE

Fill in the blanks and plot all of the points on the demand curve below. Use the **midpoint formula** to calculate price elasticity of demand, following the example shown. Plot the Total Revenue function in the space below the demand function.

Price	Q_D	Total Revenue	Price Elasticity of Demand	Elastic/Inelastic?
$2.25	100	$225		
			______________________	__________
$1.75	300	$525		
			[(200/400)/(0.5/1.5)] = [(1/2)/(1/3)] = 3/2	Elastic
$1.25	500	$________		
			______________________	__________
$0.75	700	$________		
			______________________	__________
$0.25	900	$________		

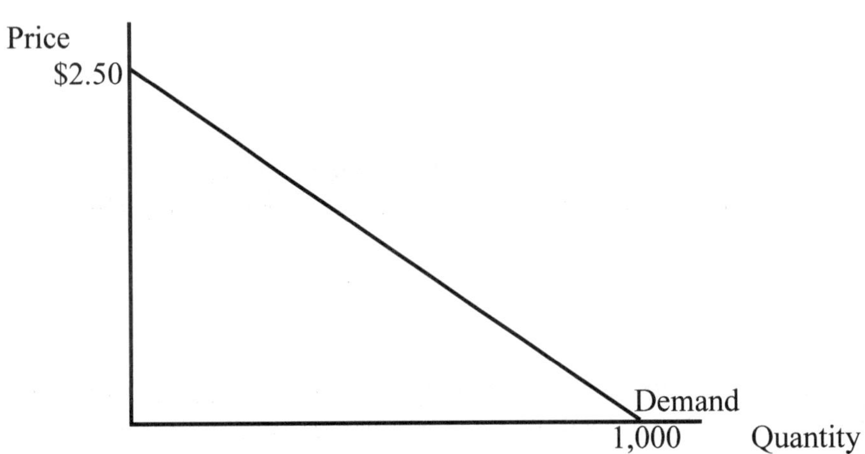

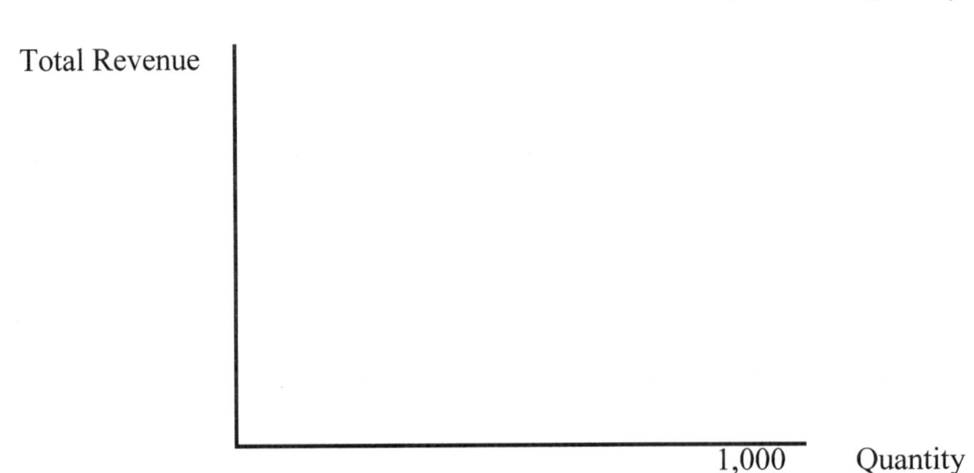

NAME____SECTION#______________

PRINT LAST NAME, FIRST NAME

OTHER ELASTICITY MEASURES

1. If the income elasticity for restaurant meals is equal to 1.4, then restaurant meals are:
   a. normal goods.
   b. inferior goods.
   c. substitute goods.
   d. complementary goods.

2. If the income elasticity coefficient for restaurant Ramen noodles is -0.5, then Ramen noodles are:
   a. normal goods.
   b. inferior goods.
   c. substitute goods.
   d. complementary goods.

3. If a 20 percent increase in consumer income results in a 5 percent increase in the quantity of potato chips sold, then the income elasticity for potato chips is equal to:
   a. -1/4 and potato chips are an inferior good.
   b. 1/4 and potato chips are a normal good.
   c. -4 and potato chips are an inferior good.
   d. 4 and potato chips are a normal good.

4. If the income elasticity for steak is equal to 0.5, then steak is a(n) _____ good and a 10% increase in income will cause a __________ % increase in the quantity demanded.
   a. normal; 5
   b. normal; 20
   c. inferior; 5
   d. inferior; 20

5. Which of the following pairs of goods is most likely to have a cross elasticity coefficient of –1.2?
   a. Beef and chicken
   b. Hot dogs and relish
   c. Hamburgers and hot dogs
   d. French fries and potato chips

6. Which of the following pairs of goods is most likely to have a cross elasticity coefficient of 1.5?
   a. Pancakes and syrup
   b. Eggs and toast
   c. Bagels and toast
   d. Coffee and cream

7. If a 10 percent increase in the price of cream cheese reduces consumption of bagels by 5 percent, the cross elasticity of demand is equal to:
   a. ½ and bagels and cream cheese are substitutes.
   b. ½ and bagels and cream cheese are complements.
   c. -½ and bagels and cream cheese are substitutes.
   d. -½ and bagels and cream cheese are complements.

NAME____SECTION#______________

PRINT LAST NAME, FIRST NAME

8. If the quantity supplied of health care increases 10 percent following a 25 percent increase in health care prices, the supply of health care is:
   a. inelastic and the price elasticity of supply coefficient is 0.4.
   b. inelastic and the price elasticity of supply coefficient is 2.5.
   c. elastic and the price elasticity of supply coefficient is 0.4.
   d. elastic and the price elasticity of supply coefficient is 2.5.

9. If a 20 percent decrease in price causes quantity supplied to decrease by 25 percent, then the price elasticity of supply is equal to:
   a. 1.25 so supply is relatively elastic.
   b. 1.25 so supply is relatively inelastic.
   c. 0.8 so supply is relatively elastic.
   d. 0.8 so supply is relatively inelastic.

10. If the supply of land is perfectly inelastic, then an increase in the demand for land caused by population growth will lead to:
    a. higher land prices, but no change in the equilibrium quantity of land.
    b. lower land prices, but no change in the equilibrium quantity of land.
    c. higher land prices and an increase in the equilibrium quantity of land.
    d. lower land prices and a decrease in the equilibrium quantity of land.

PRACTICE EXAM I

Answer the questions to the best of your ability, without relying on the book or your notes, and then check your answers using the key on ***page 112****. Use the exam to identify areas of weakness and ask questions to strengthen your understanding of these areas as you prepare for the exam.*

1. Scarcity exists because:
   a. it is impossible to increase the quantity of available resources.
   b. it is impossible to increase the productivity of available resources.
   c. currently available resources are not sufficient to produce everything people want and need.
   d. currently available resources are sufficient to produce everything people want and need.

2. "The government should raise the minimum wage" is an example of a:
   a. factual statement.
   b. ceteris paribus statement.
   c. positive statement.
   d. normative statement.

3. Which of the following would most likely be studied in a *micro*economics course?
   a. The relationship between national output and the rate of unemployment
   b. The strategy used by the owners of a competitive firm to maximize profits
   c. The relationship between the national money supply and the price level
   d. The strategy used by the Federal Reserve, the nation's central bank, to lower interest rates

4. Incorrectly concluding that because tax reform measures benefit some individuals, the measures are also beneficial for the economy as a whole is an example of the:
   a. post hoc fallacy (association-causation issue).
   b. fallacy of division.
   c. fallacy of false cause.
   d. fallacy of composition.

5. Which of the following is ***not*** an example of the factor of production or economic resource referred to as capital?
   a. An office building
   b. Computers used by a tax preparation business
   c. Lawn mowers owned by a landscaping firm
   d. Money used to start a new business

6. The *opportunity cost* of attending school is:
   a. the same for all people.
   b. highest for people who gave up good jobs to attend school.
   c. highest for people who continue to work while attending school.
   d. equal to the tuition charged by each school.

7. A command economy is characterized by:
   a. decentralized decisions about how to allocate resources.
   b. government ownership or control of most resources.
   c. voluntary exchange and incentives to exchange.
   d. efficient allocation of scarce resources.

B

8. The business sector sells goods and services in the product market in order to generate ______, which then creates ______ for the household sector.
   a. costs; revenue
   b. revenue; income
   c. profit; costs
   d. costs; profit

B

9. A country experiences a trade deficit when:
   a. the value of exports exceeds the value of imports.
   b. some of the goods and services produced in the business sector are exported.
   c. the value of imports exceeds the value of exports.
   d. some of the goods and services purchased by the household sector are imported.

C

Use the production possibilities schedule below to answer the next two questions.

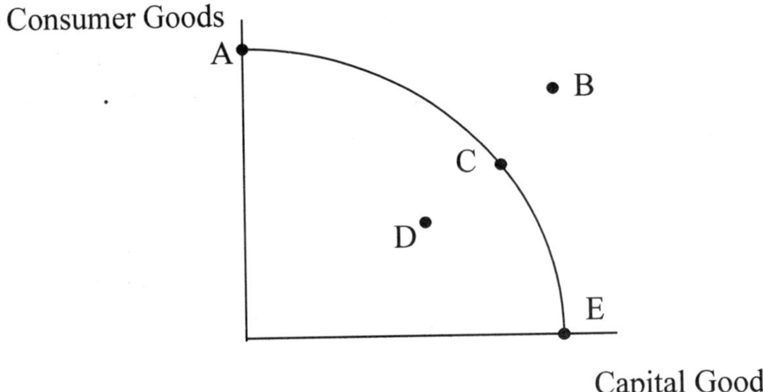

10. This economy must experience an increase in technology and/or an increase in resources in order to produce at point:
    a. A.   b. B.   c. C.   d. D.

B

11. Production is inefficient at point:
    a. A.   b. B.   c. C.   d. D.

D

12. A rightward shift of a production possibilities frontier (curve) indicates that:
    a. economic activity is declining.
    b. economic growth has occurred.
    c. opportunity costs are decreasing.
    d. opportunity costs are constant.

B

Use the production possibilities schedule below to answer the next three questions.

Combination	School Buses	Army Tanks
A	50	0
B	46	10
C	36	20
D	___	30
E	0	40

13. If the opportunity cost of moving from combination C to combination D is 14 school buses, how many school buses are produced at combination D?

a. 14
b. 22
c. 36
d. 50

14. This economy can produce 46 school buses and 20 army tanks if:

a. it uses current technology efficiently.
b. it fully employs available resources.
c. resources and technology remain fixed over time.
d. the economy experiences economic growth.

15. This production possibilities schedule:
a. illustrates a one-to-one trade-off between the production of buses and tanks.
b. reflects the law of increasing opportunity costs.
c. indicates that resources are equally well-suited to producing both tanks and buses.
d. implies that this economy is not using its available resources efficiently.

16. Protectionist policies are designed to:
a. restrict imports so domestic consumers are able to pay lower prices.
b. increase imports so domestic consumers are able to pay lower prices.
c. restrict imports so it is easier for domestic firms to compete with foreign firms.
d. increase imports so it is easier for domestic firms to compete with foreign firms.

17. Two parties can enjoy gains from trade by specializing in the activities for which:
a. an absolute advantage exists.
b. a comparative advantage exists.
c. an unlimited market exists.
d. a stratified market exists.

18. If country A can produce coffee at a lower opportunity cost than country B, then:
a. country A has an absolute advantage in the production of coffee.
b. country B has an absolute advantage in the production of coffee.
c. country A has a comparative advantage in the production of coffee.
d. country B has a comparative advantage in the production of coffee.

Use the graphs below to answer the next two questions.

Books BOB

4

0 4 Pencils

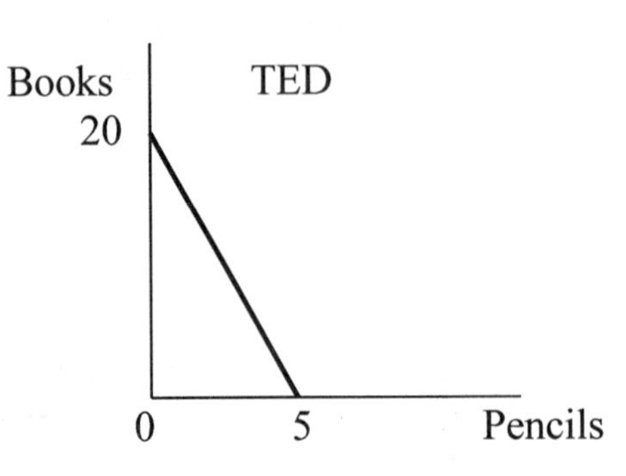

19. For Bob, the opportunity cost of 1 book is _____ pencil(s), while for Ted, the opportunity cost of 1 book is _____ pencil(s).
 a. 4; 5 b. 1; 1/4 c. 1; 4 d. 1/4; 1

20. Bob has a comparative advantage in _____ and Ted has a comparative advantage in _____.
 a. both books and pencils; neither books nor pencils
 b. neither books nor pencils; both books and pencils
 c. pencils; books
 d. books; pencils

Use the graphs below to answer the next two questions.

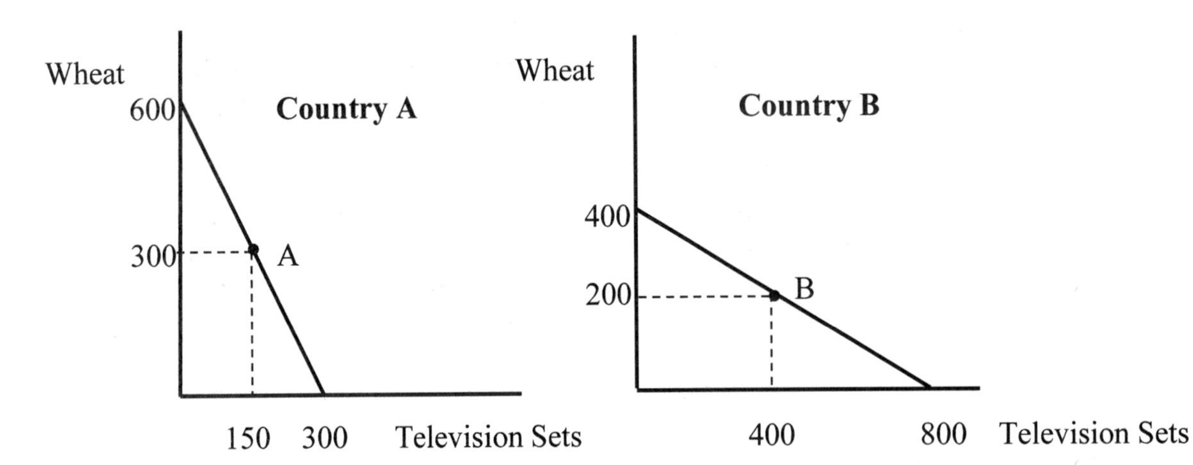

21. In the absence of trade, country A produces at point A and country B produces at point B; their combined output is then _____ units of wheat and _____ television sets.
 a. 550; 500 b. 500; 550 c. 800; 600 d. 600; 800

22. If the two countries specialize according to comparative advantage, their combined output increases to _____ units of wheat and _____ television sets.
 a. 550; 500 b. 500; 550 c. 800; 600 d. 600; 800

23. According to the law of demand, an increase in the price of personal computers will, ceteris paribus, lead to:
   a. an increase in the demand for personal computers.
   b. a decrease in the demand for personal computers.
   c. an increase in the quantity demanded of personal computers.
   d. a decrease in the quantity demanded of personal computers.

24. All of the following will lead to an increase in the demand for jeans ***except***:
   a. an increase in income, assuming jeans are normal goods.
   b. a decrease in the price of khakis, assuming khakis are substitutes for jeans.
   c. an increase in the popularity of jeans.
   d. an increase in the number of schools that allow students to wear jeans.

25. Which of the following would ***best*** explain a decrease in the demand for shrimp?
   a. An increase in consumer income, assuming shrimp is a normal good
   b. A decrease in the price of crab legs (a substitute for shrimp)
   c. An increase in the price of shrimp
   d. A decrease in the price of shrimp

26. An increase in the quantity supplied of haircuts is most likely to occur as a result of:
   a. a decrease in the supply of baseball caps.
   b. an increase in the popularity of long hair.
   c. an increase in the price of haircuts.
   d. an increase in cost of getting a license to cut hair.

27. Which of the following would ***best*** explain a decrease in the supply of bicycles?
   a. An increase in the price of bicycles
   b. A decrease in the price of bicycles
   c. An increase in the popularity of bicycling
   d. A decrease in the number of bicycle manufacturers

28. Technological improvements that reduce the cost of manufacturing personal computers combined with a decrease in the demand for personal computers results in:
   a. an increase in equilibrium quantity and a decrease in equilibrium price.
   b. a decrease in both equilibrium quantity and equilibrium price.
   c. either a. or b. could be correct
   d. none of the above

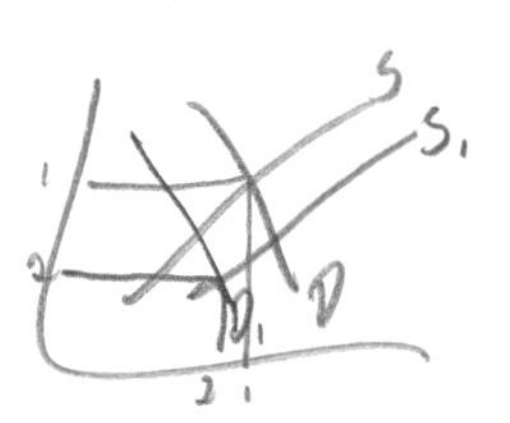

Use the graph below to answer the next three questions.

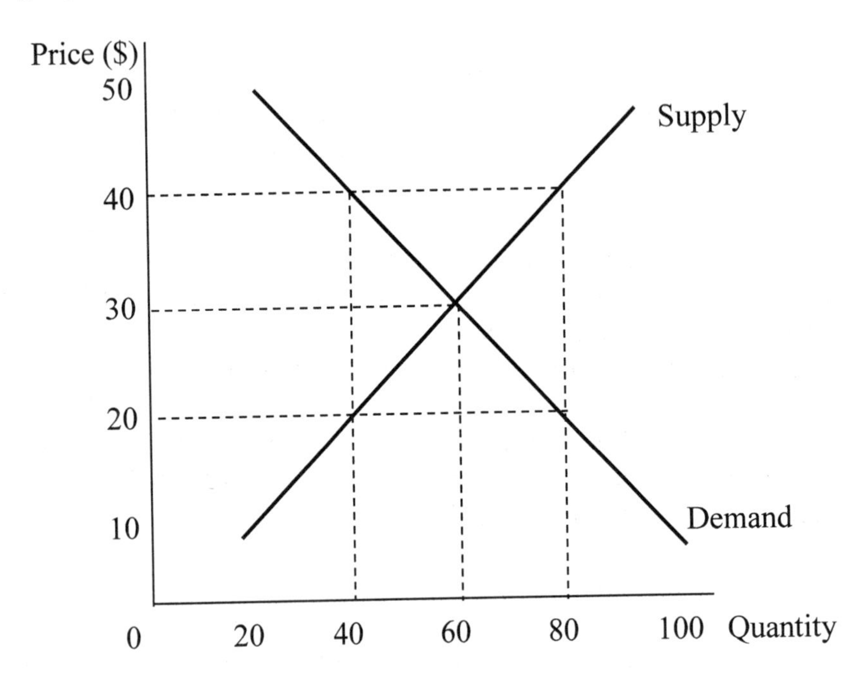

C 29. The equilibrium price is ________ and equilibrium quantity is ________.

a. $20; 20 b. $30; 40 c. $30; 60 d. $40; 80

30. If the price in this market is set at $20, a ________ of ________ units will result.

A
a. shortage; 40
b. shortage; 20
c. surplus; 40
d. surplus; 20

31. If the price in this market is set at $40, a ________ of ________ units will result.

C
a. shortage; 40
b. shortage; 20
c. surplus; 40
d. surplus; 20

32. Price elasticity of demand is calculated as:

C
a. the responsiveness of equilibrium price to a shift in the demand curve.
b. the responsiveness of equilibrium price to a shift in the supply curve.
c. the percentage change in quantity demanded divided by the percentage change in price.
d. the percentage change in price divided by the percentage change in quantity demanded.

33. If a 10 percent reduction in the price of a commodity results in a 10 percent increase in quantity demanded, the absolute value of the price elasticity of demand coefficient is _______ and demand is said to be ________.

a. 1; perfectly elastic
b. 1; unit elastic
c. <1; inelastic
d. 0; perfectly inelastic

34. If the absolute value of the price elasticity of demand coefficient for liquid hand soap is 1.67, the demand for liquid hand soap is:

a. elastic.
b. unit elastic.
c. inelastic.
d. perfectly inelastic.

35. Ceteris paribus, the demand for a product will be more elastic when:

a. the product is a necessity.
b. there are no close substitutes available.
c. only a short period of time is allowed for adjustment to a price change.
d. the price of the product is large relative to income.

36. When the price of a hotdog at the ballpark is $4, quantity demanded is 2,250. When the price of a hotdog at the ballpark is $6, quantity demanded is 1,750. The demand for hotdogs at the ballpark is relatively _____ and the price elasticity coefficient is equal to_____ using the midpoint formula.

a. inelastic; 0.625
b. elastic; 0.625
c. inelastic; 1.6
d. elastic; 1.6

37. The price elasticity of demand coefficient _________ when moving down along a linear downward sloping demand curve.

a. stays the same
b. increases
c. decreases
d. increases and then decreases.

38. If the absolute value of the price elasticity of demand coefficient for milk is 0.75, then the demand for milk is ___________ and a(n) ____________ in price will lead to an increase in total revenue.

a. elastic; decrease
b. elastic; increase
c. inelastic; decrease
d. inelastic; increase

39. If the income elasticity for canned beans is equal to -0.8, then canned beans are:

a. normal goods.
b. inferior goods.
c. substitute goods.
d. complementary goods.

40. Which of the following pairs of goods is *most* likely to have a cross elasticity that is greater than zero?

a. Bread and sandwich meat
b. Crayons and coloring books
c. Peanut butter and jelly
d. Coca-Cola and Dr. Pepper

Answers to Practice Exam I

1.	**C**	**11.**	**D**	**21.**	**B**	**31.**	**C**
2.	**D**	**12.**	**B**	**22.**	**D**	**32.**	**C**
3.	**B**	**13.**	**B**	**23.**	**D**	**33.**	**B**
4.	**D**	**14.**	**D**	**24.**	**B**	**34.**	**A**
5.	**D**	**15.**	**B**	**25.**	**B**	**35.**	**D**
6.	**B**	**16.**	**C**	**26.**	**C**	**36.**	**A**
7.	**B**	**17.**	**B**	**27.**	**D**	**37.**	**C**
8.	**B**	**18.**	**C**	**28.**	**C**	**38.**	**D**
9.	**C**	**19.**	**B**	**29.**	**C**	**39.**	**B**
10.	**B**	**20.**	**C**	**30.**	**A**	**40.**	**D**

CHAPTER 6 Market Efficiency

Many societies rely on markets to answer the fundamental economic questions (what to produce, how to produce, and for whom to produce) because markets promote economic efficiency. Recall from chapter 2 that **technical efficiency** is achieved when producers are making as much output as they can with available resources and technology. A society achieves **economic efficiency** (also known as allocative efficiency) when producers are making the goods and services that people most want and need. The condition for economic efficiency can be stated in different ways.

An outcome is efficient when

- Marginal Benefit = Marginal Cost
- The sum of Consumer Surplus and Producer Surplus is maximized
- There is no Deadweight Loss

Each of these efficiency conditions requires specialized terminology and additional explanation. The first condition (MB = MC) was demonstrated in chapter 1.

The value of something to a consumer can be estimated by the maximum amount of money the consumer is willing to pay to acquire it. **Marginal benefit** (MB) is a measure of the value of each additional unit to the consumer in terms of how much money each additional unit is worth to the consumer, or the maximum amount the consumer would pay for each additional unit. An important principle that is derived from consumer behavior theory is the notion that marginal benefit falls as consumption increases.

Suppose you would pay, at most, $3 for one slice of pizza; it can be inferred that the marginal benefit of the first slice of pizza is $3. Once you have enjoyed that first slice, you might be willing to purchase a second, but the value of the second slice is very likely to be less than $3. If you would be willing to pay, at most, $2 for a second slice and $1 for a third slice, then your MB function looks like the graph below. The marginal benefit curve reflects the value of each additional slice of pizza, not the actual price charged.

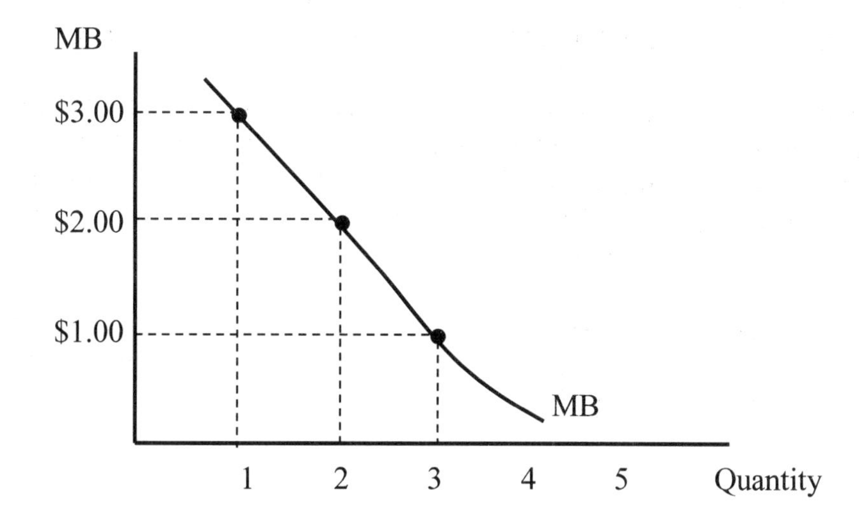

The MB curve indicates how much each slice of pizza is worth to you, or the maximum amount you would pay for each slice, so the **MB curve** can be interpreted as a **demand curve**. If the market price of a slice of pizza is $1.50, for example, you will buy two slices. The third slice is worth only $1, and no rational consumer would pay $1.50 for something that is worth only $1.

Consumer surplus is defined as the maximum amount the consumer is willing to pay for a product minus the amount the consumer actually has to pay (the market price). If you buy two slices of pizza at the price of $1.50, the first slice gives you consumer surplus equal to $1.50 and the second slice gives you consumer surplus equal to $0.50, for a total of $2.

Consumer surplus can be measured one unit at a time, but it is helpful to measure consumer surplus for an entire market using the area between the demand curve and the market price. Suppose marginal benefit exceeds price for 1,000 slices of pizza, as depicted in the graph below. Then, the shaded area corresponds to consumer surplus.

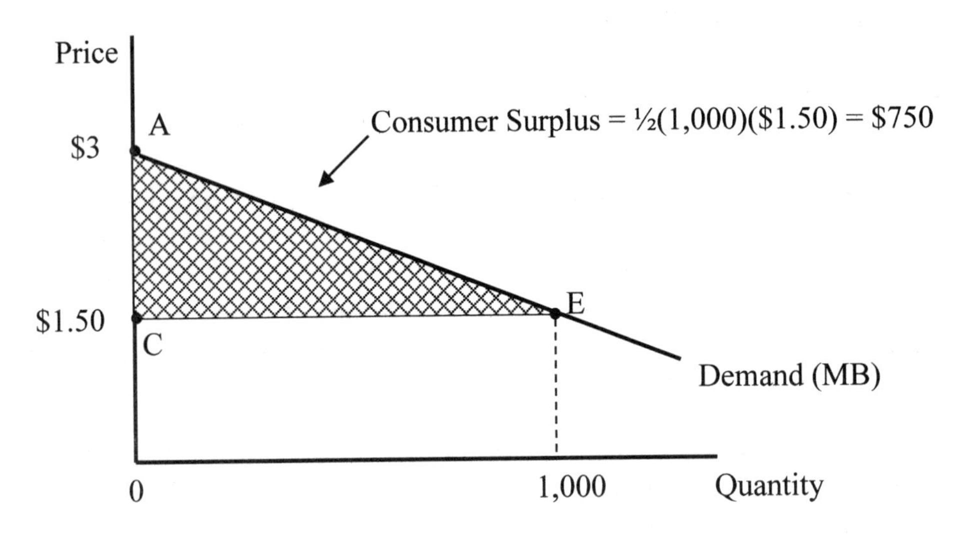

If the price in this market is $1.50 per slice, then the quantity consumed will be 1,000 slices. The marginal benefit (demand) curve lies above price from quantity 0 to quantity 1,000 slices. For every slice up to the 1,000th, marginal benefit is greater than price, and consumers enjoy a surplus on each of the slices. In other words, consumers are paying a price that is less than what they are willing and able to pay for each slice of pizza up to the 1,000th slice.

Total consumer surplus for pizza buyers in this market can be estimated by the area of the right triangle ACE in the graph, and is equal to the shaded area. This area is equivalent to calculating consumer surplus for each individual slice, up to 1,000 slices, and summing these amounts. The area of a triangle is given by the formula ½**(base)(height)**; in this instance, consumer surplus = ½(1,000)($3 - $1.50) = $750.

The amount of consumer surplus created in a market can be measured given the position of the demand curve (MB) and the market price. In general terms, consumer surplus is the area below the demand curve (MB), above the price line, and bounded by quantity.

The supply function is associated with the behavior of profit-maximizing business firms, and the economic theory of the firm is quite extensive. In later chapters, you will learn about production functions, cost functions, revenue functions, and profit functions; you will also learn that the behavior of a firm depends on the type of market in which the firm operates, or the degree of competitiveness present in the market. Although there will be a more detailed analysis in later chapters, a basic model of producer behavior is developed for use in this chapter.

Profit-maximizing sellers know that it is only worthwhile to produce and sell a unit of output if the additional revenue generated from the sale at least covers the additional cost of producing it. For example, if it costs $25 to prepare a turkey dinner and deliver it to a waiting customer, then it is profitable to do this as long as the waiting customer will pay at least $25. These cost figures do not include what are called **fixed costs** because they are not relevant to the decision; fixed costs must be paid whether the seller produces output or not. An example of a fixed cost is the cost of an oven, which does not depend on how many turkey dinners are prepared in it.

The additional cost of producing one more unit of output is the **marginal cost** (MC). The economic theory of production demonstrates that marginal cost increases as output increases (in the short run). The graph below illustrates increasing MC.

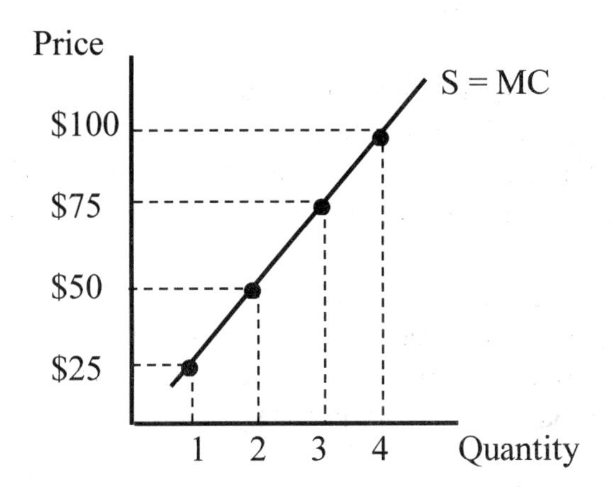

The **MC curve** is also the **supply curve** in a perfectly competitive market, because it can be used to predict how many units of output a seller is willing and able to produce at each price, where price is determined by market forces (where market supply and market demand intersect).

According to the graph above, if the going market price of a catered turkey dinner is $35, then the quantity supplied is only one because it is not profitable to pay additional costs of $50 to prepare and deliver a second turkey dinner and then only receive $35. Increasing marginal costs imply that quantity supplied will increase only when price increases, ceteris paribus.

Producer surplus is defined as the actual amount a producer receives for a product (the market price) minus the minimum amount the producer is willing to accept in exchange for the product (marginal cost). For the turkey example, if the market price is $35, then the seller enjoys a producer surplus of $10 from the first turkey supplied. This is because the minimum amount the seller would have accepted is $25, but the seller actually received $35.

Producer surplus can be measured one unit at a time, but it is helpful to measure producer surplus for an entire market using the area between the market price and the supply curve.

Returning to the pizza example, assume the price of a slice of pizza is $1.50, and quantity supplied is 1,000 slices at this price. As shown in the graph below, the marginal cost per slice is less than the market price per slice up to the 1,000th slice.

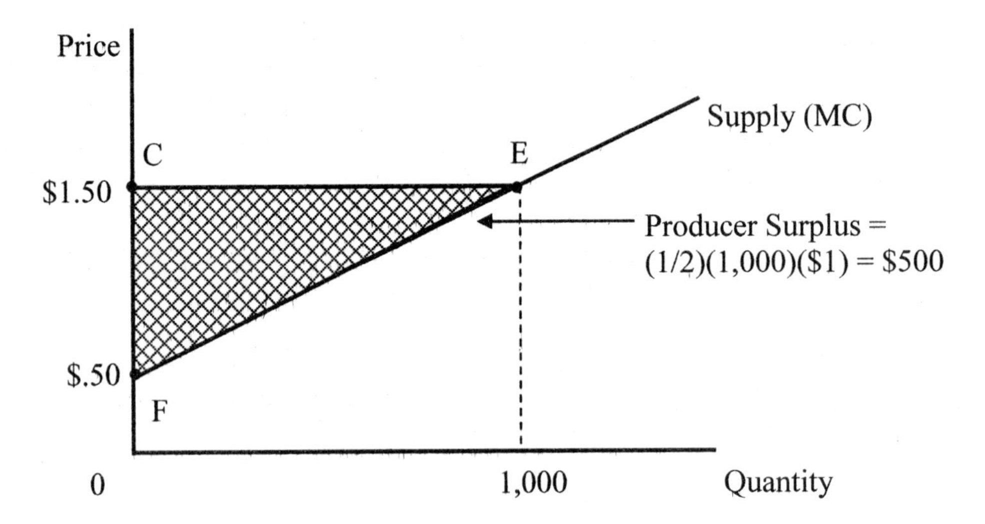

Total producer surplus for pizza sellers in this market is given by the area of the right triangle CEF, and is equal to the shaded area. This area is equivalent to calculating producer surplus for each individual slice, up to 1,000 slices, and summing these amounts. The area of a triangle is equal to **½(base)(height)**, so for triangle CEF, the area is ½ (1,000)($1.50 - $.50), which is $500.

The amount of producer surplus created in a market can be determined given the position of the supply curve (MC) and the market price. In general terms, producer surplus is the area above the supply curve (MC), below the price line, and bounded by quantity.

Since the marginal benefit function is the demand curve and the marginal cost function is the supply curve, if a market is in equilibrium where demand intersects supply, it must be true that marginal benefit equals marginal cost, or MB = MC. This is one of the conditions for efficiency listed at the beginning of the chapter. Next, it will be shown that the sum of consumer surplus and producer surplus is reduced when the price is held above or below equilibrium, and that there is deadweight loss, or inefficiency.

Total Surplus and Efficiency

When a market is in equilibrium, the sum of consumer and producer surplus, or total surplus, is maximized. This is one of the ways economists demonstrate the **efficiency** of free markets. Marginal benefit is also equal to marginal cost (MB = MC) at the competitive market equilibrium.

The graph below shows a market in equilibrium where the supply and demand curves intersect at a price of $10 and a quantity of 400.

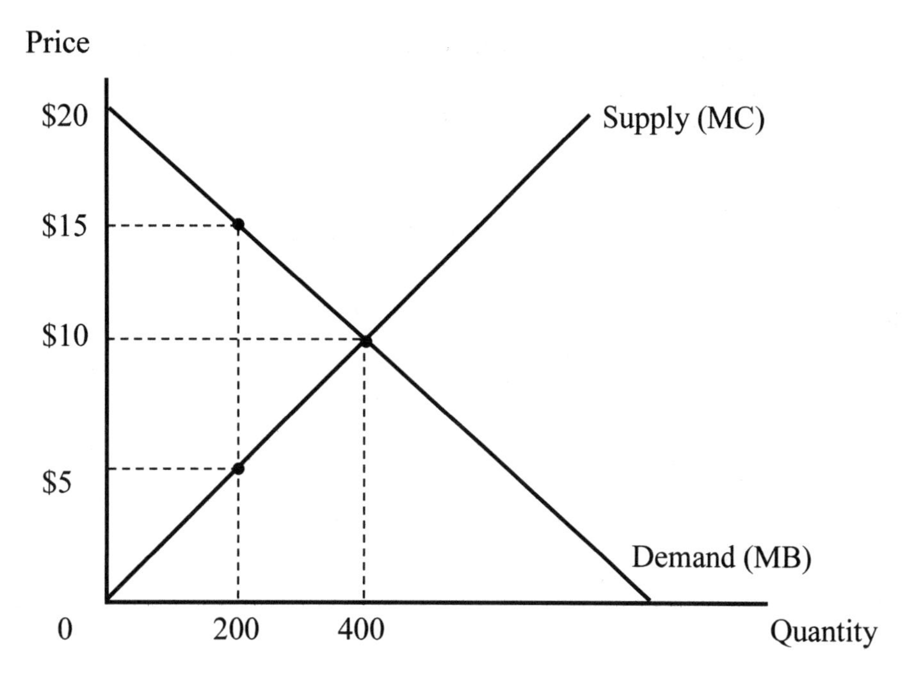

In equilibrium, when P = $10 and Q = 400, consumer surplus and producer surplus are equal to:

Consumer Surplus = ½(400)($20 - $10) = $2,000

Producer Surplus = ½(400)($10 – $0) = $2,000

and total surplus is equal to:

Total Surplus = Consumer Surplus + Producer Surplus = $2,000 + $2,000 = $4,000

Because consumer surplus measures the net gain to buyers of participating in market transactions, and producer surplus measures the net gain to sellers of participating in market transactions, total surplus (the sum of consumer surplus and producer surplus) is the net gain to all market participants. Therefore, total surplus provides a good standard against which to judge different outcomes.

Ceteris paribus, an outcome that generates more total surplus is preferred to an outcome that generates less total surplus, and the most preferred outcome is the one that maximizes total surplus; therefore, the free-market outcome is efficient when the market is perfectly competitive (and there are no externalities, as will be shown in chapter 8).

In equilibrium, 400 units are bought and sold for $10 each, and total surplus is equal to $4,000, as shown above. Free markets move toward equilibrium because price falls when quantity supplied exceeds quantity demanded (market surplus), and price rises when quantity demanded exceeds quantity supplied (market shortage).

Is it possible to create more than $4,000 in total surplus at a price and quantity other than the equilibrium price and quantity? The answer is no, and the analysis below shows why.

When price is above equilibrium, there is a surplus, and when price is below equilibrium, there is a shortage. In either of these cases, *the actual quantity that is bought and sold (exchanged) will be the smaller of the two (quantity supplied or quantity demanded).*

Suppose non-market forces, such as government limiting the price that can be charged in a market, cause the price to be $5. At a price of $5, quantity demanded is 600, but quantity supplied is only 200 units; only 200 units will be bought and sold (exchanged) since buyers cannot purchase items that have not been produced or offered for sale.

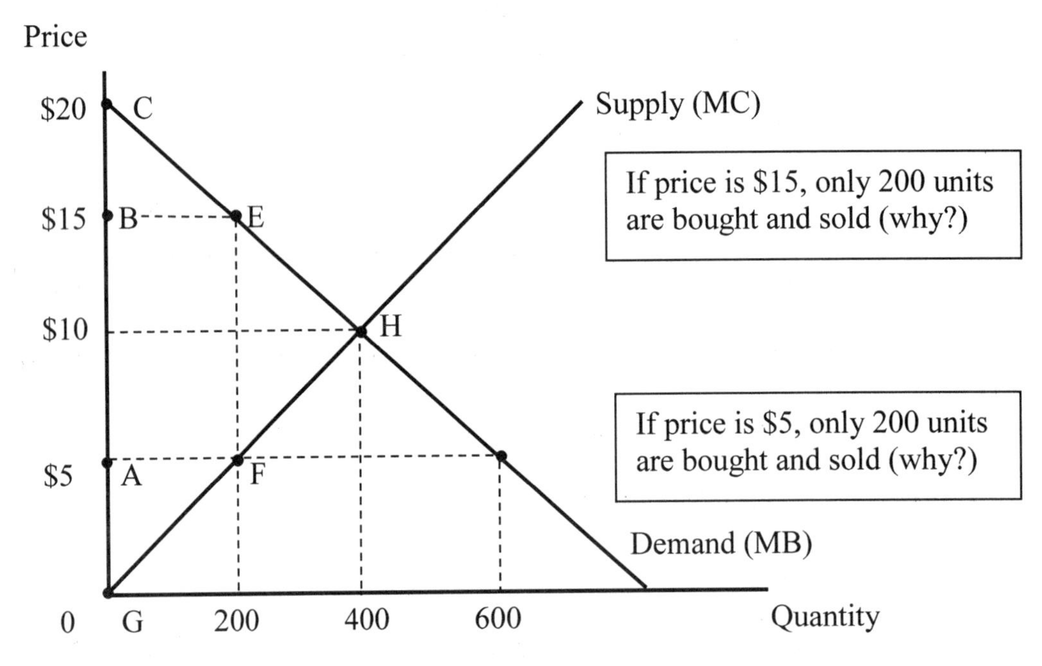

At a price of $5, consumer surplus is the area above the price of $5 and below the demand curve, or the area ACEF. Area ACEF is composed of the *right triangle* BCE and the *rectangle* ABEF, so:

Consumer Surplus = ½(200)($20 – $15) + (200)($15 – $5) = $500 + $2,000 = $2,500

Producer surplus at a price of $5 is equal to the area of the *right triangle* GAF, so

Producer Surplus = ½(200)($5 – $0) = $500

Total surplus is the sum of the two, so

Total Surplus = Consumer Surplus + Producer Surplus = $2,500 + $500 = $3,000

Recall that total surplus is $4,000 under free market conditions, so total surplus is lower at a price below equilibrium such as $5.

Similarly, total surplus is reduced if price is set above the equilibrium price. Suppose non-market forces, such as a government policy, cause the price to be $15. At a price of $15, the quantity supplied is large, but only 200 units are bought and sold because quantity demanded is equal to 200. Suppliers cannot sell output unless there are buyers.

At the price of $15, consumer surplus is reduced to the area of *right triangle* BCE, so

Consumer Surplus = ½(200)($20 – $15) = $500

Producer surplus is still calculated as the area between the price and the supply curve. If price is $15, producer surplus is now the area GBEF, which consists of the *right triangle* GAF plus the *rectangle* ABEF, so

Producer Surplus = ½(200)($5-$0) + (200)($15 – $5) = $500 + $2,000 = $2,500

Total surplus is the sum of the two, or

Total Surplus = Consumer Surplus + Producer Surplus = $500 + $2,500 = $3,000

Recall that total surplus is $4,000 under free market conditions, so total surplus is lower at a price above equilibrium such as $15.

The reduction in total surplus that occurs when output is inefficient is referred to as **deadweight loss**, defined as the loss in total surplus resulting from a particular policy or action.

In the above example, the equilibrium price of $10 resulted in a quantity bought and sold of 400 units, and total surplus of $4,000. At a price of either $5 or $15, the quantity bought and sold is only 200, and total surplus is $3,000. The difference of $1,000 is the deadweight loss that results when price is kept at either $5 or $15 because there is $1,000 less in total surplus when the price is either $5 or $15.

Deadweight loss is also represented on the graph by *triangle* EHF, so

Deadweight Loss = ½(200)($15 - $5) = $1,000

The free-market outcome, or equilibrium price and quantity, is efficient because it maximizes total surplus. The example demonstrates that other prices lead to a reduction in quantity exchanged and a reduction in total surplus, and deadweight loss measures the size of the efficiency loss.

Chapter 4 demonstrated that many different events cause demand or supply to shift, causing a change in the equilibrium price and quantity. These events also cause consumer and producer surplus to change. As an example, suppose market equilibrium is initially at a price of \$9 and quantity 90, where S_1 intersects D in the graph below.

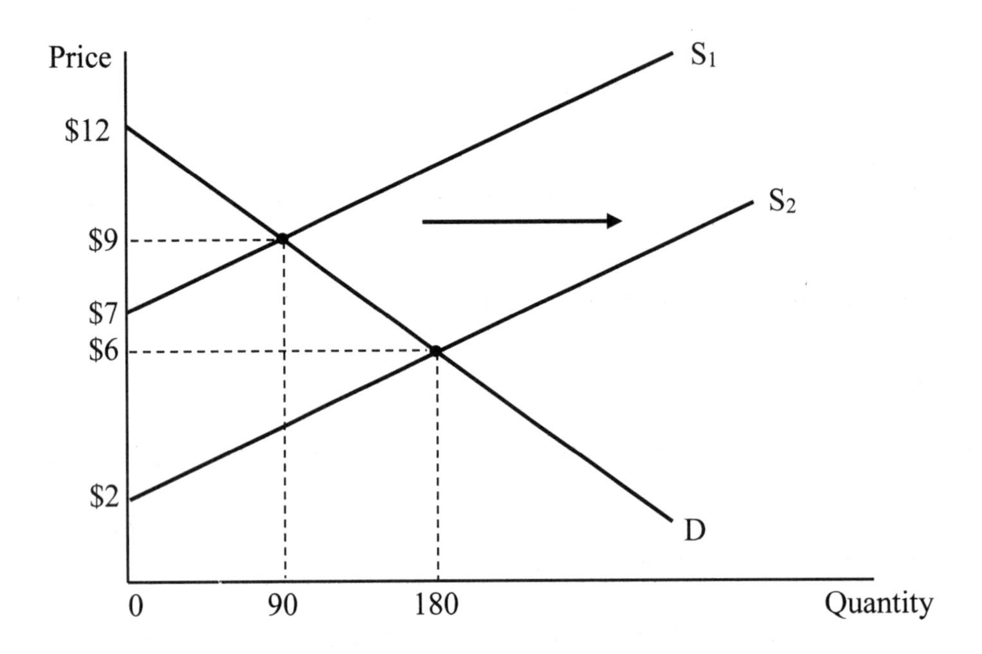

If price is \$9, consumer surplus is the area between the demand curve and the dashed line starting at \$9. This area is equal to ½(90)(\$3) = \$135. Producer surplus is the area between the dashed line starting at \$9 and the supply curve, S_1, which is ½(90)(\$2) = \$90.

Next, assume supply has shifted to the right, perhaps due to lower production costs, improved technology, or an increase in the number of sellers in the market. As a result, equilibrium price falls to \$6 and quantity increases to 180.

If price is \$6, consumer surplus is the area between the demand curve and the dashed line starting at \$6. This area is equal to ½(180)(\$6) = \$540. Producer surplus is the area between the dashed line starting at \$6 and the supply curve, S_2, which is ½(180)(\$4) = \$360.

In this example, the rightward shift of the supply curve resulted in an increase in consumer surplus, from \$135 to \$540 and an increase in producer surplus, from \$90 to \$360.

The above analysis can also be used to see how a leftward shift in supply would affect consumer and producer surplus.

Next, consider the effect of a demand shift on consumer and producer surplus.

In the example below, market equilibrium is initially at a price of $16 and quantity 100, where S intersects D_1 in the graph below.

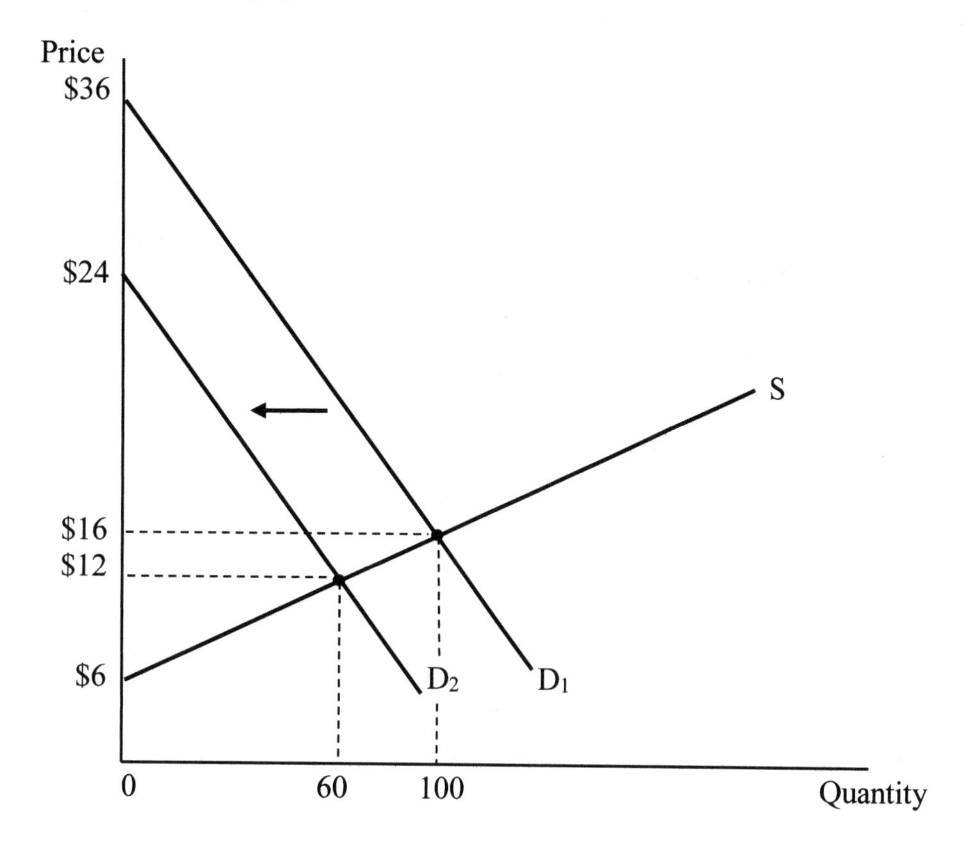

If price is $16, consumer surplus is the area between the demand curve, D_1, and the dashed line starting at $16. This area is equal to ½(100)($20) = $1,000. Producer surplus is the area between the dashed line starting at $16 and the supply curve, which is ½(100)($10) = $500.

Next, assume demand has shifted to the left, perhaps due an increase in the price of a complementary good, a decrease in the price of a substitute good, or a decrease in the number of buyers in the market. As a result, equilibrium price falls to $12 and quantity decreases to 60.

If price is $12, consumer surplus is the area between the demand curve, D_2, and the dashed line starting at $12. This area is equal to ½(60)($12) = $360. Producer surplus is the area between the dashed line starting at $12 and the supply curve, which is ½(60)($6) = $180.

In this example, the leftward shift of the demand curve resulted in a decrease in consumer surplus, from $1,000 to $360, and a decrease in producer surplus, from $500 to $180.

The above analysis can also be used to see how a rightward shift in demand would affect consumer and producer surplus.

Practice

Use the graph below to practice the calculations.

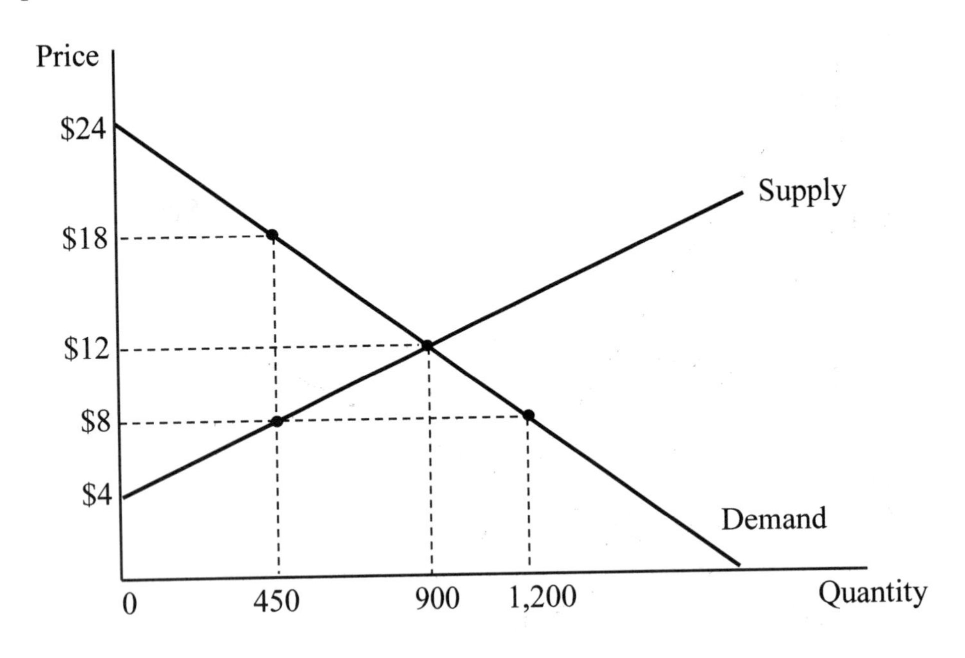

If the market is in equilibrium, price is $12 and quantity is 900. Calculate

Consumer surplus =

Producer surplus =

Total surplus =

If the product price is $18, only 450 units will be exchanged. Calculate

Consumer surplus =

Producer surplus =

Total surplus = Deadweight loss =

If the product price is $8, only 450 units will be exchanged. Calculate

Consumer surplus =

Producer surplus =

Total surplus = Deadweight loss =

NAME____SECTION#__________
PRINT LAST NAME, FIRST NAME

INEFFICIENCY AND DEADWEIGHT LOSS

Use the graph below to fill in the blanks.

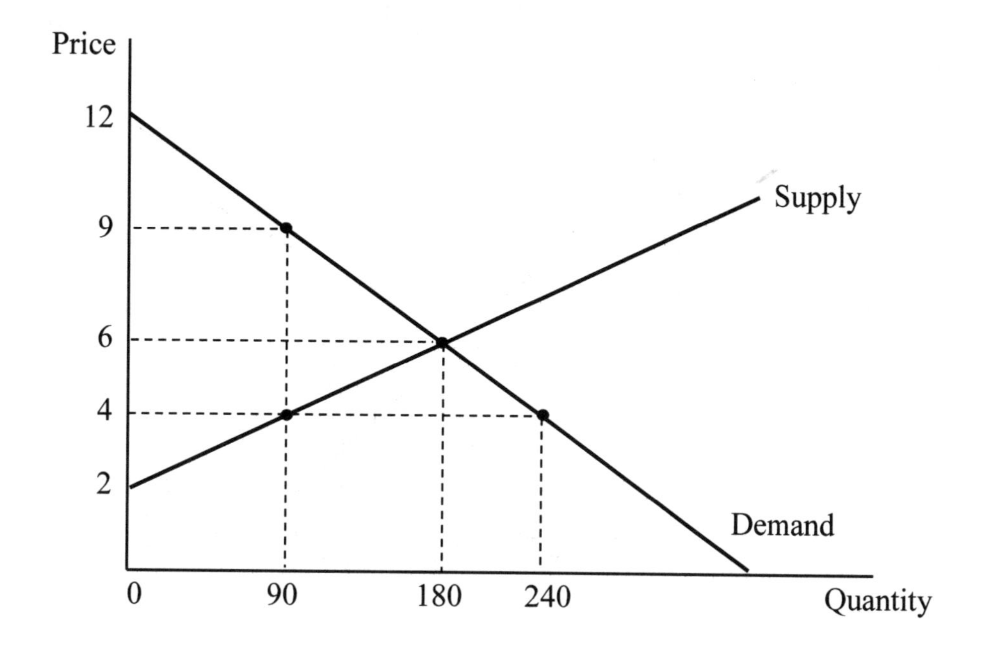

1. If the product price is $6, the quantity exchanged will equal ____________, consumer surplus will equal $____________, and producer surplus will equal $____________.

2. If the product price is $9, the quantity exchanged will equal ____________, consumer surplus will equal $____________, and producer surplus will equal $____________.

3. If the product price is $9, there will be deadweight loss equal to $____________.

4. If the product price is $4, the quantity exchanged will equal ____________, consumer surplus will equal $____________, and producer surplus will equal $____________.

5. If the product price is $4, there will be deadweight loss equal to $____________.

NAME____ SECTION#_______________
PRINT LAST NAME, FIRST NAME

MARKET EFFICIENCY

Use the graph below to fill in the blanks.

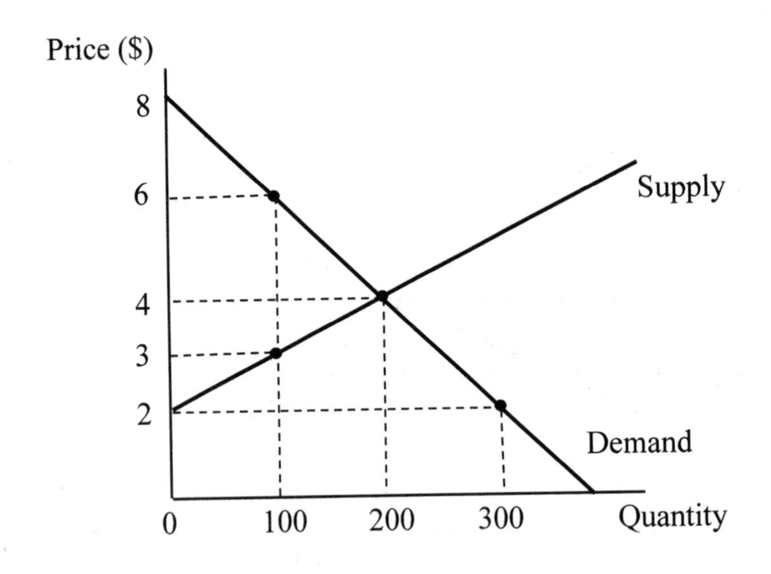

1. Equilibrium price is $____________ and equilibrium quantity is ____________.

2. In equilibrium, consumer surplus is equal to $____________.

3. In equilibrium, producer surplus is equal to $____________.

4. The efficient level of output in this market is equal to ____________, where MB = MC.

5. The efficient level of output in this market is the level of output at which combined consumer and producer surplus is __________________________.
maximized/minimized

NAME________________________________SECTION#____________

PRINT LAST NAME, FIRST NAME

CONSUMERS, PRODUCERS, AND MARKET EFFICIENCY

Use the graph below to answer questions 1 through 6.

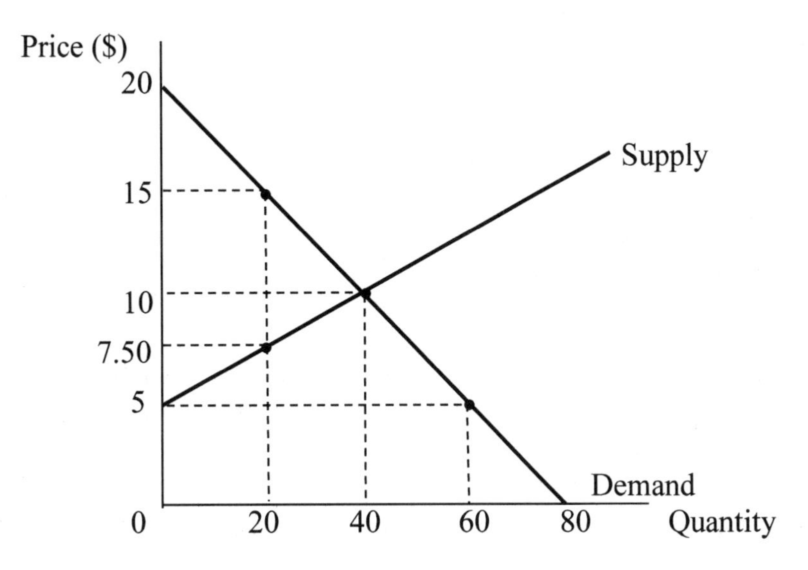

1. The marginal benefit of the 20th unit is ___ and the marginal cost of the 20th unit is ___.
   a. $7.50; $15 c. $15; $7.50
   b. $10; $10 d. $5; $5

2. The marginal benefit of the 40th unit is ___ and the marginal cost of the 40th unit is ___.
   a. $7.50; $15 c. $15; $7.50
   b. $10; $10 d. $5; $5

3. If the price of this product is $10 per unit, consumers will purchase ___ units and consumer surplus will equal $___.
   a. 20; 50 b. 20; 200 c. 40; 50 d. 40; 200

4. If the price of this product is $10 per unit, firms will sell ___ units and producer surplus will equal $___.
   a. 20; 25 b. 20; 100 c. 40; 25 d. 40; 100

5. The efficient level of output is ___ units because marginal benefit (MB) equals ____ at this output level and the sum of consumer and producer surplus is _____.
   a. 40; 40; 0 c. 40; MC; maximized
   b. 20; MC; 0 d. 20; 40; maximized

6. If the quantity exchanged in this market is limited to 20 units, the resulting deadweight loss is equal to:
   a. $50. b. $75. c. $100. d. $150.

NAME____SECTION#______________

PRINT LAST NAME, FIRST NAME

7. Consumer surplus is the difference between ________ and product price and producer surplus is the difference between ________ and product price.
   a. marginal benefit; marginal cost
   b. marginal cost; marginal benefit
   c. total benefit; total cost
   d. total cost; total benefit

8. Buyers gain consumer surplus when the market price is:
   a. greater than the highest price buyers are willing to pay.
   b. less than the highest price buyers are willing to pay.
   c. just equal to the highest price buyers are willing to pay.
   d. determined by a price floor rather than market forces.

9. Which of the following statements best illustrates the concept of producer surplus?
   a. Rose's Flower Shop is forced to sell surplus tulips at a price that is below cost because inventories are too high.
   b. A new client agrees to pay $50 a week for cleaning provided by Alice's Cleaning Service, although the business would be willing to accept $25 to perform these services.
   c. Steve found a scalper willing to sell him concert tickets for less than their original price.
   d. Maria refuses to work overtime despite being offered twice her regular wage rate because she cannot make arrangements for child care.

10. Assuming supply is upward-sloping and everything else remains the same, an increase in the demand for a product leads to:
    a. an increase in producer surplus.
    b. a decrease in producer surplus.
    c. no change in producer surplus.
    d. no change in consumer surplus.

CHAPTER 7 Price Ceilings, Price Floors, and Taxes

In a free market, the forces of supply and demand determine equilibrium price and quantity. In some real-world markets, government policy causes an outcome that is different from the free market outcome. Examples include price ceilings, price floors, and taxes.

Price Ceiling

If the free market price is deemed "too high" for some buyers in the market, policy-makers might decide to set a limit on the price sellers can charge in order to protect buyers. A **price ceiling** (sometimes referred to as a price cap) is a maximum legal price that sellers are allowed to charge. A *binding* price ceiling is one that is established below the equilibrium price because it prevents market forces from raising the price up to equilibrium and it has an ongoing impact on quantity bought and sold (exchanged).

At times, fluctuations in the price of a gallon of gasoline have prompted calls for a ceiling on the price that sellers can charge. Supply and demand analysis can be used to show the potential impact of such a policy. Suppose supply and demand conditions in the market for gasoline can be represented by the graph below.

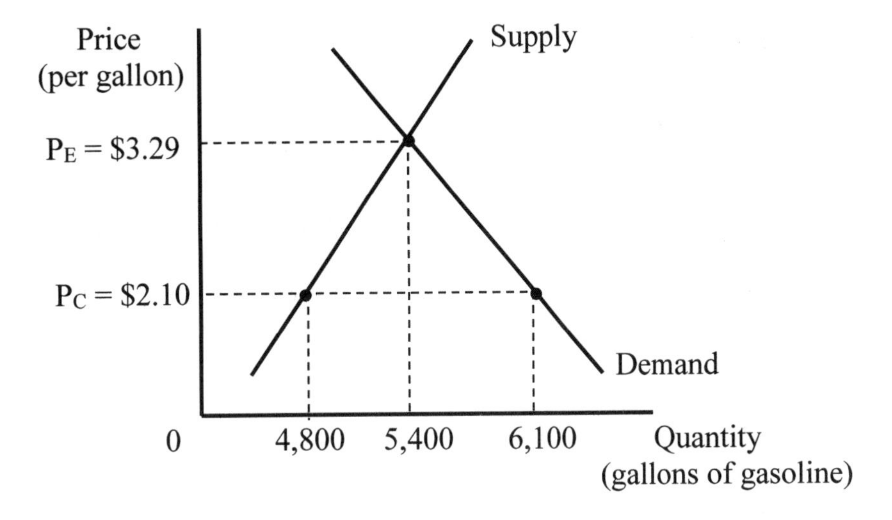

This market achieves equilibrium at a price of $3.29 per gallon, ($P_E$), when quantity demanded and quantity supplied are both equal to 5,400 gallons.

If a price ceiling (P_C) is established at a price of $2.10 per gallon, quantity supplied falls to 4,800 gallons and quantity demanded increases to 6,100 gallons. When quantity demanded exceeds quantity supplied, there is a **market shortage**. In this case, the market shortage is equal to 6,100 gallons minus 4,800 gallons, or 1,300 gallons. In the absence of the price ceiling, sellers react to a market shortage by raising price, but the legal maximum prohibits a higher price.

When there is a binding price ceiling, the quantity that will be exchanged is the smaller value (quantity supplied). The actual quantity bought and sold in the above example will be 4,800 since consumers can only purchase what is offered for sale.

In the 1970s, gasoline became very expensive because of the OPEC cartel (the Organization of Petroleum-Exporting Countries). The members of OPEC agreed to limit production in order to drive the price of oil upward. In 1971, the Nixon administration responded to the upward pressure on gasoline prices by implementing price ceilings. The predictable result was a shortage, illustrated by long lines at gas stations and gas stations running out of fuel while many customers remained in those lines.

The size of the market shortage resulting from a price ceiling depends on the elasticities of supply and demand, as the graphs below illustrate.

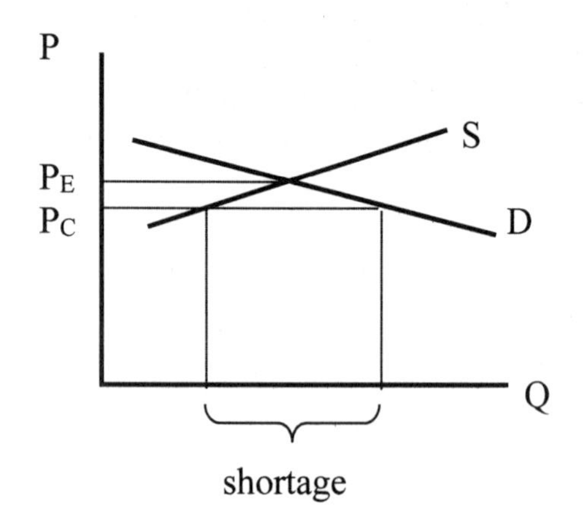

If demand and supply are price-elastic, a given price change causes a relatively large change in quantity demanded and quantity supplied. In this case, the market shortage resulting from a price ceiling at P_C is relatively large.

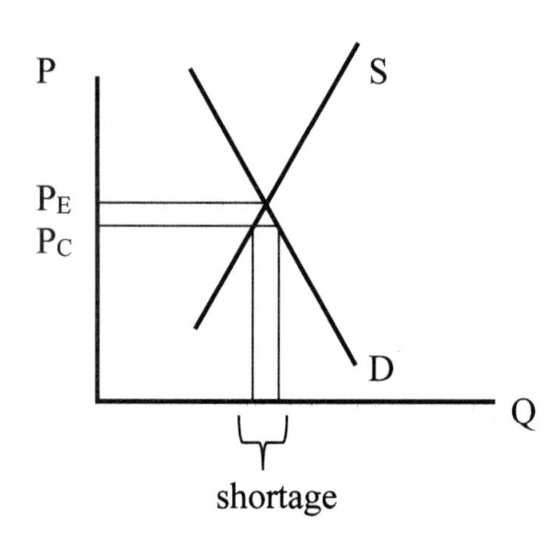

If demand and supply are price-inelastic, a given price change causes a relatively small change in quantity demanded and quantity supplied, so the market shortage resulting from a price ceiling at P_C is relatively small.

The purpose of a price ceiling is to keep price low for buyers in the market; however, the ceiling may have negative consequences for buyers, the most obvious being the inability to make a purchase because quantity supplied is limited and there is a shortage. Other possible consequences include an increase in the opportunity cost associated with obtaining the good (i.e., long lines) or the development of illegal markets (black markets) where price rises higher than the legal limit.

In the previous chapter, deadweight loss was explained as a way of measuring the loss that occurs when output is not at the intersection of the competitive supply curve and the demand curve. Economists use the concept of **deadweight loss** to measure the cost of imposing a price ceiling, and this can be illustrated graphically.

The graph below illustrates how to calculate the **deadweight loss** associated with a price ceiling established at $20. This technique was presented in chapter 6 as well.

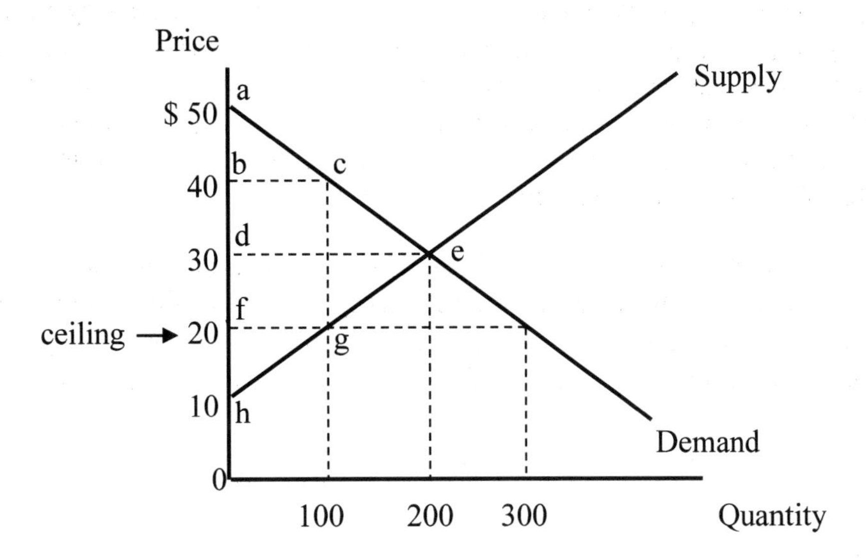

Free Market Outcome (assuming no price ceiling): P_E = $30 and Q_E = 200

Consumer Surplus = area aed = ½(200)($50 - $30) = $2,000
Producer Surplus = area deh = ½(200)($30 - $10) = $2,000
Total Surplus = area aeh = $2,000 + $2,000 = $4,000

Price Ceiling of $20: P = $20, Q_S = 100 and Q_D = 300, actual quantity exchanged = 100

Consumer Surplus = area of triangle acb + area of rectangle bcgf
Consumer Surplus = ½(100)($50 - $40) + (100)($40 - $20) = $500 + $2,000 = $2,500
Producer Surplus = area fgh = ½(100)($20 - $10) = $500
Total Surplus = area acgh = $2,500 + $500 = $3,000

Deadweight Loss: total surplus before the ceiling – total surplus after the ceiling

Deadweight loss = $4,000 - $3,000 = $1,000
Deadweight loss = area of triangle ceg = ½(100)($40 - $20) = $1,000

Since there is a deadweight loss, society experiences a net loss when a price ceiling is imposed. Although the consumers who are able to purchase the good at the reduced price are better off, the losses experienced by sellers and by consumers who are unable to obtain the product outweigh those gains.

The preceding analysis has assumed that market conditions promote an efficient outcome without government interference, or that there are no **market failures**. In the next chapter, the possibility of market failure and cases in which government policy might promote efficiency will be considered.

Price Floor

If the free market price is deemed "too low" for some sellers in a market, policymakers might decide to set a lower limit on the price buyers must pay in order to protect sellers. A **price floor** (sometimes referred to as a price support) is a minimum legal price that buyers are allowed to pay. A *binding* price floor is one that is established above the equilibrium price because it prevents market forces from lowering the price down to equilibrium and it has an ongoing impact on the quantity bought and sold (exchanged).

One important example of a price floor is the minimum wage. A minimum wage was first implemented in the U.S. in 1938. Supply and demand analysis can be used to show the potential impact of a price floor, or minimum wage, in the market for unskilled labor. Suppose supply and demand conditions in the market for unskilled labor can be represented by the graph below.

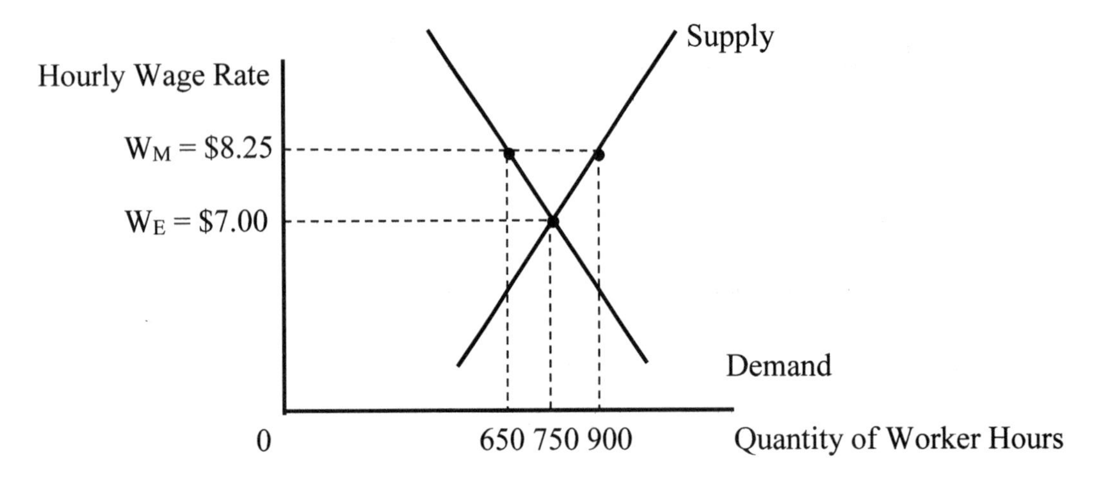

The equilibrium wage rate in this market is $7.00 per hour ($W_E$) and, at that wage rate, firms are willing to employ 750 hours of labor services. Workers are willing to supply 750 hours of labor services at a wage rate of $7.00, so everyone who is willing and able to work for $7.00 per hour can potentially find employment. Due to the existence of labor market turnover and job search time, the market may not achieve equilibrium with zero unemployment, but the potential exists.

If policymakers impose a binding price floor or minimum wage above the equilibrium wage, there will be a **market surplus**. For example, if the minimum wage (W_M) is $8.25 per hour, firms are willing to employ only 650 hours of labor services (quantity demanded is 650), but workers want to supply 900 hours of their services (quantity supplied is 900); therefore, a surplus of 250 hours exists. In the absence of the price floor, workers react to a market surplus by offering to accept a lower wage rate, but the legal minimum prevents wages from falling.

When there is a binding price floor, the quantity that will be exchanged is the smaller value (quantity demanded). The actual quantity bought and sold in the above example will be 650 since workers cannot sell their services if employers aren't hiring. The number of unemployed workers cannot be obtained from the graph since it measures worker hours, but the larger the surplus, the more unemployed workers there will be.

A minimum wage has positive as well as negative effects. For workers who are able to work as many hours as they want at the minimum wage, the consequences are clearly positive. One negative aspect of a minimum wage is the unemployment it can cause. Whether the resulting unemployment is large or small depends on the elasticities of supply and demand, as illustrated in the following graphs.

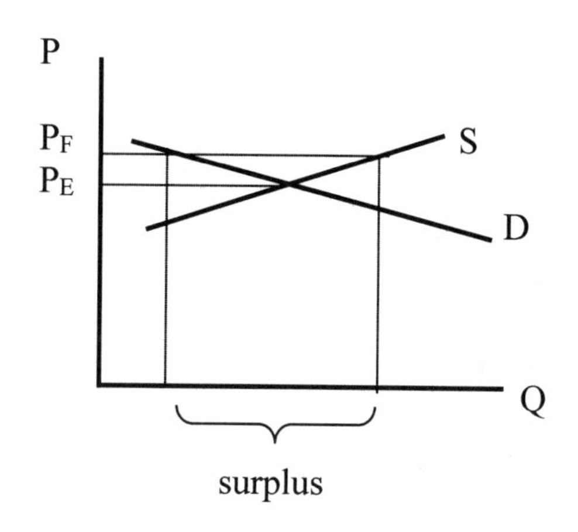

If demand and supply are price-elastic, a given price change causes a relatively large change in quantity demanded and quantity supplied. In this case, the market surplus resulting from a price floor at P_F is relatively large, so a minimum wage set above the equilibrium wage causes a large amount of unemployment.

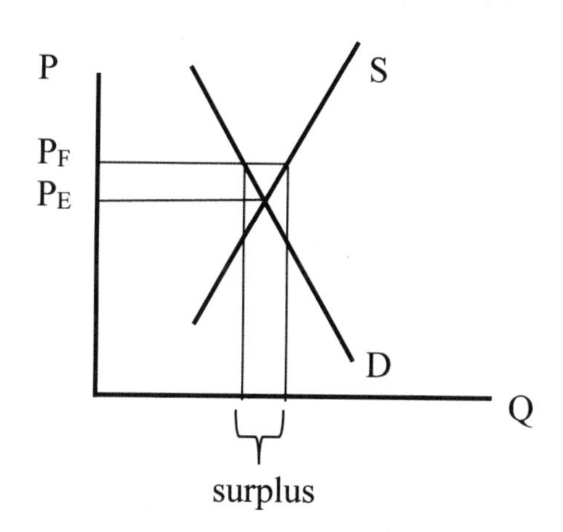

If demand and supply are price-inelastic, a given price change causes a relatively small change in quantity demanded and quantity supplied. In this case, the market surplus resulting from a price floor at P_F is relatively small, so a minimum wage set above the equilibrium wage causes a small amount of unemployment.

The minimum wage is an important topic in the political arena. The model of supply and demand indicates that there will likely be both winners and losers when a minimum wage is imposed or increased, but the adverse consequences on employment opportunities and product prices can only be quantified using empirical analysis of real-world data. This kind of analysis begins with economic principles and applies mathematical and statistical tools to create a new field of study called **econometrics**. Theory alone cannot answer the normative question of whether or not policymakers should maintain the minimum wage above market equilibrium.

Another important example of a price floor is the use of farm price supports. Because the basic model of supply and demand predicts a market surplus following the imposition of a price floor, policymakers decided to avoid that outcome by effectively paying farmers not to produce. Analysis of farm supports begins with the basic supply and demand model, but is more complicated, so analysis of U.S. farm policy is not pursued in detail here.

There is an efficiency loss associated with the imposition of a price floor. This efficiency loss, or **deadweight loss**, can be measured for a price floor of \$4, as shown in the graph below.

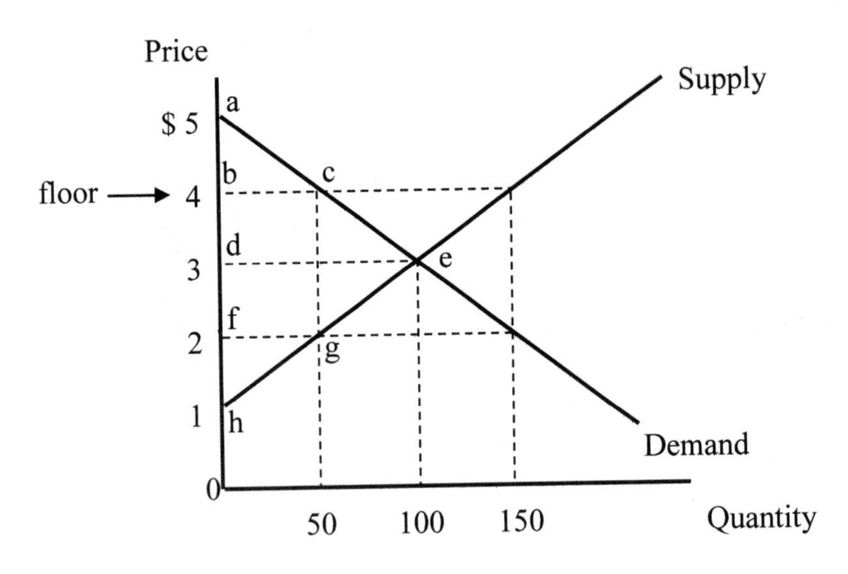

Free Market Outcome (assuming no price floor): P_E = \$3 and Q_E = 100

Consumer Surplus = area aed = ½(100)(\$5 - \$3) = \$100
Producer Surplus = area deh = ½(100)(\$3 - \$1) = \$100
Total Surplus = area aeh = \$100 + \$100 = \$200

Price Floor of \$4: P = \$4, Q_D = 150 and Q_S = 50, actual quantity exchanged = 50

Consumer Surplus = area of triangle acb = ½(50)(\$5 - \$4) = \$25
Producer Surplus = area of triangle fgh + area of rectangle bcgf
Producer Surplus = ½(50)(\$2 - \$1) + (50)(\$4 - \$2) = \$25 + \$100 = \$125
Total Surplus = area acgh = \$25 + \$125 = \$150

Deadweight Loss: total surplus before the floor – total surplus after the floor

Deadweight loss = \$200 - \$150 = \$50
Deadweight loss = area of triangle ceg = ½(100 - 50)(\$4 - \$2) = \$50

Since there is a deadweight loss, society experiences a net loss when a price floor is imposed. Although some sellers are made better off by the higher price, the losses experienced by those who are unable to sell at the higher price, as well as buyers, outweigh those gains.

In some cases, the loss in efficiency resulting from government policy provides a good reason to remove or change the policy, but it is important to consider the underlying purpose of policies that interfere with free markets. There may be equity goals that override efficiency concerns, or it may be that the market equilibrium is inefficient due to market failure, which is a topic that will be pursued in chapter 8.

Taxes can also have a significant effect on markets because they alter product prices and create a wedge between the amount consumers pay and the amount sellers receive.

Commodity Tax

The **statutory** incidence (burden) of a tax refers to which party has the legal obligation to pay the tax. For example, the statutory burden of the sales tax that is collected on many products is on business firms because the seller is legally responsible for collecting the tax and sending the money to the government. As a consumer, you may feel that you are the one who actually pays the tax, because the amount is added to the price when you pay for your purchases, and this leads us to consider the economic burden of a tax. Keep in mind that the pre-tax price of a product may differ from the price that would have been charged if there was no tax. The economic model developed in this section helps to clarify this distinction.

The **economic** incidence (burden) typically differs from the statutory incidence. Often, consumers bear at least part of the economic burden of taxes in the form of higher prices. Economic analysis is used to predict what percentage of the economic burden of the tax falls on buyers and what percentage falls on sellers. The answer depends on **elasticities** of demand and supply. An important conclusion is that statutory incidence does not determine economic incidence.

A commodity tax can be either per-unit or ad valorem. A **per-unit** tax is a fixed amount collected on each unit of a product sold. An **ad valorem** tax is levied as a percentage of the product's price. For example, the sales tax in some Texas cities is 8.25 percent of the price of taxable commodities. Additionally, taxes are classified as either general or **excise taxes**. Excise taxes are levied on specific items, such as gasoline or wine, and are usually a fixed amount per unit. For simplicity, the analysis that follows focuses on per-unit excise taxes.

Suppose there is currently no tax levied on peanuts and the price of a bag of peanuts is $1. If the government decides to collect ten cents on each bag of peanuts sold, then peanut sellers would obviously like to charge $1.10 per bag, but they will almost certainly find that the quantity demanded is lower at this higher price, leaving them with a surplus of peanuts. Most often, a new equilibrium is achieved in which the after-tax price to the consumer ends up somewhere between $1 and $1.10. The economic burden, or tax incidence, is then partly on consumers because they have to pay more than $1 due to the tax. If sellers charge $1.05 per bag of peanuts and then send 10 cents to the government to cover the tax, they are effectively selling peanuts for 95 cents now, so sellers bear part of the tax burden as well. In this example, 50 percent of the burden fell on consumers and 50 percent fell on sellers.

The type of reasoning used in the example above can be applied to any product. It is very useful to use a supply and demand graph to illustrate the consequences of a tax placed on a commodity. The diagram makes it clear how the tax affects the price consumers pay, the price sellers keep, and the quantity bought and sold in the market. The graph can also be used to illustrate how economic incidence depends on supply and demand elasticity.

Market forces dictate a price where supply and demand intersect (equilibrium), so that is always a good starting point, but a tax changes the situation. The graph below shows free market equilibrium at a price of $7 and a quantity of 240. When the price is $7 and quantity is 240 units, consumer surplus equals (½)(240)($3) = $360 and producer surplus is (½)(240)($6) = $720. Total surplus is $360 + $720 = $1,080. In order to see how the tax affects total surplus, first examine how the tax affects equilibrium price and quantity.

Suppose a tax of **$3 per unit** is imposed on this product. Sellers can't just raise the price by the full amount of the tax and still sell 240 units because quantity demanded falls as price rises (law of demand). Specifically, the demand curve below indicates that the quantity demanded is zero at a price of $10, so it is clear that the sellers in this market will not pass the entire tax to consumers by raising price from $7 to $10. They can, however, shift some of the tax burden to consumers by raising the price consumers must pay.

The line labeled **Supply + Tax** helps identify how much sellers will raise the price in this situation. This line is found by shifting the supply curve straight up by the amount of the tax per unit, so it is parallel to the original supply line. At each value of quantity supplied, the price associated with the Supply + Tax line is $3 higher. For example, before the tax, sellers would have supplied 160 units at a price of $5, but after the tax, sellers must receive $8 per unit before they are willing to supply 160 units.

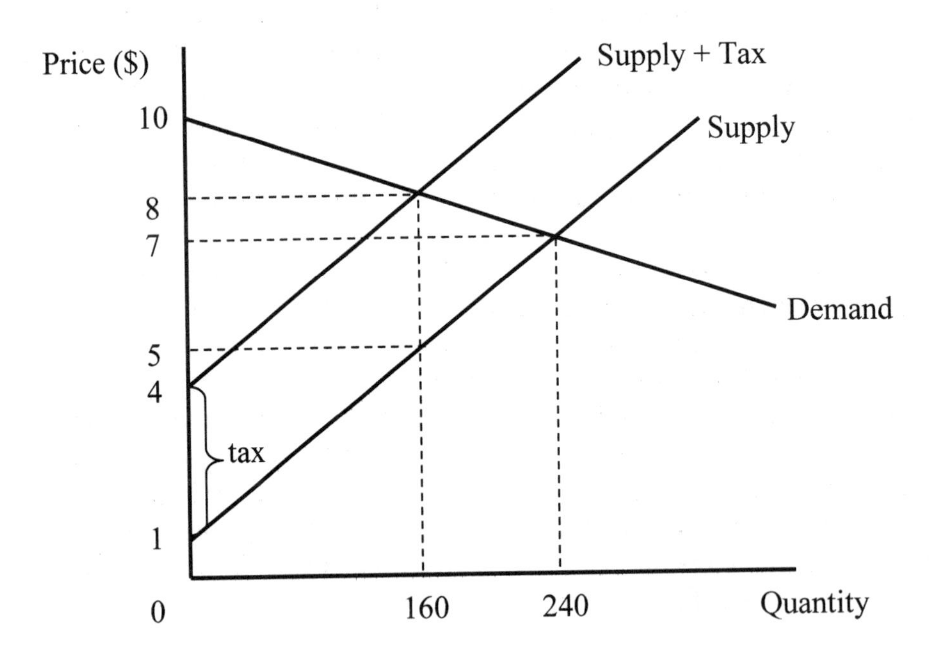

The new **equilibrium** occurs at the intersection of the Supply + Tax line and the Demand curve. The quantity supplied is 160 when sellers receive $5 per unit, and the quantity demanded is 160 when buyers pay $8 per unit; quantity supplied equals quantity demanded when the price to consumers is $8 and the price retained by sellers is $5. Government collects **tax revenue** equal to the new equilibrium quantity of 160 multiplied by the amount of tax collected on each unit, which is $3. In this case, tax revenue is (160)($3) = $480.

Consumers must pay $8 per unit rather than $7 per unit, or $1 more, when a $3 tax is imposed, so they bear one-third of the economic burden of this tax illustrated in the graph on the previous page. Sellers receive $5 per unit, as compared to the $7 they received before the tax was levied, so they bear two-thirds of the economic burden of the tax.

Economists have spent a lot of time studying tax incidence in order to learn which groups are likely to bear the burden of various taxes. One of the most important lessons of this analysis is that economic burden depends on supply and demand elasticities, not on statutory burden. It can be shown that the percentage of a tax that is borne by consumers will equal the price elasticity of supply coefficient divided by the sum of the supply and demand elasticity coefficients. For example, if the price elasticity of supply coefficient is equal to 0.5 (relatively inelastic) and the price elasticity of demand coefficient is equal to 1 (unit elastic), this indicates that one-third of the economic burden of the tax will fall on consumers since 0.5/1.5 equals 1/3.

Some examples involving graphs are presented to illustrate tax burdens when demand is perfectly inelastic or perfectly elastic. In the graph below, demand is **perfectly inelastic**, so an increase in the price of this product has no effect on equilibrium quantity.

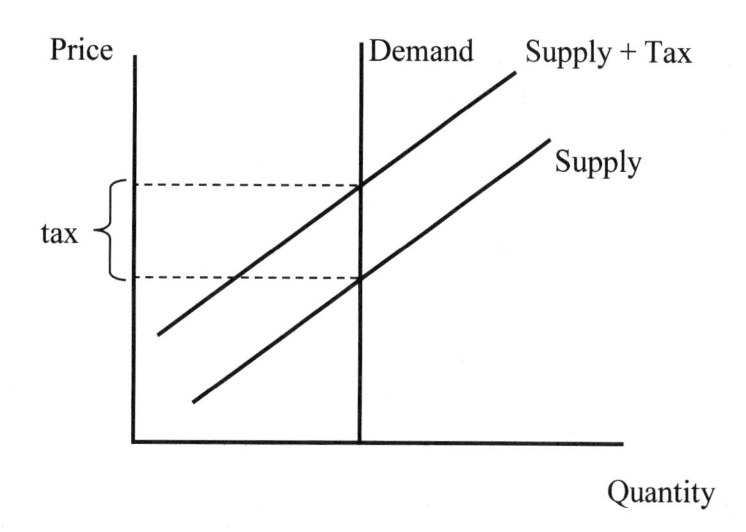

When demand is perfectly inelastic, it is possible for sellers to raise the price of the product by the full amount of the tax because a higher price does not cause quantity demanded to fall. In this case, consumers bear the full economic burden of the tax. A demand curve is likely to be perfectly inelastic when the product is a necessity with no close substitutes so that consumers have no choice but to pay the higher price resulting from the tax.

This extreme case leads to an important generalization: other things the same, *the more inelastic the demand, the more buyers will bear the economic burden of a tax*. Policymakers are aware of this result, so they are usually careful to avoid placing heavy taxes on necessities, such as food, because the burden of such taxes is likely to fall on consumers, many of whom cannot afford to pay substantially higher prices.

On the other hand, if demand is **perfectly elastic**, there are perfect substitutes available, so consumers will not purchase any of the taxed item, assuming the perfect substitutes are not taxed. In this case, the seller will bear the full economic burden of the tax, as illustrated in the graph below.

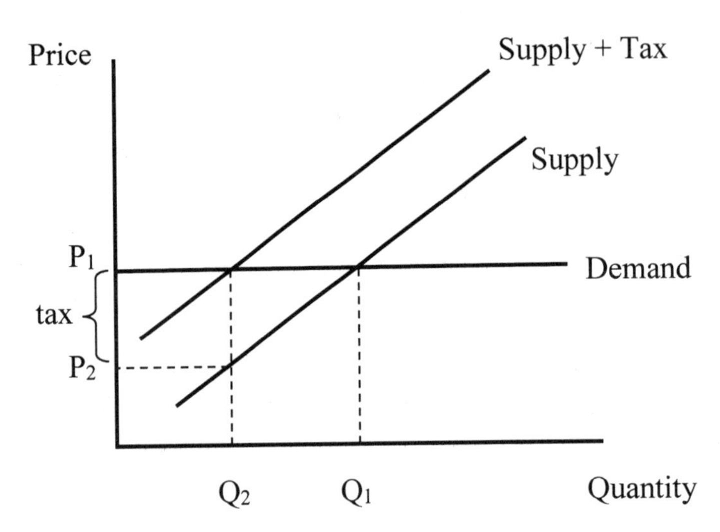

If demand is perfectly elastic, sellers cannot pass any of the tax on to consumers in the form of a higher price. The after-tax equilibrium occurs at a lower quantity, but the price paid by consumers is unaffected by the tax. In the above graph, sellers are forced to accept a per-unit price of P_2; otherwise sales will drop to zero. Consumers pay the same price as they did before the tax (P_1), so the entire economic burden of the tax falls on sellers. This analysis leads to another generalization: *other things the same, the more elastic the demand, the more sellers will bear the economic burden of a tax.*

Recall that one of the determinants of price elasticity of demand indicated that demand is likely to be more elastic when a product is considered a luxury. When policymakers imposed a special tax on luxury yachts, they discovered that the tax did not yield a lot of revenue because consumers substituted away from the taxed product and chose to purchase foreign-produced yachts instead. The tax was quickly removed since it harmed domestic producers, cost domestic jobs, and did not generate a lot of tax revenue. These results could have been anticipated using the analysis developed in this chapter.

Similar results can be reached in the extreme cases of perfectly inelastic or perfectly elastic supply: sellers bear the economic burden of a tax when supply is perfectly inelastic, while buyers bear the economic burden when supply is perfectly elastic. Similar general results can also be reached: *other things the same, the more inelastic the supply, the more sellers will bear the economic burden of a tax; the more elastic the supply, the more buyers will bear the economic burden of a tax.* **General result: the more inelastic side bears the tax burden.**

If supply and demand elasticities are the same, then the burden of the tax is split evenly between buyers and sellers. Graphically, this kind of situation occurs when the absolute value of the slope of the downward-sloping demand curve is equal to the slope of the upward-sloping supply curve (so they look like an "X" when drawn).

There is an efficiency loss associated with commodity taxation. This efficiency loss, or **deadweight loss**, can be measured as shown in the graph below, which is the same as the graph that was shown earlier in the chapter and is repeated for convenience.

Recall that in free market equilibrium, price is $7, quantity is 240, consumer surplus equals (½)(240)($3) = $360 and producer surplus equals (½)(240)($6) = $720. Total surplus is $360 + $720 = $1,080.

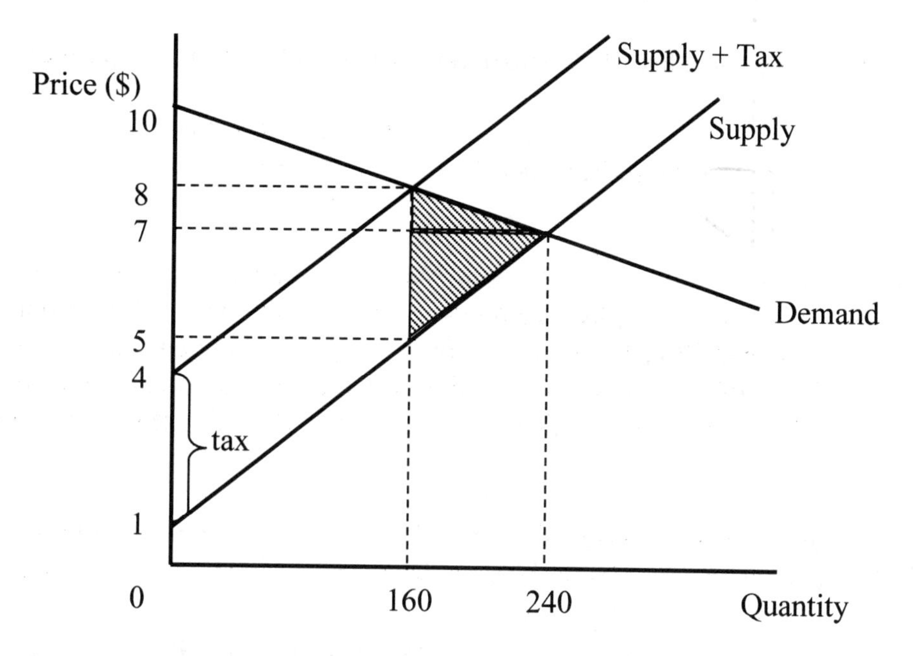

In the after-tax equilibrium, consumer surplus is (½)(160)($10 - $8) = $160 and producer surplus is (½)(160)($5 - $1) = $320. Total surplus fell from $1,080 to $480 as a result of this tax.

The amount of **tax revenue** collected by government is ($3)(160) = $480, so part of the lost consumer and producer surplus is simply being transferred to government. Assume that government will use the $480 in tax revenue to pay for something of value to society, such as roads, schools, or police protection, so tax revenue does not represent a loss to society.

The net loss (in this case, the total $1,080 surplus before the tax minus the total $480 surplus after the tax minus the tax revenue of $480) is therefore $120. This net loss is also referred to as the **deadweight loss** or the **excess burden of the tax**, and is equal to the <u>shaded area</u> in the above graph.

Deadweight Loss = ½(240 – 160)($8 – $5) = ½(80)($3) = $120

In some cases, government uses taxes to deliberately reduce the quantity consumed or produced in order to achieve a specific goal. For example, government might impose a tax on alcohol or tobacco (a so-called sin tax) to discourage use of these products. Additionally, environmental policy sometimes relies on taxes as a way to reduce output when there is pollution. If the initial market equilibrium is not efficient, taxation may not cause deadweight loss.

The U.S. Income Tax

Ideas for reforming the U.S. income tax structure are numerous. Sometimes the goal of reform is to simplify the tax code, sometimes to make taxation more progressive, or less progressive, or eliminate the marriage penalty, or improve incentives to invest. You will no doubt encounter many arguments for tax changes in the years to come. It is helpful to understand some basic tax concepts when evaluating the U.S. income tax and various reform proposals.

The *average* income tax rate is calculated by dividing income tax payments by income:

$$\text{Average Tax Rate} = \frac{\text{income tax payments}}{\text{income}}$$

A **proportional** income tax is one with a constant average tax rate. For example, if every person paid exactly 20 percent of income in taxes, the income tax would be proportional. The U.S. income tax is **progressive**, meaning that the average tax rate increases as income increases. Families with relative low incomes pay a small percentage of their income in taxes, while families with higher incomes pay a higher average tax rate. A tax is **regressive** if the average tax rate falls as income rises.

The marginal tax rate measures the *additional* income tax paid on *additional* income, or the change in income tax payments divided by the change in income. The symbol Δ (delta) means "change in," so:

$$\text{Marginal Tax Rate} = \frac{\Delta\text{income tax payments}}{\Delta\text{income}}$$

If the marginal tax rate is greater than the average tax rate, then the average tax rate increases with income, and the income tax is progressive. The table below provides hypothetical data to illustrate the relationship between marginal tax rates and average tax rates.

Taxable Income	Marginal Tax Rate
0 - $20,000	10 percent
$20,001 - $40,000	15 percent
$40,001 - $80,000	25 percent

Suppose a family's taxable income is $30,000. According to the hypothetical tax table above, this family pays 10 percent of the first $20,000, or $2,000, plus 15 percent of the next $10,000, or an additional $1,500, so this family's income tax liability is $3,500 and their average tax rate is 11.67 percent ($3,500/$30,000). Notice that their average tax rate is lower than the highest marginal tax rate they pay. A family with $40,000 in taxable income would pay income taxes of $5,000, for an average tax rate of 12.5 percent. Thus, the average tax rate increases as income increases, but be careful not to confuse the average tax rate with the marginal tax rate. This confusion can be costly if you refuse a raise on the grounds that it will move you into a higher tax bracket, so keep in mind the high marginal rate only applies to additional income.

NAME Drew Dollar SECTION#__________
PRINT LAST NAME, FIRST NAME

PRICE CEILINGS AND PRICE FLOORS

1. Policymakers are more likely to impose a price **ceiling**:
   a. above equilibrium price in order to protect buyers from high prices.
   b. above equilibrium price in order to protect sellers from low prices.
   c. below equilibrium price in order to protect buyers from high prices.
   d. below equilibrium price in order to protect sellers from low prices.

C

2. Policymakers are more likely to impose a price **floor**:
   a. above equilibrium price in order to protect buyers from high prices.
   b. above equilibrium price in order to protect sellers from low prices.
   c. below equilibrium price in order to protect buyers from high prices.
   d. below equilibrium price in order to protect sellers from low prices.

B

3. A binding price ceiling causes a market _____, while a binding price floor causes a market _____.
   a. shortage; shortage
   b. surplus; surplus
   c. shortage; surplus
   d. surplus; shortage

A

Use the graph below to answer questions 4 and 5.

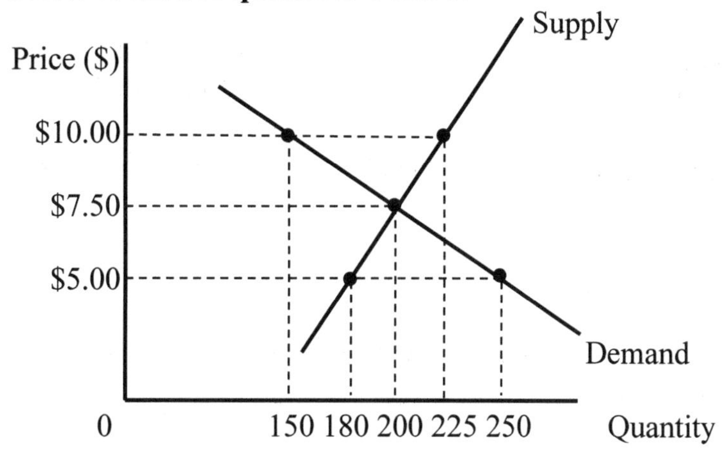

4. If there is a price floor set at $10.00, the quantity bought and sold in this market will be equal to _____ and there will be a market __________.
   a. 150; shortage
   b. 225; shortage
   c. 150; surplus
   d. 225; surplus

C

5. If there is a price ceiling set at $5.00, the quantity bought and sold in this market will be equal to _____ and there will be a market __________.
   a. 180; shortage
   b. 250; shortage
   c. 180; surplus
   d. 250; surplus

A

NAME____SECTION#________________
PRINT LAST NAME, FIRST NAME

Use the graph below to answer questions 6 through 10.

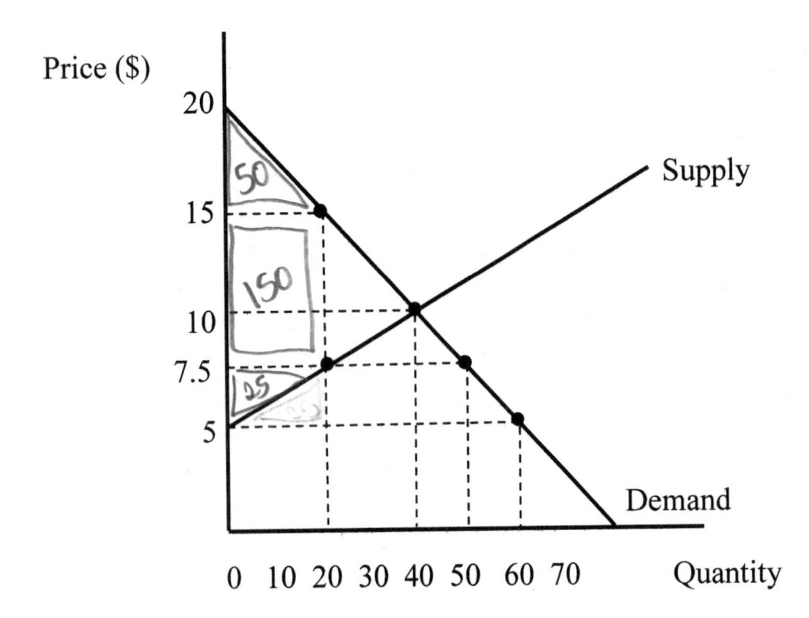

6. When this market is in equilibrium, consumer surplus is equal to _______ and producer surplus is equal to ________.

a. $200; $100 c. $400; $200
b. $100; $200 d. $200; $400

7. If there is a price floor set at $15, the quantity bought and sold (exchanged) in this market will be equal to:

a. 20. c. 60.
b. 40. d. 80.

8. If there is a price floor set at $15, consumer surplus will be equal to ____ and producer surplus will be equal to ____.

a. $50; $100 c. $100; $100
b. $50; $175 d. $100; $175

9. If there is a price ceiling set at $7.50, the quantity bought and sold (exchanged) in this market will be equal to:

a. 20. c. 60.
b. 40. d. 80.

10. If there is a price ceiling set at $7.50, consumer surplus will be equal to ____ and producer surplus will be equal to ____.

a. $175; $25 c. $200; $25
b. $175; $50 d. $200; $50

NAME____SECTION#________________
PRINT LAST NAME, FIRST NAME

PRICE FLOOR

Use the graph below to fill in the blanks.

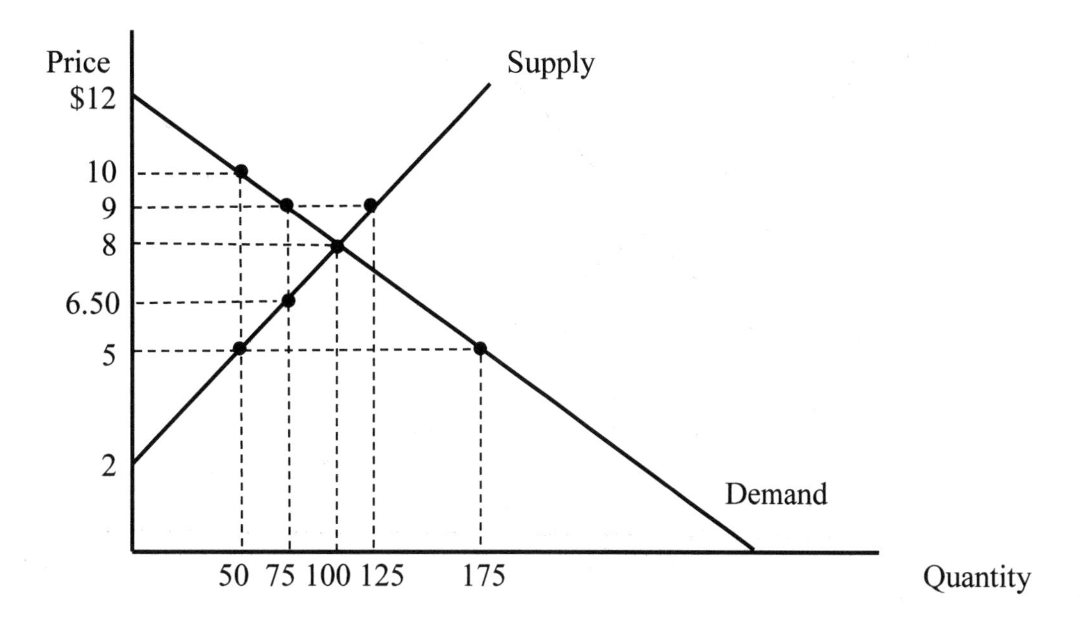

1. In equilibrium, price is $____________ and the quantity exchanged (bought and sold) will equal ____________ units; consumer surplus is equal to $____________ and producer surplus is equal to $____________.

2. If government sets a **price floor** at $9, quantity demanded will equal ____________ units, quantity supplied will equal ____________ units, and the actual quantity exchanged will equal ____________ units.

3. If government sets a **price floor** at $9, consumer surplus will equal $____________.

4. If government sets a **price floor** at $9, producer surplus will equal $____________.

5. If government sets a **price floor** at $9, deadweight loss will equal $____________.

NAME____SECTION#________________
PRINT LAST NAME, FIRST NAME

PRICE CEILING

Use the graph below to fill in the blanks.

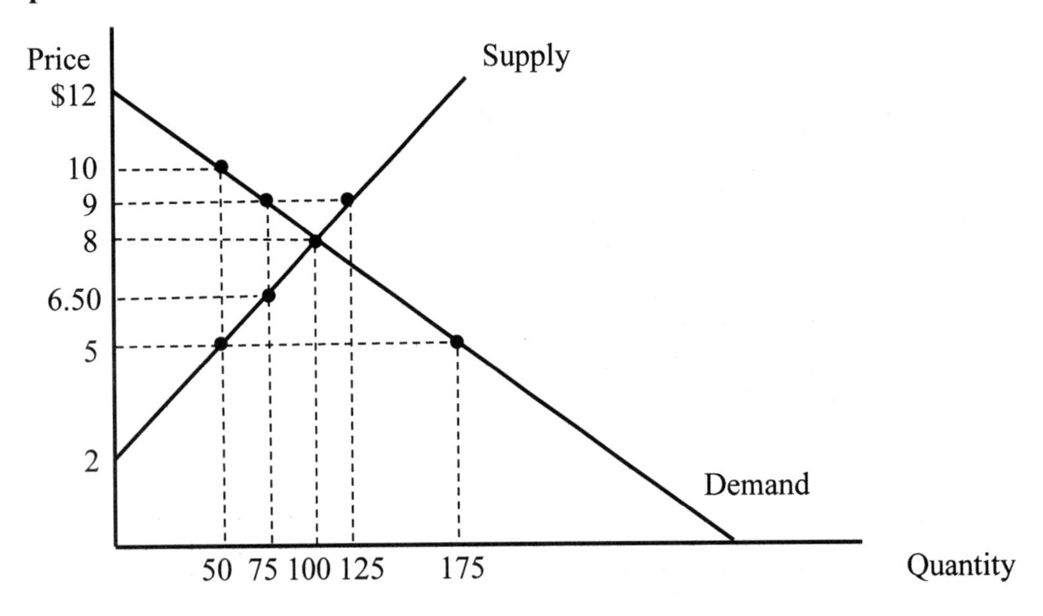

1. In equilibrium, price is $____________ and the quantity exchanged (bought and sold) will equal ____________ units; consumer surplus is equal to $____________ and producer surplus is equal to $____________.

2. If government sets a **price ceiling** at $5, quantity demanded will equal ____________ units, quantity supplied will equal ____________ units, and the actual quantity exchanged will equal ____________ units.

3. If government sets a **price ceiling** at $5, consumer surplus will equal $____________.

4. If government sets a **price ceiling** at $5, producer surplus will equal $____________.

5. If government sets a **price ceiling** at $5, deadweight loss will equal $____________.

NAME____SECTION#______________

PRINT LAST NAME, FIRST NAME

PRICE CEILINGS, PRICE FLOORS, AND TAXATION

Use the table below to answer questions 1 and 2.

Price	Quantity Demanded	Quantity Supplied
$8	200	1,000
$6	400	800
$4	600	600
$2	800	400

1. Setting a price floor of $8 would cause a market surplus in the amount of:
   a. 400 units. b. 500 units. c. 600 units. d. 800 units.

2. Setting a price ceiling of $2 would cause a market shortage in the amount of:
   a. 400 units. b. 500 units. c. 600 units. d. 800 units.

3. The economic incidence (burden) of a tax refers to:
   a. the legal limit on how much sellers can raise price in an attempt to shift tax burdens to consumers.
   b. how much revenue the tax is able to generate.
   c. what percentage of the tax burden falls on buyers and what percentage of the tax burden falls on sellers.
   d. which party has the legal obligation to send the tax dollars to the government.

4. The statutory incidence (burden) of a tax refers to:
   a. the legal limit on how much sellers can raise price in an attempt to shift tax burdens to consumers.
   b. how much revenue the tax is able to generate.
   c. what percentage of the tax burden falls on buyers and what percentage of the tax burden falls on sellers.
   d. which party has the legal obligation to send the tax dollars to the government.

5. Regardless of the statutory incidence of a commodity tax, the economic incidence of the tax is:
   a. entirely on buyers if supply is perfectly inelastic.
   b. entirely on buyers if demand is perfectly inelastic.
   c. entirely on buyers if demand is perfectly elastic.
   d. entirely on sellers if demand is perfectly inelastic.

6. Suppose aluminum foil and plastic wrap are perfect substitutes. If a tax is placed on aluminum foil but not on plastic wrap, the burden of the tax will fall on:
   a. sellers since they cannot raise the price of aluminum foil.
   b. sellers since the price of aluminum foil will increase by the amount of the tax.
   c. buyers since the price of aluminum foil will increase by the amount of the tax.
   d. both buyers and sellers since the price of aluminum foil cannot increase by the amount of the tax.

NAME____SECTION#________________

PRINT LAST NAME, FIRST NAME

Use the graph below to answer questions 7 through 10:

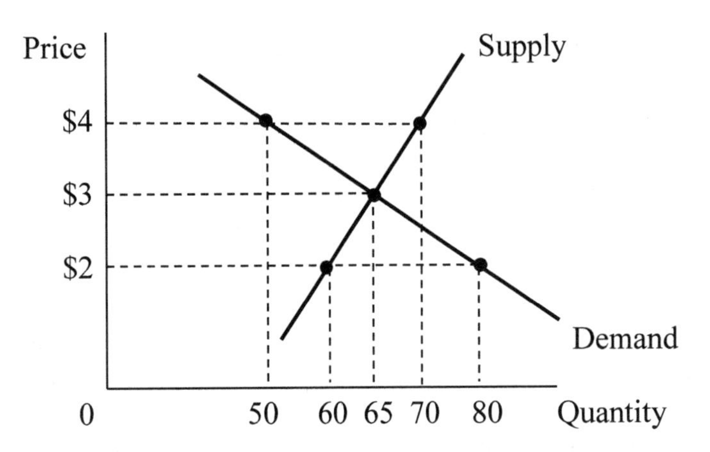

7. If there is a price floor of $4 in this market, there will be:
   a. no effect on quantity because this is not a binding floor.
   b. a decrease in demand and an increase in supply.
   c. a market surplus of 20.
   d. a market shortage of 20.

8. If there is a price floor of $2 in this market, there will be:
   a. no effect on quantity because this is not a binding floor.
   b. a decrease in demand and an increase in supply.
   c. a market surplus of 20.
   d. a market shortage of 20.

9. If there is a price ceiling of $2 in this market, there will be:
   a. no effect on quantity because this is not a binding ceiling.
   b. an increase in demand and a decrease in supply.
   c. a market surplus of 20.
   d. a market shortage of 20.

10. If the price ceiling of $2 is *removed*, market forces will cause the price to:
    a. increase to $3, which will cause quantity demanded to rise and quantity supplied to fall.
    b. increase to $3, which will cause quantity demanded to fall and quantity supplied to rise.
    c. stay at $2 because sellers prefer to have a surplus.
    d. stay at $2 because sellers prefer to have a shortage.

NAME Drew Dollar SECTION#________
PRINT LAST NAME, FIRST NAME

COMMODITY TAXATION

1. If the price of a cup of coffee is $2.00 in the absence of any tax, and a $0.30 per cup tax is levied on coffee, ceteris paribus, then:
   a. consumers will be forced to pay $2.30 per cup.
   b. sellers will be forced to accept $1.70 per cup.
   c. the after-tax price per cup will most likely be between $2.00 and $2.30.
   d. the after-tax price per cup will most likely be greater than $2.30.

   C

2. The economic burden of a tax:
   a. is always shifted to consumers by raising the product price by the amount of the tax.
   b. is borne by sellers if supply is perfectly elastic.
   c. is partially shifted to consumers through higher prices in most cases.
   d. falls on sellers if the statutory burden of the tax is on sellers.

   C

Use the graph below to answer questions 3 and 4:

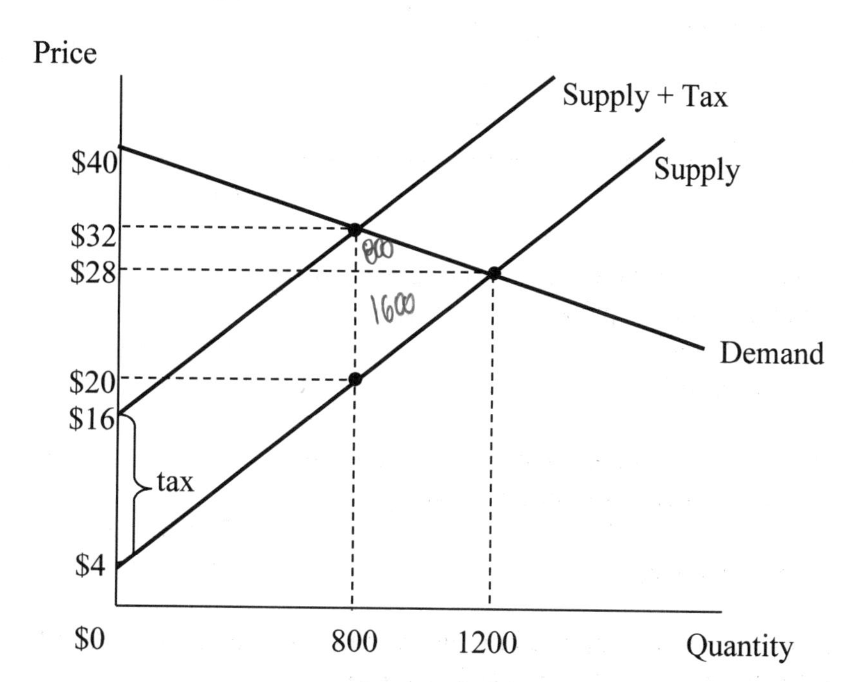

3. As a result of the $12 per-unit tax imposed on this commodity, the quantity produced and consumed in this market changes to ____ and there is a deadweight loss of ____.
   a. 800; $2400
   b. 800; $3200
   c. 1200; $2400
   d. 1200; $3200

   A

4. If a $12 per-unit tax is imposed in this market, buyers will bear ____ percent of the tax burden because demand is relatively _____.
   a. 33; elastic
   b. 67; elastic
   c. 33; inelastic
   d. 67; inelastic

   A

NAME________________________________ SECTION#____________

PRINT LAST NAME, FIRST NAME

5. Commodity taxes usually result in deadweight loss because a tax causes quantity to:
   a. fall, increasing both consumer surplus and producer surplus.
   b. fall, decreasing both consumer surplus and producer surplus.
   c. rise, increasing both consumer surplus and producer surplus.
   d. rise, decreasing both consumer surplus and producer surplus.

Use the graph below to answer questions 6 through 10.

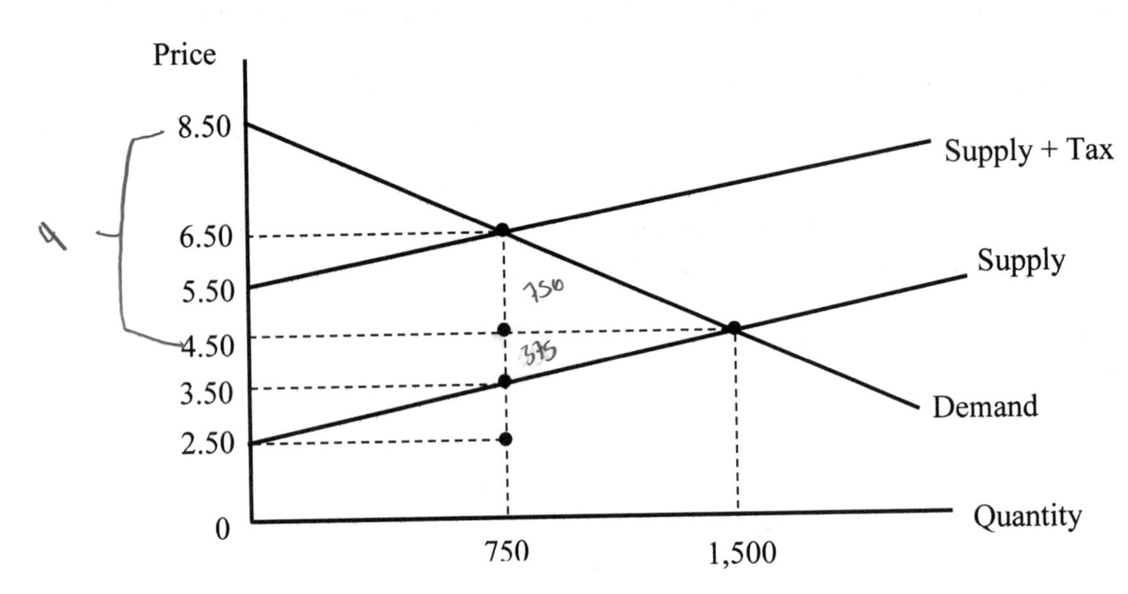

6. If there is no tax and the market has achieved equilibrium, then _____ units will be bought and sold for a price of ____ each.
   a. 750; $6.50
   b. 750; $3.50
   c. 1,500; $6.50
   d. 1,500; $4.50

7. If there is no tax and the market has achieved equilibrium, consumer surplus is equal to _____ and producer surplus is equal to _____.
   a. $3,000; $1,500
   b. $1,500; $3,000
   c. $1,500; $750
   d. $750; $1,500

8. If a $3 per-unit tax is imposed in this market, the quantity consumed changes to _____ and the price paid by consumers changes to _____.
   a. 750; $6.50
   b. 750; $3.50
   c. 1,500; $6.50
   d. 1,500; $4.50

9. If a $3 per-unit tax is imposed in this market, the quantity produced changes to _____ and the price retained by sellers changes to _____.
   a. 750; $6.50
   b. 750; $3.50
   c. 1,500; $6.50
   d. 1,500; $4.50

10. If a $3 per-unit tax is imposed in this market, there is a deadweight loss of:
   a. $750
   b. $1,125
   c. $2,250
   d. $4,800

NAME____SECTION#_______________
PRINT LAST NAME, FIRST NAME

COMMODITY TAXATION

Use the graph below to fill in the blanks.

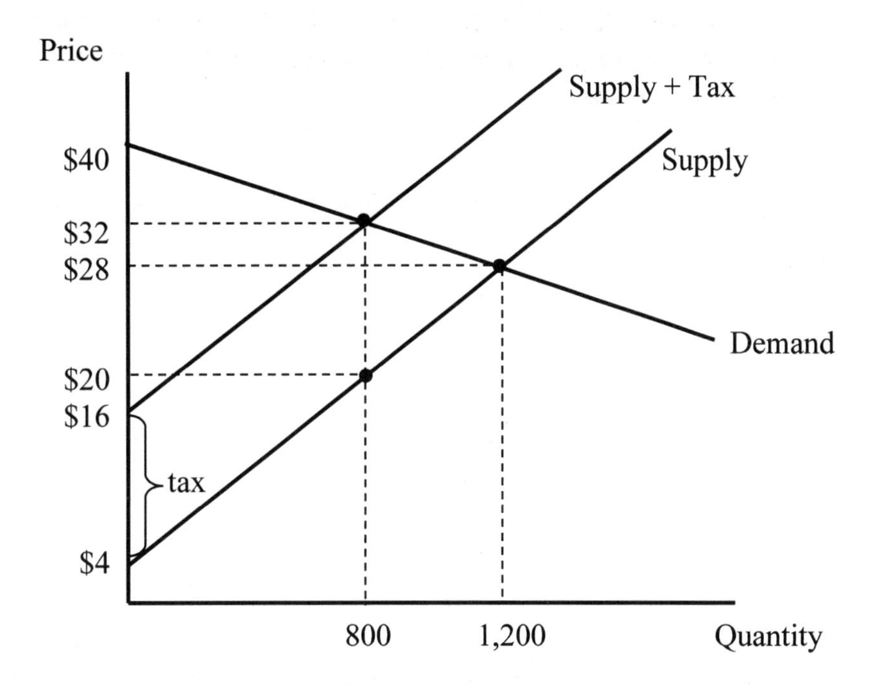

Assuming this market is in equilibrium with no tax, the price of this good is 1) $_________, and the quantity bought and sold is 2) _______________. Before the tax, consumer surplus is equal to 3) $_______________ and producer surplus is equal to 4) $_______________. Assume government levies a $12 per-unit tax on this good. With a $12 per-unit tax, the price buyers must pay will rise to 5) $___________, and the price sellers receive falls to 6) $___________. The after-tax quantity bought and sold is 7) _________. After the tax, total surplus (consumer surplus plus producer surplus) is equal to 8) $____________. Tax revenue is equal to 9) $____________ and the deadweight loss is equal to 10) $______________.

NAME____SECTION#______________

PRINT LAST NAME, FIRST NAME

INCOME TAXATION

Suppose the existing tax structure imposes a tax rate of 10 percent on taxable income up to $60,000 and a marginal tax rate of 25 percent on taxable income above $60,000. Assume there are no tax credits and the average tax rate is tax liability divided by taxable income. Use this information to complete the table.

Taxable Income	Tax Liability	Average tax rate
$20,000	$__________	____________
$30,000	$__________	____________
$60,000	$__________	____________
$100,000	$__________	____________
$200,000	$__________	____________

Define the terms progressive, proportional, and regressive as they relate to income taxation:

Is this tax structure progressive, proportional, or regressive? ______________________

CHAPTER 8 Market Failure and the Role of Government

Economic theory demonstrates that free markets can promote an **efficient** allocation of resources in which the goods and services people want are produced at the least cost. In the real world, however, an efficient outcome may be prevented by market failure. There are four primary **sources of market failure**.

1) **Imperfect (Asymmetric) information** – buyers and sellers make choices regarding the use of scarce resources based on the information available to them. If the information is incorrect or incomplete, then the choices may not promote efficiency. Efficient transactions cause all participants to be made better off, but imperfect information can lead to inefficient transactions.

2) **Imperfectly competitive markets** – profit-motivated sellers are driven to produce the goods and services people want at the lowest possible price by the forces of competition. As shown by the model of supply and demand, market forces promote efficiency, but the model was based on an assumption that markets are perfectly competitive. With imperfect competition, sellers are able to charge higher prices by restricting output, so the result is no longer efficient.

3) **Externalities** – in some cases, the benefits or costs of a transaction can spill over to third parties. When there are spillover benefits, or **positive externalities**, the free market equilibrium is likely to correspond to a level of output that is lower than the socially efficient quantity. When there are spillover costs, or **negative externalities**, the free market equilibrium is likely to correspond to a level of output that is higher than the socially efficient quantity.

4) **Public goods and common resources** – free markets do not efficiently provide **public goods** because of the nature of public goods. Once provided, the benefits of a public good cannot be denied to those who do not pay, leading to a **free-rider problem**. For example, if a private group of individuals formed a security force to prevent foreign invasion, it would be difficult to force all those who benefit to share in the cost. Free markets may also lead to inefficient use of **common resources** when property rights are not well-established. Common resources, like wild animals, clean air, and clean water, may be overused if there is no mechanism in place to encourage conservation.

Market failure means that the free-market outcome is not efficient and, in many cases, economists recommend specific government policies designed to correct market failure and promote efficiency. The sources of market failure are examined in more detail before moving on to an analysis of how government might improve the outcome. When government takes action, there is also the possibility of **government failure** because the incentives that motivate efficient behavior in the private sector are often absent from bureaucratic agencies. It is necessary to understand that the realistic choice is sometimes between an inefficient market outcome and an inefficient government outcome.

Imperfect Information

Market participants require information to make decisions. Consumers must know what products are available, and at what price, in order to choose an optimal bundle of goods and services. Entrepreneurs must know how much potential profit exists in various markets in order to decide what kind of business to start. Borrowers must know the costs of credit in order to decide how much and when to borrow. In many cases, society has elected to rely on private incentives to acquire information. In other cases, however, it may be that information is too difficult or expensive to acquire; or it may be that some participants would deliberately provide false or misleading information, so government sometimes steps in.

When there is **asymmetric information**, one party in the transaction knows more than the other. For example, if a consumer purchases a used car based on the seller's assurance that the car has no major defects, but in fact the seller knows that the engine block is cracked, the consumer is not made better off from this transaction. For this reason, U.S. law typically voids transactions or contracts based on fraudulent information. Insurance markets are characterized by asymmetric information. For example, individuals seeking health insurance may have knowledge about family history which they do not choose to disclose to the insurance provider.

The **Truth in Lending Act of 1968** protects consumers by requiring clear disclosure of the costs of credit. This act requires lenders to disclose all costs of credit up front, such as the annual percentage rate (APR) to be paid on the loan. The purpose of this legislation is to protect borrowers from potentially misleading claims about the true cost of a loan. Generally, lenders have better information than borrowers as a group, so this is an example of asymmetric information. Although it is possible for borrowers to read a finance textbook and learn the difference between the annual percentage rate and the annual interest rate compounded monthly, a more efficient arrangement is to require lenders to provide clear and consistent information about loan costs so that consumers can make informed decisions.

The U.S. legal system offers many forms of protection from false or misleading information. The **Federal Trade Commission** was created in 1914 to investigate instances of false advertising and force firms to provide only truthful information. Contracts based on fraudulent information are routinely set aside by courts. Tobacco companies and pharmaceutical companies are required to provide accurate information on product risks.

Government plays an important role in the market for information by potentially making information more credible and improving **transparency**. When you purchase a home, you can rely on the seller's assurance that the home is not infested with termites. This is not because sellers would never provide false information, but because past legal cases have made it clear that sellers have a legal responsibility to provide truthful information, or face the prospect of an expensive lawsuit resulting in an order to pay monetary damages to the injured party. Market purists may argue that there is no need for government to intervene because sellers who provide false information will not survive for long in a competitive environment. This would not apply to the seller of just one house, though, because that seller is not concerned with survival in the marketplace. Current government policy reflects a belief that efficient transactions require full information, and the legal system can be used to make information more accessible and reliable.

Imperfectly Competitive Markets

An industry is imperfectly competitive when a firm can raise the price of its product without losing all sales of that product. Firms in imperfectly competitive markets set price above marginal cost and produce an inefficiently low level of output. In the extreme, an industry that is controlled by a single firm, called a **monopoly**, has no competition and the price and output chosen by an unregulated, profit-maximizing monopolist can be very different from the efficient outcome likely to emerge in a competitive market.

The next three chapters provide a foundation for business by introducing important concepts like cost, revenue, and profit. The supply function, which was presented in Chapter 4 as the relationship between price and quantity supplied, is more formally derived based on the behavior of profit-maximizing sellers operating in perfectly competitive markets. Chapters 12, 13, and 14 demonstrate how the outcome changes when firms operate in imperfectly competitive markets, and information about how government promotes competition and regulates big business is also provided. Therefore, this chapter will not go further into the analysis of imperfectly competitive markets beyond asserting that government promotes competition by using **antitrust legislation** to prevent the formation of monopolies and the use of anticompetitive practices such as price-fixing.

Externalities

Government provides for education, public health, police and fire protection, roads and highways, and a host of other goods and services that generate **external** or **spillover benefits**. When the consumption of a good or service creates benefits that spill over to third parties, a **positive externality** exists and the **marginal social benefit** (MSB) exceeds the marginal private benefit. MSB is the marginal benefit to society, and includes both private and spillover benefits.

Many unregulated producers would likely emit pollutants and toxins into the air, ground, and water, which would generate **external** or **spillover costs**. When the production of a good or service creates costs that spill over to third parties, a **negative externality** exists. Perfectly competitive firms set marginal benefit equal to marginal cost, resulting in an efficient level of output when all the costs have been taken into account. In some cases, private marginal cost curves do not include all costs. When a negative externality exists, the **marginal social cost** (MSC) exceeds the marginal private cost that firms must pay. MSC is the marginal cost to society, and includes both private costs and spillover costs.

The free market equilibrium corresponds to the intersection of marginal private benefit (demand) and marginal private cost (supply), but the socially efficient level of output requires that marginal social benefit equal marginal social cost. In the absence of an externality, the free market equilibrium and the socially efficient level of output are the same. An externality creates a discrepancy between the demand function and the marginal social benefit curve, when there is a positive externality; and between the supply function and the marginal social cost curve, when there is a negative externality, resulting in a discrepancy between the market equilibrium output and the socially efficient output.

The inefficiency created by either a positive or negative externality can be illustrated graphically. In the absence of government intervention, the equilibrium price is determined by free market forces, and consumers will purchase Q_1 in the graph below. Thus, Q_1 is the market equilibrium quantity. The **efficient quantity**, however, is Q_2 where MC = MSB, and the **efficient price** is the price that induces consumers to purchase the efficient quantity. Since the market equilibrium level of output (Q_1) is less than the efficient level (Q_2), the market is said to **underallocate** resources when there is a **positive externality**.

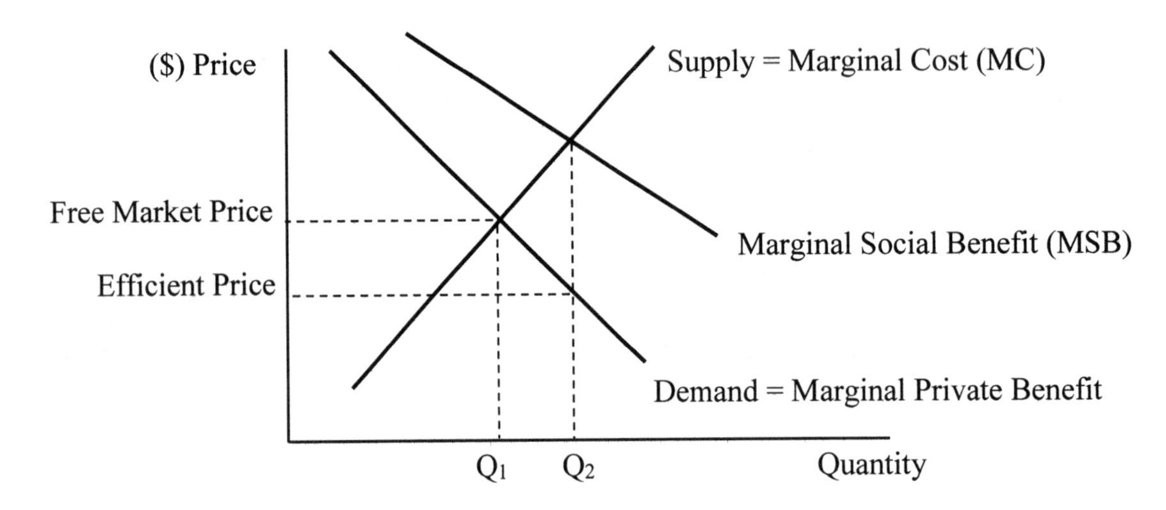

Government may **subsidize** production or consumption or it may directly provide the good or service to ensure an efficient quantity. In many cases, government uses a combination of these approaches. For example, the quantity of education is increased when government builds schools, hires teachers, and makes attendance mandatory. Government also subsidizes higher education by giving students grants and low-interest loans. A subsidy lowers the price buyers pay so they will choose a larger quantity.

In the absence of government intervention, the private market for education would provide profit-driven schools, for example. The theory of externalities implies that this privately-achieved equilibrium is inefficient, because society would benefit from the education of more children, including many whose parents could not afford private schooling. Current subsidies for education are probably motivated by more than a desire to correct an externality problem. Education improves earnings potential and is seen as an important tool for reducing poverty.

The theory of positive externalities leads to the conclusion that some goods and services that provide external benefits will be produced in a free market economy, but that society benefits from a larger quantity. With no government, many people would purchase protection from private security companies. When government intervenes and uses tax dollars to pay police officers, it ensures that society has a greater level of protection and security. The goal of government policy is to increase the quantity from Q_1 to Q_2 in the above graph depicting a positive externality. The practical difficulty is to determine the efficient quantity in such markets, and this process involves both economic analysis and political compromise since tax dollars are required to provide subsidies and directly fund programs.

In the absence of government intervention, when the equilibrium price is determined by free market forces, firms set marginal benefit equal to marginal private cost and produce Q_1 in the graph below. Thus, Q_1 is the market equilibrium quantity. The **efficient quantity**, however, occurs where MSC = MB at Q_2 and the **efficient price** is the price that induces consumers to purchase the efficient quantity. Since the market equilibrium level of output (Q_1) is above the efficient level of output (Q_2), the market is said to **overallocate** resources when there is a **negative externality**.

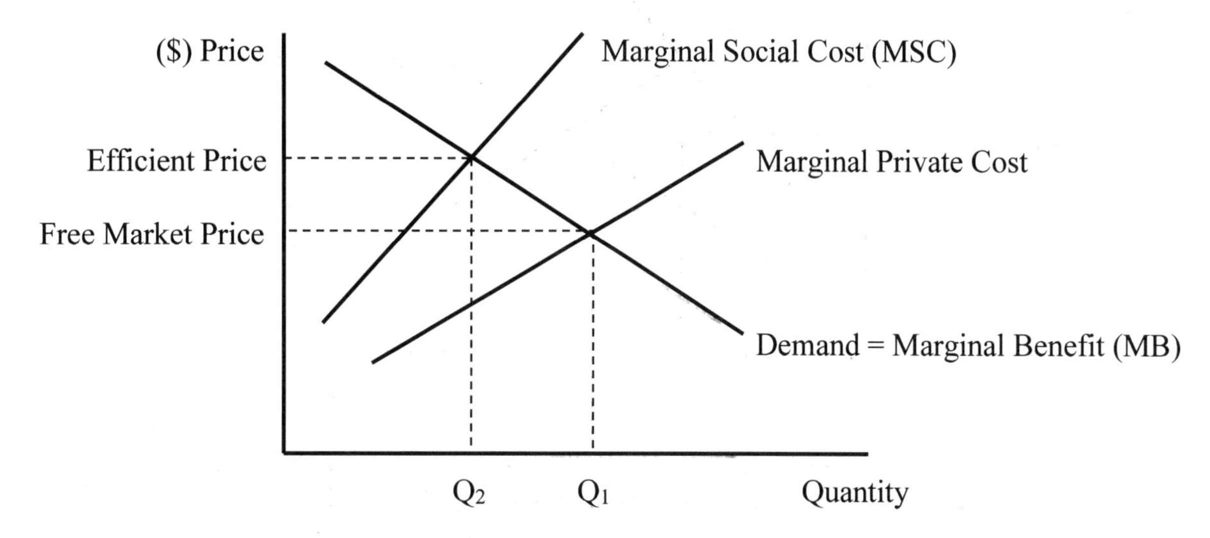

In the absence of government intervention, firms could dispose of waste products by dumping them into a river, for example. The theory of externalities implies that society is better served when firms dispose of waste in a manner that does not pollute the river too much. Government corrects negative externalities through regulation in some cases. For example, zoning regulations might prevent a factory from locating in a residential neighborhood where families would be harmed by emissions from the factory.

U.S. environmental policy relies on regulations that are enforced by the Environmental Protection Agency (EPA). For example, regulation may require that a factory reduce harmful emissions, requiring the installation of scrubbers on smokestacks. Note that an efficient requirement in terms of measurable pollutants leaves firms free to choose the most cost-effective method of achieving the required outcome. The challenge for policymakers is to set efficient standards. Compliance with environmental regulations causes the firm's costs to increase, leading to a higher product price and lower level of production and consumption. This approach is sometimes called **internalizing** the externality because it changes external costs (costs that are borne by society or third parties) to internal costs (costs that are borne by the firm).

Government might also address a negative externality through taxation. Efficiency requires a high price to discourage consumption, but society doesn't necessarily want producers to receive a high price because that would encourage over-production. A potentially efficient solution is to create a wedge between the price consumers pay and the price firms receive. Recall that a tax creates such a wedge. In Chapter 7, the imposition of a tax led to an inefficient outcome because it was assumed that the market equilibrium outcome was efficient. When there is a negative externality, a tax can actually result in an efficient outcome.

One policy solution to a negative externality is to impose a tax on the good whose production creates the external cost. This tax is called a **Pigouvian tax** after the economist, A.C. Pigou, who proposed it. The way the Pigouvian tax works is illustrated in the graph below.

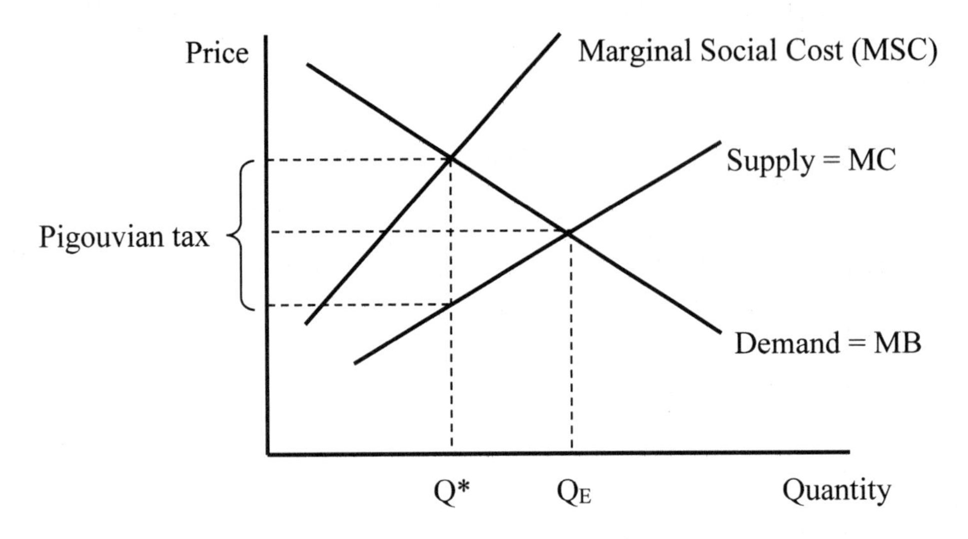

In the graph, Q_E is the level of output that would be produced in a free-market equilibrium where the external costs are borne by society. The position of the marginal social cost function allows us to identify the socially efficient level of output at Q*.

A tax levied on a commodity creates a wedge between the price paid by buyers and the amount received by sellers. The size of the Pigouvian tax is determined by how large a tax wedge is needed to reduce output in this market to the efficient level of Q*. The tax creates the desired effect by forcing consumers to pay a higher price, while reducing the price sellers receive. In the case where a tax is imposed to correct a negative externality, the tax does not create a deadweight loss.

Taxation corrects a negative externality by inducing lower production levels, because less production means less pollution. Economic analysis does not conclude that efficiency requires zero pollution, but only that environmental costs be taken into account just as labor costs and other input costs are taken into account. U.S. environmental policy relies more heavily on regulation than taxation, most likely because policymakers cannot easily determine the size of the Pigouvian tax needed to bring about an efficient outcome.

When regulation or taxation does not correct a negative externality, injured parties may seek legal remedy through either an injunction (a court order to cease the activity causing the injury) or payment of compensatory damages. A legal solution, achieved through tort law, requires courts to determine which party holds property rights. For example, does a factory owner have the right to use a nearby stream to dispose of waste, or does the community surrounding the stream have the right to an unpolluted water source?

The Coase Theorem, proposed by Nobel economist Ronald Coase in 1960, emphasizes the need for clearly defined property rights. According to the **Coase theorem**, an efficient outcome can be achieved without any need for active government involvement as long as property rights are clearly defined and transaction costs are sufficiently low. Transaction costs are obstacles to private bargaining and would be prohibitively high if, for example, the party affected by the spillover cost did not know who was causing the damage. Another obstacle to bargaining occurs when there are too many parties involved. For example, it would be difficult for an individual to work out a private solution to second-hand smoke in a public place; after having paid one smoker to refrain from lighting up, another smoker could come along.

Coase also argued that it makes no difference how property rights are assigned, as long as they are clearly assigned to one party or the other. An efficient outcome can be reached regardless of which party holds the initial property right, but the assignment of rights has distributional consequences. As an example, suppose that a factory is very noisy, and the noise from the factory reduces the profits of a nearby restaurant. With specific information on the costs of different solutions, the efficient solution can be identified. Suppose the problem can be solved by having the factory relocate, having the restaurant relocate, or installing sound-proofing in the factory. If relocation of either business is expensive compared to the sound-proofing option, then the efficient solution is to install sound-proofing. If the factory is assigned the property right, the restaurant owner will offer to pay for sound-proofing if this is cheaper than relocating or losing customers due to noise, assuming transaction costs do not interfere. If the restaurant is assigned the property right, then the factory will install sound-proofing to avoid having the restaurant seek an injunction which would force the factory to relocate or close. In either case, merely the threat of legal action is sufficient to induce the parties to work out the best solution, as long as transaction costs are sufficiently low.

If transaction costs are too high, then disputes may have to be resolved in court, but the Coase Theorem does not guarantee that a court-ordered remedy will always be efficient. It might be more effective to use regulations to avoid situations that would create disputes. As an example, the government typically decides the best place to locate an airport in order to minimize the damage to neighborhoods and businesses associated with noise and traffic. Local zoning restrictions potentially prevent negative externalities that would be difficult to resolve through private bargaining. Government involvement in such decisions reflects a belief that efficiency is enhanced by rules and regulations, but people are wary about regulations that become too restrictive and do more harm than good.

Public Goods and Common Resources

Pure **public goods** have the characteristics of being both **nonrival** and **nonexcludable**. A good is nonrival if the use of that good by one consumer does not preclude the use of it by another consumer. For example, one person's decision to watch a program on public television does not interfere with another person's ability to watch that program. Nonrival goods can be consumed by many at the same time. Nonexcludable means that once a public good is provided, it is impossible to keep non-payers from receiving the benefits of it. For example, when a program is aired on public television, anyone can view the program, whether they have made a contribution to public television or not.

Since public goods are nonexcludable, there is a **free-rider problem**, so government might have to require each person to pay his or her fair share in order to guarantee that the desired quantity of a public good is produced. It is sometimes possible to rely on voluntary support, as with public television, but a public good like national defense is considered so important that government is justified in using its power of taxation to ensure that sufficient resources are devoted to defense.

In some cases, the theory of positive externalities can be applied to goods that, while not pure public goods, create external benefits that have public good characteristics. Such goods are referred to as impure or quasi-public goods. For example, someone who finds a cure for cancer will obviously own something of value in the marketplace, but the potential benefits to society are so large that it makes sense for government policy to encourage and support research. The market will provide incentives for some research, but a greater amount may be socially efficient.

Goods that are rival but nonexcludable are **common resources**. Rival means that one person's use of this good diminishes other people's use of the same good. If there is no government policy to restrict the use of common resources, these resources will likely be overused because they are nonexcludable and therefore subject to a free-rider problem. Examples of common resources include fish in the ocean, clean air and water, and congested highways. The tendency for common resources to be used more than is desirable from society's point of view is sometimes referred to as the **Tragedy of the Commons**. Government policy can promote efficiency by regulating the use of the resource, taxing the use of the resource, or converting the common resource into a private good (which involves clearly defining property rights). For example, government might restrict fishing in certain areas to prevent depletion of marine life.

The theory of negative externalities led to the conclusion that if unregulated firms harm the environment while producing and do not incur any costs as a result (because the costs are borne by others), then the market equilibrium quantity will be inefficiently high. By the same token, if ownership of common resources like clean air is unassigned, there will be too much environmental damage. Whether we rely on the theory of negative externalities or the theory of common resources, we reach the conclusion that government should intervene in some way to promote efficient use of scarce resources, avoid depletion of natural resources, and prevent inefficient damage to the environment.

Even when there is no market failure and the free-market outcome is efficient, there may be situations in which government intervention is recommended in order to promote **equity** (fairness). For example, the United States is often considered to be a land of opportunity. For many, income and wealth inequality is justified when individuals are all given a chance to succeed, and some choose to work harder than others. However, government intervention may be necessary in order to provide opportunities for all. The need for government to act as a guardian of fairness and opportunity is controversial and must be balanced with concerns about the adverse effects of government handouts on incentives to work. While many agree that government has a role to play, there are different viewpoints regarding how government should be involved in promoting equity.

The Functions of Government

In the U.S. economy, government is involved in many different areas at the local, state, and federal levels. Many of the functions of government relate to some type of market failure.

1) **Providing a legal framework** – markets work best when property rights are clearly assigned and protected and when contracts are enforced. Transactions based on perfect information are much more likely to promote efficiency, so the law often requires full disclosure of contract terms and product features.

2) **Promoting competition and regulating business** – antitrust legislation was passed to prevent the formation of monopolies and the use of anticompetitive practices such as price-fixing. In certain cases, business firms are permitted to operate a monopoly, but they are subject to government regulations limiting the price they can charge. The purpose of such intervention into business practices is to avoid the inefficient outcome associated with imperfectly competitive markets. An important exemption is granted to firms eligible for patents, which protect a firm's monopoly for 20 years as a means of encouraging new inventions.

3) **Correcting externalities** – government provides for education, public health, police and fire protection, roads and highways, and a host of other services because these services create external benefits. Government is also involved in environmental protection to correct the problem of external costs.

4) **Providing public goods and regulating the use of common resources** – it is difficult to imagine business firms profitably providing public goods since consumers can enjoy the benefits without paying. Because of the free-rider problem, it is necessary for government to require each person to pay his or her fair share for public goods like national defense. Similarly, government regulates the use of common resources to prevent overuse and depletion.

5) **Assisting families in poverty (redistributing income)** – even if a market allocation is efficient, society's notions of fairness or equity may require some assistance to those in need. Such programs include some cash assistance (TANF, or Temporary Assistance for Needy Families), food stamps, Medicaid, and housing assistance. The progressive income tax system is also designed to help low-income families with the Earned Income Tax Credit (EITC). Government supports education partly to promote efficiency and partly to promote equity by creating opportunities for people to succeed in a market economy.

6) **Promoting economic growth and macroeconomic stabilization** – macroeconomic policies are designed to pursue the goals of full employment, low inflation, and a healthy rate of economic growth. There is substantial debate among macroeconomists regarding the best way to achieve all three of these important goals, and these topics are addressed in a Macroeconomics course.

The list of government's functions does not mention an important category: **social insurance** programs. Social insurance programs have become the most important, the most expensive, and often the most controversial aspect of government domestic policy; not only in the United States but also in many other countries, including developing and industrial nations. In the United States, social insurance programs include Social Security (retirement, disability and survivor insurance), unemployment insurance, and Medicare (health insurance for those age 65 and older). In the 1950s, 69 cents of every $1 spent by the federal government paid for national defense, while only 4 cents of every $1 was for social security. Now, approximately 20 cents of every federal $1 is for national defense, while 21 cents is for social security and 22 cents is for health care.

A detailed study of social insurance programs is beyond the scope of this course, but no discussion of government's role would be complete without at least a brief mention of these programs. Most discussions about the federal government focus on the difficulties inherent in maintaining social insurance for an aging population, and no discussion of the national debt can avoid an attempt to anticipate the future growth of entitlements.

The next chapters focus on **business** decision-making, taking into account the costs of production, potential revenues, and resulting profits. The models of business decision-making are based on the assumption that each firm's goal is to earn maximum profit. There are some contradictions to this assumption in practice, as when a manager is more interested in the short-run value of stock options than in the firm's overall profitability, for example. However, the assumption that the firm's goal is to maximize profit provides a general theory of behavior and a good starting point for the analysis of real-world firms and markets.

NAME________________________________SECTION#________
PRINT LAST NAME, FIRST NAME

MARKET FAILURE

1. In the market for information, government sometimes steps in to:
   a. enforce sales that were made on the basis of misleading information.
   b. prevent sellers from making false and misleading claims.
   c. enforce contracts that were made on the basis of false information.
   d. prevent sellers from providing information to buyers.

2. When consumers lack perfect information about product prices:
   a. the outcome will be efficient because product prices will always be the same under perfectly competitive conditions.
   b. the outcome may not be efficient because consumers may pay a high price for a product that is available for a lower price elsewhere.
   c. they will not buy the product until they have obtained full information.
   d. the outcome will be efficient because consumers will only pay a high price for a product if they think it is worth it.

3. Which of the following is an example of a *negative* externality?
   a. A Boy Scout troop cleaning up a neighborhood park
   b. Toxic chemicals dumped into a river that is used as a water supply
   c. A neighbor who plants a beautiful garden in his front yard
   d. A wealthy citizen donating land for use as a public park

4. When there is a negative externality, the unregulated market results in a level of output that is ________ than the socially efficient level because the private costs are ________ than the social costs.
   a. higher; greater
   b. higher; less
   c. lower; greater
   d. lower; less

5. Which of the following is an example of a *positive* externality?
   a. The noise created by an auto racetrack located near a residential area
   b. Toxic chemicals dumped into a river that is used as a water supply
   c. A neighbor who refuses to mow his yard or paint his house
   d. A lower crime rate in a neighborhood patrolled by a security company

6. When there is a positive externality, the unregulated market results in a level of output that is ________ than the socially efficient level because the private benefits are ________ than the social benefits.
   a. higher; greater
   b. higher; less
   c. lower; greater
   d. lower; less

NAME____SECTION#________________

PRINT LAST NAME, FIRST NAME

7. Because a pure public good is:
   a. excludable, it is not possible for any consumer to be a free rider.
   b. excludable, it is possible for some consumers to be free riders.
   c. nonexcludable, it is not possible for any consumer to be a free rider.
   d. nonexcludable, it is possible for some consumers to be free riders.

8. All of the following are examples of public goods ***except***:
   a. national defense.
   b. a lighthouse.
   c. a bagel with cream cheese.
   d. a fireworks display.

9. The "free-rider" problem refers to a situation in which:
   a. some people receive welfare benefits to which they are not entitled.
   b. the benefits associated with public goods cannot be denied to users, whether or not they are willing to pay for them.
   c. government must subsidize public transportation.
   d. the benefits associated with private goods cannot be denied to those who are unwilling to pay for them.

10. Since common resources are non-excludable, government policy:
   a. can promote efficiency by regulating the use of common resources, taxing their use, or converting them into privately-owned resources.

   b. will only reduce efficiency since common resources are efficiently used in free market equilibrium.
   c. can promote efficiency by taxing the use of common resources, but any other policy would result in a less efficient outcome.
   d. does not have any effect on efficiency since common resources cannot be depleted.

NAME______________________________SECTION#__________
PRINT LAST NAME, FIRST NAME

EXTERNALITIES

Use the graphs to fill in the blanks:

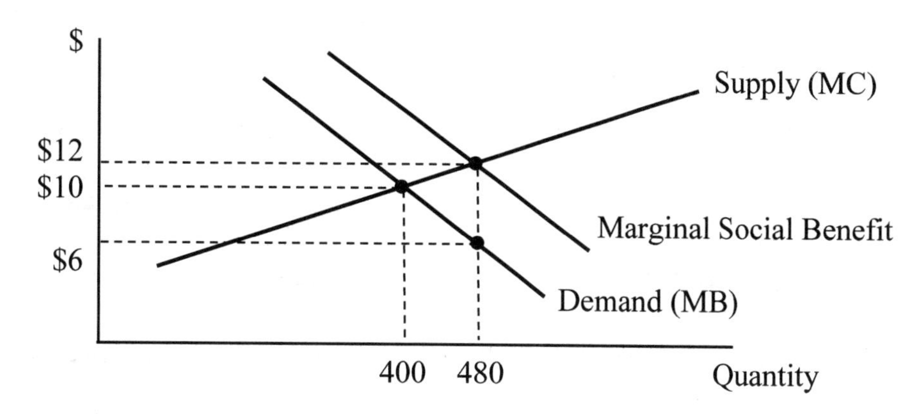

The above graph depicts a 1) ______________ externality. In this market, the equilibrium level of output is 2) __________ units and the price of the product will be 3) $__________ if no action is taken by government. The socially efficient level of output is 4) __________ units, indicating that market forces result in an output level that is 5) ______________ than the efficient level.

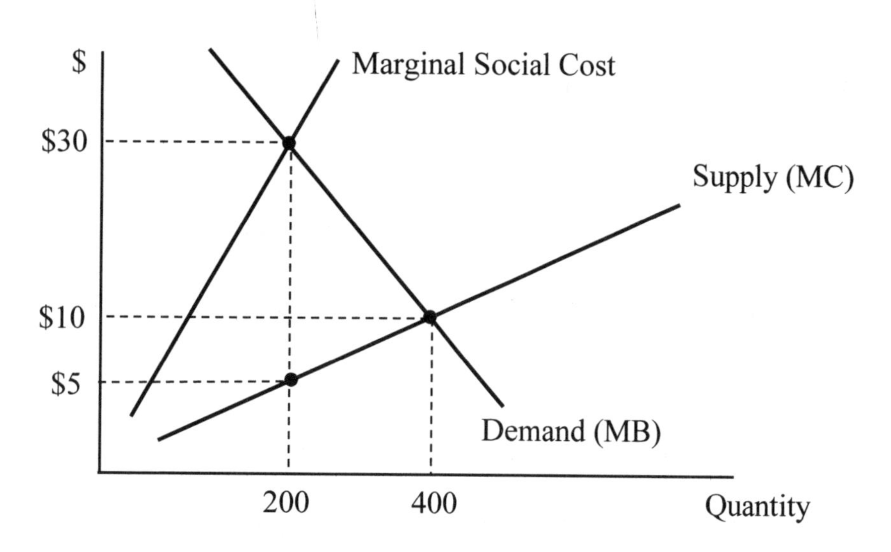

The above graph depicts a 6) ______________ externality. In this market, the equilibrium level of output is 7) __________ units and the price of the product will be 8) $__________ if no action is taken by government. The socially efficient level of output is 9) __________ units, indicating that market forces result in an output level that is 10) ______________ than the efficient level.

NAME____SECTION#________________

PRINT LAST NAME, FIRST NAME

FUNCTIONS OF GOVERNMENT

Fill in the blanks:

1) Government must provide a ____________________________________ because markets work best when property rights are protected and contracts are enforced.

2) Government may need to promote _________________________ and regulate business to avoid the inefficient outcomes associated with monopolized markets.

3) Government provides services like education and police protection because these services create a ____________________ externality.

4) Government tends to _____________________ activities like education and police protection in order to promote efficiency.

5) Government is involved in environmental protection because of _____________________ externalities.

6) Government tends to use _____________________ to discourage pollution and promote a more efficient allocation of resources.

7) Because of the _______________________ problem, government cannot provide national defense and then expect each person to pay an amount equaling the value of defense.

8) Even if a market allocation is efficient, society's notions of ______________________ may require that government provide some assistance to those in need.

9) Macroeconomic policies are designed to pursue the goals of full employment, price stability, and ________________________________.

10) _____________________________________ programs have become the most important, expensive, and often the most controversial aspect of domestic policy.

NAME____SECTION#______________

PRINT LAST NAME, FIRST NAME

MARKET FAILURE AND THE ROLE OF GOVERNMENT

1. The government agency that investigates instances of false advertising is called the:
   a. Securities and Exchange Commission.
   b. Federal Trade Commission.
   c. Consumer Watchdog Organization.
   d. Department of the Treasury.

2. The Truth in Lending Act of 1968 protects consumers by:
   a. requiring clear disclosure of the costs of credit.
   b. setting the interest rate lenders can charge.
   c. setting the interest rate borrowers can pay.
   d. requiring all lenders to set the same costs of credit.

3. Financial aid grants given to college students are expected to:
   a. increase production but reduce consumption of education.
   b. reduce production but increase consumption of education.
   c. increase production and consumption of education, which *harms* society.
   d. increase production and consumption of education, which *benefits* society.

4. A tax levied on gasoline is predicted to:
   a. reduce production and consumption, leading to more pollution.
   b. reduce production and consumption, leading to less pollution.
   c. increase production and reduce consumption and pollution.
   d. reduce production, leading to more consumption and pollution.

5. According to the Coase Theorem, an efficient outcome can be achieved without any need for active government involvement as long as:
   a. property rights are clearly defined and transaction costs are sufficiently high.
   b. property rights are clearly defined and transaction costs are sufficiently low.
   c. there are no ownership rights which might be affected by a spillover (external) cost.
   d. the parties causing the spillover (external) costs cannot be identified.

6. The tendency to use common resources more than is desirable from society's point of view is called the:
   a. Coase theorem.
   b. law of diminishing marginal utility.
   c. rivalry problem.
   d. Tragedy of the Commons.

7. The designation of an owner of a good or resource with the legal authority to control its use is known as the establishment of:
   a. property rights.
   b. human rights.
   c. uncommon resources.
   d. common resources.

NAME____SECTION#_______________

PRINT LAST NAME, FIRST NAME

8. Government programs designed to redistribute income:
   a. have never been successful in reducing poverty and inequality.
   b. generally benefit high-income households more than low-income households.
   c. are meant to reduce poverty and inequality.
   d. are intended to create a perfectly equal distribution of income.

9. Government promotes and protects competition by using antitrust legislation to:
   a. prevent the formation of monopolies and the use of anticompetitive practices such as price-fixing.
   b. establish a fair price for each product and prevent firms from charging a price that exceeds this value.
   c. provide strong incentives for innovation by protecting patent rights.
   d. clearly define and protect property rights.

10. Which of the following is ***not*** one of the functions of government in the U.S.?
   a. Providing a legal framework and protecting property rights
   b. Providing public goods and correcting externalities
   c. Promoting full employment, low inflation, and economic growth
   d. All of the above are functions of the U.S. government

CHAPTER 9 The Firm: Economic Costs, Profits and Production

A **firm** is an organization that transforms inputs into outputs for the purpose of sale. The firm is the primary producing unit in a market-based economy, and it is generally assumed that the firm's main objective is to **maximize profit.** Firms in the economy are commonly classified along two different lines: by legal organization or by market structure.

The legal organization of firms refers to the ownership of the firm and the legal structure under which the firm operates. Three broad classifications of firms are proprietorships, partnerships, and corporations. A **proprietorship** has a single owner of all assets and profits of the firm and unlimited liability for all debts of the firm. A **partnership** has two or more owners, all sharing in the profits and debts (liabilities) of the firm. A **corporation** is a legal entity separate from its owners. The liability of an owner, or **stockholder,** of a corporation is limited to the stockholder's initial investment. Approximately 70% of all firms in the U.S. are organized as sole proprietorships, but corporations account for over 80% of all revenues. This course pays more attention to the market structure in which a firm operates than the legal organization.

Firms may also be classified based on the type of competition that exists in the market or industry in which they operate. The level of competition present defines the market structure. Market structure ranges from perfect competition to pure monopoly. **Perfectly competitive** industries have many firms, each producing identical output, with no barriers preventing new firms from entering the industry in the long run. **Pure monopoly** is on the opposite end of the spectrum, with only one firm producing an output for which there is no close substitute. Monopoly markets are characterized by significant barriers to entry. Barriers to entry are obstacles that make it unprofitable or impossible for new firms to enter an industry or market. **Monopolistic competition** and **oligopoly** are market structures that lie in between perfect competition and monopoly.

The pricing and output behavior of a firm depends on several factors, including the competitive conditions and characteristics of the market in which the firm operates. There are many similarities among firms regardless of market structure. All firms face the same type of input and technology constraints, are subject to diminishing returns in the short run, and are assumed to attempt to maximize profits.

Total Revenue, Total Cost, and Profit

Total revenue is the price of the good (P) multiplied by the quantity sold (Q):

Total Revenue = Price x Quantity = PQ

As an example, a firm that sells 1,000 units of output at a price of $5 per unit has total revenue of ($5)(1,000) = $5,000 from the sale of the output.

Total cost represents total **economic cost,** which includes all opportunity costs associated with production. The assumed goal of all firms is to maximize profit. To accomplish this, the firm must consider all costs incurred in the production of output. Total economic cost has two components: explicit costs and implicit costs.

Costs that require direct monetary payments to the factors of production are called **explicit costs.** Most resources require the firm to make an explicit payment in order to use the resource. For example, firms must pay wages in order to hire labor. In addition to compensating employees for their hours of labor, a firm may also provide other benefits, such as contributions made by the firm to an employee retirement plan and medical insurance. All the payments the firm must make in order to hire labor are included in the firm's costs. Similarly, the firm may have to make direct monetary outlays in order to hire other factors of production, such as capital and entrepreneurial ability. Explicit costs are recorded as accounting costs in bookkeeping, and the firm can declare them as expenses for tax purposes.

Some resources used in production may not require the firm to make a direct monetary payment. If a firm owns a factor of production outright, then it does not have to make a money outlay to use that resource. However, the resource may have alternative uses, so there is an opportunity cost associated with using it. **Implicit costs** are the opportunity costs to the firm for the use of factors of production for which it does not make a direct monetary payment.

Firms want to make the best *economic* use of resources and must consider all costs of production. For example, a firm may own a building. The building could be used by the firm as a retail outlet, and the firm would not have to make a direct payment to use the building. The alternative use of the building may be to lease it to another firm and simply collect the rent checks. To make the best economic decision about the use of the building, the firm must consider the rent that would be foregone if the firm uses the building itself.

Total economic cost consists of explicit and implicit costs.

Total Economic Cost = Explicit Costs + Implicit Costs

Suppose the owner of a painting company spends $10,000 in one year on paint and other supplies, so explicit costs are $10,000. If the next best use of the owner's time is working at a job that pays $20,000 a year, then implicit costs are $20,000 and total economic cost for the year is $10,000 + $20,000 = $30,000. The $20,000 in foregone income is assumed to be an implicit cost, but the owner could make this an explicit cost by paying herself a salary of $20,000.

To model the decision-making behavior of firms in a market economy, it will be assumed that the ultimate goal of the firm is to earn the maximum profit. The simplest definition of profit is the total amount of payments received from the sale of an output in a given period, which defines the firm's total revenue, minus the total economic cost of producing the output. Economic profit is abbreviated using the Greek letter pi (π) and is expressed as:

Economic Profit = π = Total Revenue – Total Economic Cost

In an economics course, the economic definition of profit is generally used. The next section explains the distinction between economic and accounting profit, but in the remainder of the book, keep in mind that references to "profit" are actually references to "economic profit" and references to "costs" are actually references to "economic costs."

Accounting Profit versus Economic Profit

Profit can be viewed from an accounting perspective or from an economic perspective. **Accounting profit** is total revenue minus total explicit costs; implicit costs cannot be used for tax purposes and are neither included as a bookkeeping entry nor considered when calculating accounting profit. **Economic profit** is total revenue minus total explicit *and* implicit costs. In other words, economic profit is total revenue minus total economic costs. Because accounting profit does not factor in implicit costs, it will usually be greater than economic profit. The assumed goal of the firm is maximum profit, which requires making the best economic use of resources. From the firm's perspective, then, the appropriate profit to consider in decision making is **economic profit.** In the study of the principles of microeconomics, total cost refers to total economic cost, and profit refers to economic profit.

A firm earns **zero economic profit** when total revenue is equal to total economic costs; a firm that is earning zero economic profit is not earning zero accounting profit because it is earning enough to cover all opportunity costs. A firm that is earning zero economic profit is said to be earning a **normal profit** because normal profit is the minimum required to keep the firm in business. When economic profit is zero, the owners and investors of the firm are making just enough to be satisfied and stay in business because they are covering all opportunity costs and could not get a better return elsewhere.

Example

Suppose Nathan owns a consulting business and, in order for him to provide the consulting services needed to make his business a success, he gave up a job that paid $100,000 per year. Therefore, one of the costs Nathan should consider when analyzing how well his business did is the $100,000 per year he could have earned elsewhere. The $100,000 per year is an implicit cost and represents the opportunity cost of his labor services. If his total revenue is $150,000 for the year and his explicit costs equal $50,000, then he is earning a normal profit, or as much as he could make in the job he gave up, and his **economic profit is zero**. His economic profit can be written as:

Economic Profit = $150,000 – ($50,000 + $100,000) = $150,000 - $150,000 = 0

In the above example, if Nathan's explicit costs are $25,000 per year, rather than $50,000 per year, then he will earn a **positive economic profit** of $25,000: total revenue of $150,000 per year minus explicit costs of $25,000 per year and implicit costs of $100,000 per year. The existence of positive economic profit might attract new entrants into this industry.

Economic Profit = $150,000 – ($25,000 + $100,000) = $150,000 - $125,000 = $25,000

If Nathan's explicit costs are $60,000 per year, he will incur a **negative economic profit**, or an **economic loss**, of $10,000: total revenue of $150,000 per year minus explicit costs of $60,000 per year and implicit costs of $100,000 per year. Firms that incur persistent economic losses may choose to exit the market and move resources to another, more profitable, industry.

Economic Profit = $150,000 – ($60,000 + $100,000) = $150,000 - $160,000 = -$10,000

Production and Time

The production process can be separated into periods based on the availability and variability of the factors of production. In economics, the **short run** is a period of time in which one or more factors of production are held constant. The factors of production that are held constant are referred to as **fixed inputs**. Capital equipment and plant (factory) capacity are often difficult and expensive to change, and will be fixed inputs. In the short run, the firm will have **variable inputs**, such as labor, that it applies to its fixed inputs to produce an output. The firm can change variable inputs in order to increase or decrease output, but the amount of output that can be produced is constrained, or limited, by the fixed input in the short run. Although capital is usually the input that is fixed in the short run, highly specialized labor may also be difficult to hire and may be the fixed input that constrains a firm's ability to produce.

The **long run** is a period of time in which a firm can vary all inputs. It is a time period sufficient for the firm to change all inputs, including capital and plant capacity; in the long run, all factors of production are **variable.** The long run is not defined as a specific unit of time and it varies across industries; it is a period sufficient for all inputs to be altered, which means it is sufficient for existing firms to expand production capacity and for new firms to build production capacity and enter a market. The long run has two identifiers: 1) in the long run, all factors of production are variable; and 2) in the long run, new firms can start up and enter a market. Entrepreneurs engage in both short-run production decision-making and long-run production planning. Routine decisions about input usage and production levels are usually short-run decisions for an established firm because most capital inputs (factory space, retail space, computer systems, equipment, etc.) are not changed very often. When market conditions warrant changing the firm's entire scale of operation, or plant capacity, entrepreneurs make what economists call long-run decisions.

A firm that is making a decision about how many units of output to produce and supply to the market, using its available resources and production capacity, is making a short-run production decision. The theory of how firms make short-run decisions is used to derive the **supply curve** (as introduced in chapter 4). Sometimes, market conditions cause the price to fall so low that the firm cannot earn a profit. However, it is sometimes the case that a firm will minimize losses by continuing to produce in the short run since the firm must pay some costs even if it goes out of business, such as the remaining rent due on a lease. In some cases, the losses are so great that the firm chooses to shut down immediately. To make a clear distinction, a firm that goes out of business in the **short run** is said to **shut down** (this can happen very suddenly and the owners must still pay for fixed inputs), but a firm that waits until all fixed cost commitments are satisfied and goes out of business in the **long run** is said to **exit** the industry
(a firm typically exits only after a long period of persistent losses).

The Production Function

The production method chosen by the firm depends on several factors, including technology and input prices. Once the production method is chosen, there will be a mathematical relationship between the inputs and the output. This relationship is called the **production function.** A **short-run production function** assumes that at least one input is fixed.

The table below provides a hypothetical example of the mathematical relationship between a single variable input, labor, and output, assuming all other inputs are fixed (held constant).

Quantity of Labor (L)	Output per Time (Q)
0	0
1	7
2	18
3	33
4	44
5	48
6	46

In the short run, one or more inputs are being held constant and the output obtained from an additional unit of an input is called **marginal product.** If labor is assumed to be the only variable input, then the marginal product of labor (MP_L) is expressed by the equation:

$$MP_L = \frac{\text{change in output}}{\text{change in labor}} = \frac{\Delta Q}{\Delta L} = \frac{Q_2 - Q_1}{L_2 - L_1}$$

where Q is output and L is labor (the number of workers hired). In the table above, output (Q) is 18 when 2 workers (L) are hired, and output is 33 when 3 workers are hired. Output increased from 18 to 33, or by 15, when the third worker was hired; thus, the marginal product of the third worker is equal to15, as shown by the calculation below.

$$MP_L = \frac{\text{change in output}}{\text{change in labor}} = \frac{\Delta Q}{\Delta L} = \frac{33 - 18}{3 - 2} = 15$$

Initially, adding variable inputs to fixed inputs increases marginal product. However, as additional units of the variable input are added, marginal product will eventually decline. This principle is referred to as the **law of diminishing returns** or **the law of diminishing (marginal) product**. Diminishing returns sets in when the marginal product of the variable input begins to decline.

Based on the data in the above table, output increased by 7 when the first worker was hired, by 11 when the second worker was added, by 15 when the third worker was employed, and by 11 with the addition of the fourth worker. In this case, diminishing returns sets in with the fourth worker.

In the short run, all firms encounter diminishing returns because at least one input is fixed and cannot increase as variable inputs increase. However, all inputs are variable in the long run, so the law of diminishing returns does not apply to the long run. For example, if the size of a sandwich shop is 1,200 square feet, there is a limit to how many workers can be employed and diminishing returns will set in at some point. If the owner of the sandwich shop can open new stores in different locations, this limit no longer applies.

Average product is the measurement of how many units of output, on average, are produced by each unit of input. The average product of labor (AP_L) gives output per worker and is calculated as:

$$AP_L = \frac{\text{Output}}{\text{Labor}} = \frac{Q}{L}$$

For example, if output is equal to 18 when 2 workers are hired, average product is equal to 18/2 or 9 units of output per worker. The production function from the previous page is expanded below to include values for marginal product (defined on the previous page) and average product (defined above).

Quantity of Labor L	Output per Time Q	Marginal Product $MP = \Delta Q/\Delta L$	Average Product $AP = Q/L$
0	0		
1	7	7	7
2	18	11	9
3	33	15	11
4	44	11	11
5	48	4	9.6
6	46	-2	7.67

The law of diminishing marginal product indicates that the MP function will usually rise initially, but will eventually begin to fall. Marginal product can even be negative if there are so many workers that they get in each other's way and cause total output to drop. The behavior of average product also follows a typical pattern of initially rising and then falling. In this example, worker productivity improves at first, most likely because workers are able to specialize and avoid running around too much. Eventually, though, worker productivity falls.

The relationship between marginal product and average product is illustrated in the graph below. As long as the marginal product of the additional input is greater than the average product, the average product will increase; once marginal product and average product are equal, average product is at its maximum; when marginal product falls below average product, it causes average product to fall. This is similar to the relationship between a student's grade in one class and the student's grade point average (if a student with a 3.0 GPA earns an A in a class, this grade causes the GPA to rise, and so on).

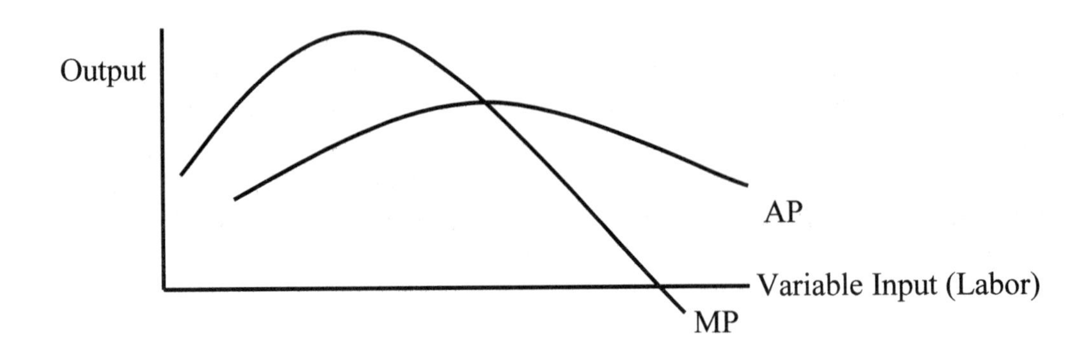

NAME____ SECTION#______________
PRINT LAST NAME, FIRST NAME

ACCOUNTING VERSUS ECONOMIC PROFIT

Use the information below to answer questions 1 through 5.

Assume you gave up a $60,000 per year job at an accounting firm to start your own tax preparation business. To simplify, assume your tax personal obligations are the same whether you run your own firm or work for another firm.

1. If your revenue during the first year of business is $75,000, and you incurred $5,000 in expenses for equipment and supplies, how much is your accounting profit?

2. If your revenue during the first year of business is $75,000, and you incurred $5,000 in expenses for equipment and supplies, how much is your economic profit?

3. If your accounting profit is $60,000, much is your economic profit?

4. If your revenue during the first year of business is $60,000, and you incurred $5,000 in expenses for equipment and supplies, how much is your accounting profit?

5. If your revenue during the first year of business is $60,000, and you incurred $5,000 in expenses for equipment and supplies, how much is your economic profit?

NAME____SECTION#______________

PRINT LAST NAME, FIRST NAME

THE PRODUCTION FUNCTION

The table below represents a production schedule for Quincy's Quiche Corner, a small shop in a mall that sells quiches. Assume Quincy's operates in a perfectly competitive environment (in both input and output markets).

Complete the table and then will in the blanks below using the information in the table:

Number of Workers (L)	Output (quiches/hour = Q)	MP_L	AP_L
0	0		
1	________	________	10
2	22	________	________
3	36	________	________
4	________	12	________
5	55	________	________
6	________	________	10
7	63	________	________

With only 1 worker, Quincy's is able to produce and sell 1) __________ quiches per hour. Adding a 2nd worker increases output to 22 quiches per hour, so the marginal product of the 2nd worker is 2) __________. The marginal product of the 3rd worker is 3) ______________ than the marginal product of the 2nd worker; however, diminishing marginal product sets in when the 4) __________ worker is hired. Starting with zero workers, average product first 5) ______________ and then 6) ______________. Average product and marginal product are equal at the 7) ____________________ point of the AP function. The marginal product of the 5th worker is 8) __________ quiches per hour and average product is 9) __________ quiches per hour when 5 workers are employed. The marginal product of the 7th worker is 10) __________ quiches per hour and this number will continue to fall if more workers are hired.

NAME____SECTION#______________

PRINT LAST NAME, FIRST NAME

BUSINESS FIRMS, COSTS, AND PROFIT

1. Which business organization offers investors the protection of limited liability, so the most an investor can lose is the initial investment?
   a. Sole proprietorship
   b. Oligopoly
   c. Corporation
   d. Partnership

2. The market structures that lie in between perfect competition and pure monopoly are called:
   a. proprietorship and partnership.
   b. corporation and oligopoly.
   c. oligopoly and monopolistic competition.
   d. profit-maximizing and revenue-maximizing structures.

3. Accounting profit is equal to:
   a. total revenue minus total explicit cost.
   b. total revenue multiplied by total cost.
   c. total revenue minus total economic cost.
   d. zero in all cases.

4. Economic profit is equal to:
   a. total revenue minus total explicit cost.
   b. total revenue multiplied by total cost.
   c. total revenue minus total economic cost.
   d. zero in all cases.

5. Betty left her $50,000 per year job in advertising to start a lawn service and be her own boss. In her first year, Betty received $75,000 in payments from customers and paid $5,000 for equipment and supplies. Betty's economic profit in her first year is:
   a. $5,000.
   b. $15,000.
   c. $20,000.
   d. $70,000.

6. The opportunity cost of the time an owner puts into a business:
   a. is relevant only if the owner pays herself an explicit salary.
   b. is the income foregone by not working in the best alternative job.
   c. varies depending on the legal organization of the firm.
   d. cannot be measured and so should not be considered in the economic decision-making process.

NAME____SECTION#______________

PRINT LAST NAME, FIRST NAME

7. The long run is:
   a. that period of time in which all factors of production are fixed.
   b. that period of time in which at least one factor of production is fixed.
   c. that period of time in which all factors of production are variable.
   d. a time horizon of up to one year.

8. In the short run, firms:
   a. can only vary capital inputs.
   b. can vary all inputs.
   c. have at least one fixed input.
   d. have only fixed inputs.

9. Which of the following ***best*** represents a fixed input?
   a. An oil exploration rig
   b. A pool of unskilled labor waiting outside a factory's gates each day
   c. The material and thread used in clothing production
   d. Fresh fruit and vegetables served at a local restaurant

10. A firm deciding how many workers it should hire to manufacture kitchen countertops using existing equipment is making a:
    a. permanent decision.
    b. short-run decision.
    c. long-run decision.
    d. capital-usage decision.

NAME____SECTION#________________
PRINT LAST NAME, FIRST NAME

COSTS, PROFIT, AND PRODUCTION

1. Suppose ABC Corporation sold 2,000 units of output at a price of $2 per unit. If ABC Corporation's explicit cost to produce the 2,000 is $1,500 and its implicit cost to produce the 2,000 units is $2,000, then ABC Corp. has total revenue of 4000________, an accounting profit of 2500________, and an economic profit of 500________.

   a. $1,500; $0; $1,000
   b. $4,000; $1,000; $0
   c. $4,000; $500; $2,500
   d. $4,000; $2,500; $500

2. Firms encounter diminishing marginal product (diminishing returns) in the short run because:
   a. all inputs are fixed.
   b. at least one input is fixed.
   c. inputs can only be varied proportionally.
   d. at some point, firms must hire inferior labor to increase output.

3. If total output is 40 units when 4 workers are employed and 48 units when 5 workers are employed, then:
   a. average product is 10 units when 4 workers are employed.
   b. the marginal product of the 5th worker is 8 units.
   c. average product must be falling because the marginal product of the 5th worker is lower than the average product for 4 workers.
   d. all of the above are true.

Use the information in the table below to answer questions 4 and 5.

Number of Workers	Output
0	0
1	8
2	18
3	30
4	44
5	52
6	56
7	52

4. The marginal product of the 4th worker is:
   a. 4 units of output.
   b. 12 units of output.
   c. 14 units of output.
   d. 18 units of output.

5. When 5 workers are hired, average product is ______ units of output.
   a. 8
   b. 9.6
   c. 10.4
   d. 14

NAME____SECTION#______________

PRINT LAST NAME, FIRST NAME

6. Suppose 9 workers can repair 36 television sets per day. If a tenth worker is hired and the total number of repaired T.V. sets increases to 39, then:
   a. each worker repairs, on average, 4 T.V. sets per day when nine workers are hired.
   b. the marginal product of the tenth worker is 3.9 T.V. sets.
   c. average product must be rising because the marginal product of the tenth worker is greater than average product when nine workers are hired.
   d. All of the above are true

Use the information below to answer questions 7 through 10.

Hal's Holiday Hats produces Santa hats in a small factory on the edge of town. There is a fixed amount of capital used to produce the hats, yet plenty of labor is available for work. The following table is a hypothetical production schedule for Hal's shop.

Labor	Quantity of hats produced per day
0	0
1	20
2	50
3	75
4	90
5	100
6	100
7	90

7. The marginal product of the second worker is _____ hats per day.
   a. 20
   b. 25
   c. 30
   d. 50

8. When 3 workers are hired, average product is _____ hats per day.
   a. 10
   b. 25
   c. 50
   d. 75

9. If the marginal product of the fourth worker is 15 units of output, the quantity of hats produced per day when four workers are employed is equal to _____.
   a. 80
   b. 90
   c. 95
   d. 100

10. Diminishing marginal product (or "diminishing returns") sets in ***with*** the addition of the _____ worker.
   a. first
   b. second
   c. third
   d. fourth

CHAPTER 10 Costs of Production

Firms attempt to earn profits, but their efforts are constrained by the production technology, the prices of inputs (workers, machines, and so on), and the price at which they can sell the final good or service. A firm earns positive (economic) profit when total revenue, calculated by multiplying price times quantity, exceeds total cost. If production is potentially profitable, the economic model assumes that firms choose the output level associated with the *largest possible profit.*

In order to determine how much output to produce to earn the largest possible profit, a firm must know both the revenue and the cost associated with producing each level of output. The relationship between revenue and output depends on market structure. A revenue function is derived assuming a perfectly competitive market structure in chapter 11. Other market structures are examined in chapters 12 through 14. The production function and input costs, which determine the firm's cost structure, are not dependent on market structure. The cost functions developed in this chapter apply to all firms, regardless of market structure.

In the short run there are both fixed and variable inputs, so there are both fixed and variable costs. Fixed costs are costs that *do not change with the level of output*, such as payments that are a set amount and are specified in a contract (for example, the lease on a building). Fixed costs must be paid even if the firm produces zero output. Variable costs are costs that *change when output changes* and are incurred only if the firm produces output.

A firm's **total cost (TC)** is the sum of **total fixed cost (TFC)** and **total variable cost (TVC)**, and is written:

TC = TFC + TVC

At an output level of zero, the firm's variable costs are zero. However, the firm must pay its fixed costs even if it does not produce, so at output equal to zero, total cost is equal to total fixed cost. If the firm produces output, it must employ variable inputs and pay variable costs, so its total cost will include both fixed and variable costs. These cost measures can be used to calculate TC, TFC or TVC if two of the values are known.

As an example, if a firm has total cost of $200,000 and total variable cost of $150,000 when it produces 1,000 units of output, then the firm's total fixed cost is the difference between them. If the firm's total fixed cost is $50,000, then the firm has total cost of $50,000 when output is zero.

TFC = TC – TVC = $200,000 - $150,000 = $50,000

Recall from the previous chapter that total cost represents total *economic* cost, so the amounts are assumed to include both explicit and implicit costs. For example, if an entrepreneur gave up a salary of $40,000 per year to start a business, then the total fixed costs of this business would include $40,000 per year to cover that opportunity cost. However, the amount given for TFC typically does not indicate the specific components and it is not necessary to know the components in order to derive the cost functions and graphs.

Average Costs

Output is usually priced and sold on a *per unit* basis, so costs expressed on a per unit basis are often more useful. Per unit costs are referred to as **average costs** and are calculated by dividing the appropriate total cost by the number of units of output (Q) produced.

Average total cost **(ATC)** is total cost per unit of output; average fixed cost **(AFC)** is fixed cost per unit of output; and average variable cost **(AVC)** is variable cost per unit of output. The equations for each of these measurements are given below, followed by examples.

$$\mathbf{ATC} = \frac{\mathbf{TC}}{\mathbf{Q}} \qquad \mathbf{AFC} = \frac{\mathbf{TFC}}{\mathbf{Q}} \qquad \mathbf{AVC} = \frac{\mathbf{TVC}}{\mathbf{Q}}$$

If total cost is $20,000 when output is 1,000 units, then average total cost (ATC) is $20,000/1,000 = $20. In other words, each unit of output costs $20 to produce when the firm produces 1,000 units of output.

If total variable cost is $15,000 when output is 1,000 units, then average variable cost (AVC) is $15,000/1,000, or $15.

If total cost is $20,000 and total variable cost is $15,000, then total fixed cost must be equal to $5,000.

Average fixed cost (AFC) at 1,000 units of output can be calculated in two ways, both of which yield the same answer:

1) AFC = TFC/Q = $5,000/1,000 = $5 or
2) AFC = ATC – AVC = $20 - $15 = $5

Since TC = TFC + TVC, it must also be true that ATC = AFC + AVC, which implies that AFC = ATC - AVC.

The table below provides cost data for a hypothetical producer of gadgets.

Q	TC	TFC	TVC	ATC	AVC	AFC
0	$100	$____	$ 0	---	---	---
1	160	____	60	________	________	________
2	210	____	110	________	________	________
3	260	____	160	________	________	________
4	320	____	220	________	________	________
5	410	____	310	________	________	________

Use the formulas presented so far to fill in the missing numbers and check your work against the completed table on the next page.

The values in the table reflect the relationships between TC, TFC, and TVC. When output is 4 gadgets per time period, total cost is $320 and total fixed cost is $100, which means total variable cost must be $220 because TVC = TC – TFC. Note that total fixed cost is constant and equal to $100 at every level of output. Fixed costs do not change with the level of output. Total variable cost, however, depends on the level of output and increases as output increases. This means total cost must also increase as output increases because TC = TFC + TVC.

Q	TC	TFC	TVC	ATC = TC/Q	AVC = TVC/Q	AFC = TFC/Q
0	$100	$100	$ 0	---	---	---
1	160	100	60	160/1 = $160	60/1 = $60	100/1 = $100
2	210	100	110	210/2 = $105	110/2 = $55	100/2 = $50
3	260	100	160	260/3 = $86.67	160/3 = $53.33	100/3 = $33.33
4	320	100	220	320/4 = $80	220/4 = $55	100/4 = $25
5	410	100	310	410/5 = $82	310/5 = $62	100/5 = $20

The values in the above table also show that both average total cost and average variable cost initially decrease, hit a minimum value, and then begin to increase. Average fixed cost, however, decreases over the entire range of output. This is because total fixed cost does not change with the level of output, and the same value for total fixed cost, $100, is being divided by an increasingly greater number of units of output. As output increases, the portion of the cost of producing each unit of output that goes to pay for fixed factors of production, or overhead, is declining. The decline in AFC as output increases is referred to as "spreading the overhead."

The graph below shows the general shapes of the TC, TVC, and TFC curves. Note that the TFC curve is a horizontal line because total fixed costs do not change as output increases. Since TC = TFC + TVC, it must be true that TFC = TC – TVC. This means that TFC is the vertical distance between the TC and TVC curves. Because TFC can be determined from the TC and TVC curves, the TFC curve is redundant and does not really need to be included.

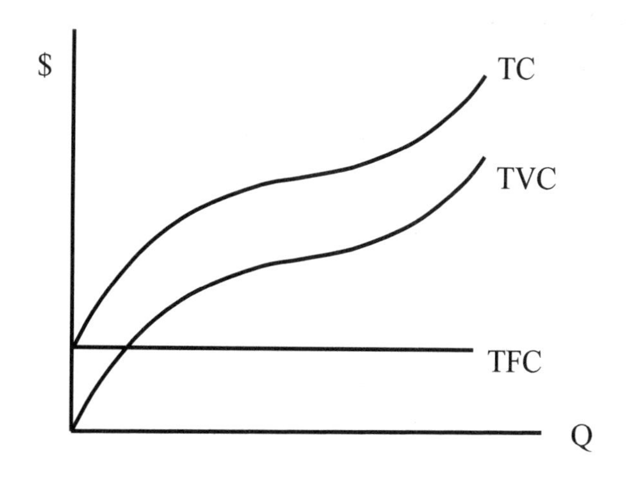

The graph below shows the general shapes of the ATC, AVC, and AFC curves. Note that both the ATC and AVC curves decline from the initial starting point, hit a minimum, and then increase. The AFC curve falls over the entire range of output because TFC, a constant, is being divided by an increasingly larger quantity of output. Since ATC = AFC + AVC for a given level of output, it must be true that AFC = ATC – AVC. This means AFC is the vertical distance between the ATC and AVC curves. Note that ATC and AVC become closer together as output increases because AFC is decreasing. Since AFC can be determined from the ATC and AVC curves, the AFC curve is redundant and does not really need to be included.

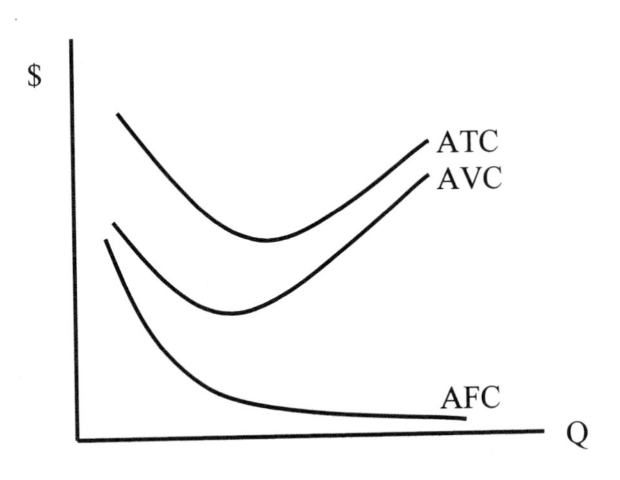

Marginal Cost

A firm may also want to know how much cost will change when the level of output changes. **Marginal cost (MC)** gives the change in total cost associated with producing one more unit of output:

$$MC = \frac{\text{change in total cost}}{\text{change in output}} = \frac{TC_2 - TC_1}{Q_2 - Q_1} = \frac{\Delta TC}{\Delta Q} = \frac{\Delta TVC}{\Delta Q}$$

Note that the change in total cost is the same as the change in total variable cost because the difference between these two values is total fixed cost (TFC) and TFC does not change with output. Marginal cost is not related to average fixed cost because total fixed cost is assumed constant for a given short-run production function.

Marginal cost is related to both average variable cost **(AVC)** and average total cost **(ATC)** in the following ways:

1) As long as MC is **less** than AVC, AVC declines; as long as MC is **less** than ATC, ATC declines. That is, if the marginal cost is below the average, the marginal "pulls" the average down.

2) MC intersects AVC at minimum AVC; MC intersects ATC at minimum ATC. The MC curve is increasing when it intersects both AVC and ATC.

3) When MC is **greater** than AVC, AVC increases; when MC is **greater** than ATC, ATC increases.

The relationships between marginal cost, average variable cost, and average total cost are illustrated on the graph below. The marginal cost curve passes through the minimum points of both the average total cost and average variable cost curves. The average total cost and average variable cost curves get closer together at higher levels of output, showing that average fixed cost is declining.

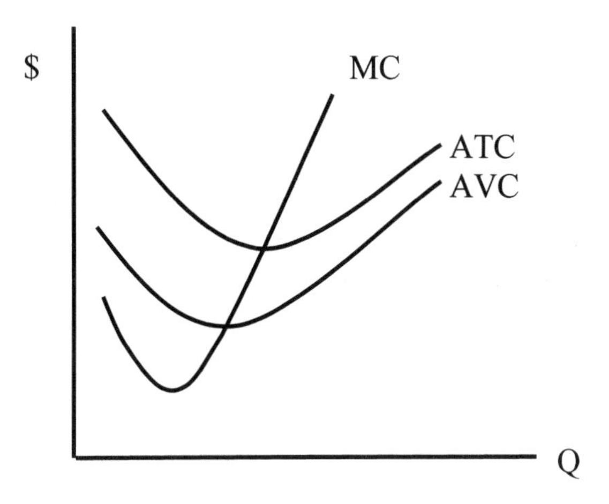

The exact position of each of the cost curves depends on short-run production function data as well as on input prices, so each firm has its own set of cost curves. Most of the time, though, the cost curves have the same general appearance as those shown here, and often a sketch depicting these cost measures can be used to arrive at general principles.

Firms increase output by adding variable inputs; the graph below assumes the variable input is labor (L). Marginal cost **(MC)** falls when marginal product **(MP)** is rising, and rises when marginal product begins to fall, due to the law of diminishing returns. The relationship between MC and MP, sort of a mirror-image relationship, is depicted in the graphs below.

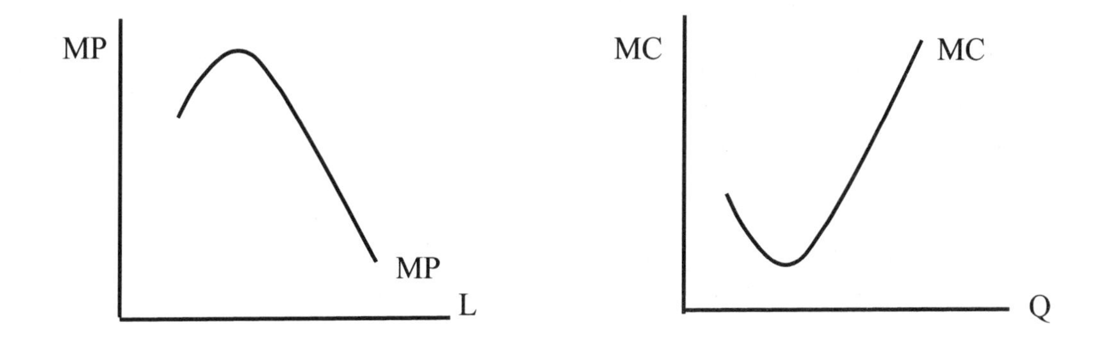

The law of diminishing returns dictates that marginal product must eventually fall as additional units of a variable input are added to existing fixed inputs; as a result, the law of diminishing returns also dictates that marginal cost must eventually begin to rise as additional units of a variable input are added to existing fixed inputs. As will be shown in the next chapter, part of the upward-sloping portion of the firm's MC function is the firm's supply function, so this is an important result that will confirm the **law of supply** presented in chapter 4.

Consider an example in which the firm increases output by hiring additional workers, holding capital fixed. Then, the **wage** (W) paid to a worker is the change in total cost associated with a one-unit change in labor, or W = ΔTC/ΔL. Recall that marginal product (MP) is defined as ΔQ/ΔL. Dividing the wage (W) by marginal product (MP) illustrates the inverse relationship between MP and MC:

$$\frac{W}{MP} = \frac{\Delta TC/\Delta L}{\Delta Q/\Delta L} = \frac{\Delta TC}{\Delta Q} = MC$$

A profit-maximizing firm does not stop hiring workers before fully exhausting the benefits of division of labor, implying that the firm does not choose a level of employment corresponding to the upward-sloping portion of the marginal product function. For this reason, a profit-maximizing firm will not choose a level of output corresponding to the downward-sloping portion of the marginal cost curve. The operating region of the marginal cost curve is the upward-sloping part.

Long-Run Costs

The theory of supply emphasizes the behavior of costs in the short run. However, real-world business planning involves making decisions in the long run as well. The last section of the chapter provides a brief introduction to the behavior of costs in the long run.

For most industries, average costs vary as the scale of production changes. For example, a firm that manufactures paper plates will probably face a very high per-unit cost if it only produces 100 paper plates per week. This is because the firm would not be able to obtain expensive equipment to automate production if it produces at such a small scale.

A firm moves to a larger scale of production by increasing inputs. There are three possible relationships between inputs and output in the long run:

1) **Economies of scale** (increasing returns to scale) occur when a firm increases inputs by some percentage, and output increases by an even larger percentage; in this case, average costs fall as production (output) increases.

2) **Constant returns to scale** occur when a firm increases inputs by some percentage and output increases by the same percentage; in this case, average costs remain constant as production (output) increases.

2) **Diseconomies of scale** (decreasing returns to scale) occur when a firm increases inputs by some percentage, but output increases by a smaller percentage; in this case, average costs rise as production (output) increases.

The typical pattern is for a firm to experience economies of scale initially, followed by constant returns to scale, until reaching a production level that is high enough for diseconomies of scale to kick in.

A long-run average cost (LRAC) curve shows how average cost changes as output is increased, given that inputs are being increased to bring about the increased output. The output level **Q_0** in the graph below corresponds to the firm's **minimum efficient scale**, which is defined as the level of output at which economies of scale are fully exhausted or used up.

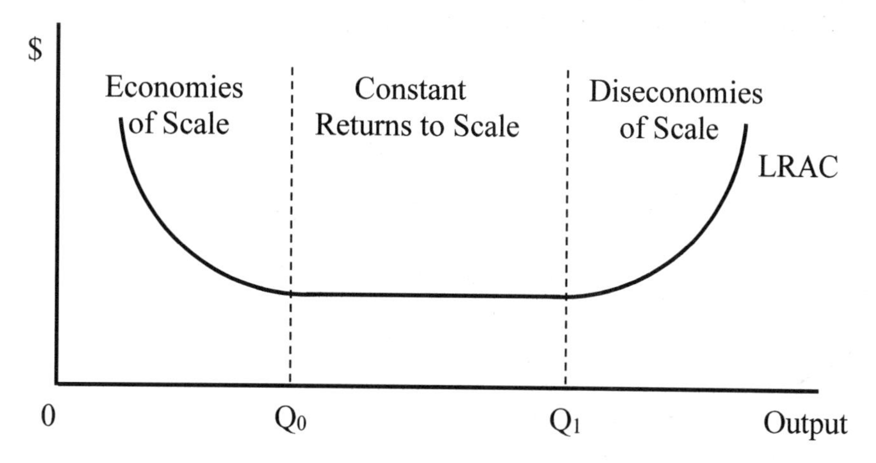

Smaller firms generally enjoy economies of scale as they expand because they are able to acquire more specialized capital that raises productivity, and they are able to spread capital overhead costs when more output is produced. For example, when a movie theater spreads the cost of a projector over thousands of customers, the cost per movie-goer is lower than if the theater had only a few hundred customers. At some point, the firm reaches its minimum efficient scale (where economies of scale have been fully exploited), and then a period of constant returns will likely begin, causing per-unit cost to remain constant as the firm continues to expand its scale of operation. It is possible for firms to reach a point where diseconomies of scale occur, though real-world firms would take steps to avoid this by, for example, operating as separate divisions (like GM). Bigger is better only up to a point; size can eventually become a liability due to communication and monitoring problems which can reduce productivity and raise per-unit costs.

Consider a simple example to see the relationship between returns to scale (increasing, constant, or decreasing) and long-run average cost (LRAC). Assume that when inputs are increased by a certain percentage, total cost (TC) increases by the same percentage. The following hypothetical data illustrates how LRAC behaves as the scale increases.

Scale 1	Scale 2	Scale 3	Scale 4
TC = $200	TC = $400	TC = $800	TC = $1,600
Q = 100	Q = 400	Q = 800	Q = 1,000
LRAC = $2	LRAC = $1	LRAC = $1	LRAC = $1.60

At Scale 1, total cost (TC) = $200 and output (Q) = 100 units, so long-run average cost is TC/Q = $200/100 = $2. As the firm expands to Scale 2 by increasing inputs, total costs double, from $200 to $400, and output more than doubles, from 100 units to 400 units, so the firm is experiencing economies of scale, and average cost falls from $2 to $1. When the firm moves from Scale 2 to Scale 3, inputs are doubled, costs double, output exactly doubles, and average cost remains the same, indicating constant returns to scale. If the firm grows from Scale 3 to Scale 4, doubling inputs and costs, output grows by only 25 percent. As a result, average cost rises from $1 to $1.60. As previously discussed, real-world firms will take steps to prevent unit costs from rising as they grow, usually by reorganizing.

Example: Calculating Short-Run Costs From a Graph

The graph below reflects typical marginal cost, average variable cost, and average total cost curves for a firm. From these three curves, all of the short-run costs of production can be identified or calculated for the output levels shown in the graph.

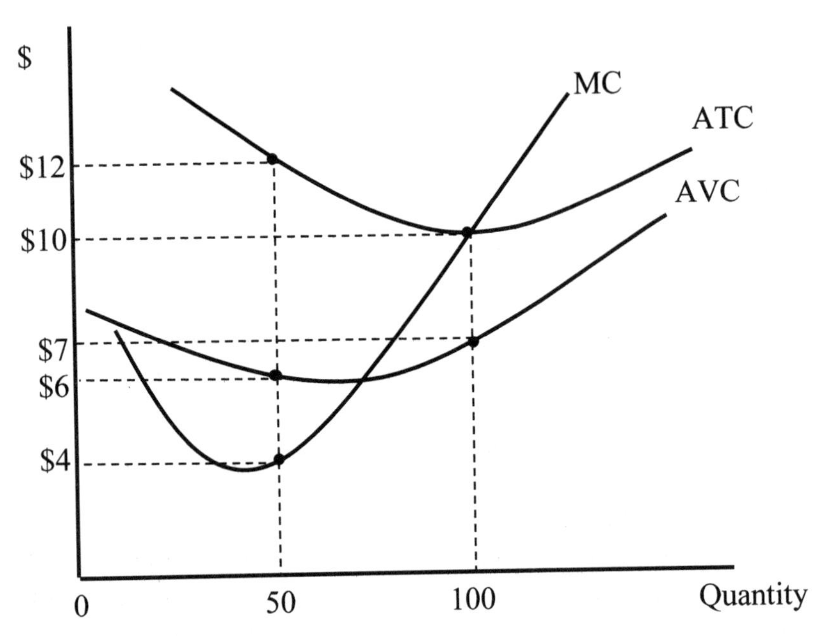

To determine ATC, AVC, AFC and MC:

Draw a vertical line through all curves from the quantity axis at the identified level of output. Follow that line up to the ATC, AVC, or MC curve, and read the $ cost from the vertical axis. AFC is the vertical distance between the ATC and AVC curves, so at each given level of output, **AFC = ATC – AVC.**

At output of 50 units, ATC = $12, AVC = $6, MC = $4, and AFC = $12 – $6 = $6

At output of 100 units, ATC = $10, AVC = $7, MC = $10, and AFC = $10 – $7 = $3

To determine TC, TVC, and TFC:

The equations for ATC, AVC, and AVC are:

ATC = TC/Q **AVC = TVC/Q** **AFC = TFC/Q = (ATC – AVC)**

To get TC, TVC, and TFC, multiply the average by quantity:

TC = ATC(Q) **TVC = AVC(Q)** **TFC = AFC(Q) = (TC – TVC)**

At output of 50 units, TC = $12(50) = $600; TVC = $6(50) = $300; TFC = $6(50) = $300

At output of 100 units, TC = $10(100) = $1,000; TVC = $7(100) = $700; TFC = $3(100) =$300

Notice that TC and TVC both increase when output increases. TFC, however, is the same at all levels of output because total fixed cost does not change with the level of output. So regardless of which level of output is used, TFC is the same.

NAME____SECTION#____________

PRINT LAST NAME, FIRST NAME

CALCULATING SHORT-RUN COSTS FROM A GRAPH

Use the graph below to fill in the blanks.

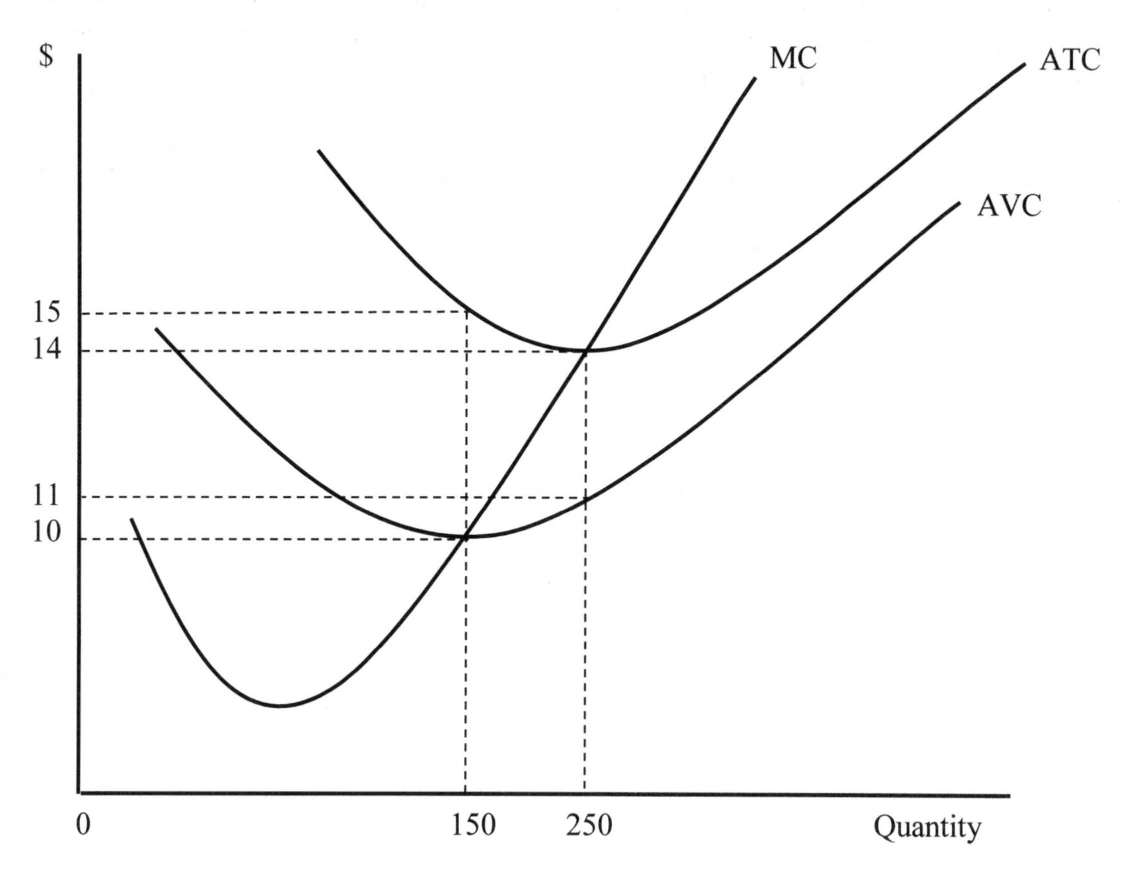

1. If output is 150 units, then average total cost (ATC) = $_______________.

2. If output is 150 units, then average variable cost (AVC) = $_______________.

3. If output is 150 units, then average fixed cost (AFC) = $_______________.

4. If output is 150 units, then total cost (TC) = $_______________.

5. If output is 150 units, then total variable cost (TVC) = $_______________.

6. If output is 150 units, then total fixed cost (TFC) = $_______________.

7. If output is 250 units, then ATC = $_______________ and AVC = $_______________.

8. If output is 250 units, then average fixed cost (AFC) = $_______________.

9. If output is 250 units, then TC = $_______________ and TVC = $_______________.

10. If output is 250 units, then total fixed cost (TFC) = $_______________.

NAME______________________________________SECTION#______________

PRINT LAST NAME, FIRST NAME

SHORT-RUN COSTS

Fill in the missing values for total cost (TC), total fixed cost (TFC), total variable cost (TVC), average total cost (ATC), average variable cost (AVC), and marginal cost (MC) in the table below; use the data to fill in the blanks.

Q	TC	TFC	TVC	ATC	AVC	AFC	MC
0	$10	$____	$____				
1	$15	$____	$____	$____	$____	$____	$____
2	$____	$____	$____	$____	$____	$____	$3
3	$____	$____	$____	$8	$____	$____	$____
4	$____	$____	$22	$____	$____	$____	$____
5	$____	$____	$____	$____	$7	$____	$____

Total fixed costs are equal to 1) $__________ at every level of output, while total variable costs 2) ____________________ as output increases. Average total cost and average variable cost first 3) ____________________, then 4) ____________________ as output increases.

The marginal cost of producing the second unit of output is $3, so total cost is 5) $__________ when Q = 2. When Q = 3, total cost is 6) $__________ since average total cost is $8. When Q = 4, total cost is 7) $__________ since total variable cost is $22. When Q = 5, total variable cost is 8) $__________ since average variable cost is $7.

Marginal cost is calculated by dividing the change in total cost by the change in output, so the marginal cost of producing the fourth unit is 9) $__________ and the marginal cost of producing the fifth unit is 10) $__________.

NAME____SECTION#______________

PRINT LAST NAME, FIRST NAME

SHORT-RUN COSTS OF PRODUCTION

1. Costs that change as the level of output changes are called:
   a. overhead.
   b. variable costs.
   c. fixed costs.
   d. sunk costs.

2. Costs that must be paid in the short run even when no output is produced are called:
   a. average variable costs (AVC).
   b. total fixed costs (TFC).
   c. total variable costs (TVC).
   d. marginal costs (MC).

3 Marginal cost (MC) is:
   a. the change in total cost (TC) divided by the change in output (Q).
   b. the change in total variable cost (TVC) divided by the change in output (Q).
   c. not affected by the level of fixed costs.
   d. All of the above

4. Which of the following is ***true*** in the short run?
   a. TC = TVC - TFC
   b. AFC = AVC + ATC
   c. TFC = TC - TVC
   d. All of the above are true

5. Which of the following is ***not true*** in the short run?
   a. MC = $(\Delta TVC/\Delta Q)$
   b. MC = $(\Delta TC/\Delta Q)$
   c. (TC/Q) = (TVC/Q)
   d. ATC = AVC + AFC

6. Suppose the total cost of production in the short run is $500,000 when 2,000,000 units are produced. Then, average total cost (ATC) is:
   a. 25 cents per unit and average fixed cost (AFC) is 15 cents per unit.
   b. $4 per unit, and average fixed cost (AFC) is $2 per unit.
   c. 25 cents per unit, and average fixed cost (AFC) is unknown given the available information.
   d. $4 per unit, and average fixed cost (AFC) is unknown given the available information.

NAME______________________________________SECTION#______________
PRINT LAST NAME, FIRST NAME

7. If, in the short run, producing 100 units of output results in a total cost to the producer of \$5,000, while the producer must pay \$2,000 when no output is produced, then all of the following are true **except**:
   a. ATC = \$50 when Q = 100.
   b. AVC = \$30 when Q = 100.
   c. AFC = \$10 when Q = 100.
   d. AFC = \$10 when Q = 200.

Use the information below to answer questions 8 through 10.

Tinker's Tools produces one product, hammers. Fixed costs for Tinker's Tools include rent on the building, interest payments to the bank, insurance costs and property taxes, which total \$70 per day. The following represents a short-run cost schedule for Tinker's Tools.

Output/day	Total cost/day
0	\$ 70
100	100
200	140
300	230
400	340
500	470
600	620

8. When output is 400 units, average variable cost (AVC) is equal to ______.
   a. \$0.275
   b. \$0.675
   c. \$0.80
   d. \$0.85

9. The marginal cost of increasing output from 400 units to 500 units is ______ per unit.
   a. \$0.30
   b. \$0.50
   c. \$1.30
   d. \$1.50

10. When output is 500 units, average fixed cost (AFC) is equal to ______.
    a. \$0.85
    b. \$0.80
    c. \$0.35
    d. \$0.14

NAME____SECTION#______________

PRINT LAST NAME, FIRST NAME

SHORT-RUN COSTS OF PRODUCTION

1. A firm producing 30 units of output has average total cost equal to $12 and average variable cost equal to $8. This firm's total fixed costs are therefore equal to:

   B

   a. $4. b. $120. c. $240. d. $360.

2. If marginal cost is greater than average total cost, then:

   A

   a. average total cost is rising.
   b. average total cost is falling.
   c. average total cost is at a maximum.
   d. average total cost is at a minimum.

3. If the total cost of producing 2 units of output is $100 and the total variable cost of producing 2 units of output is $80, then:

   D

   a. average variable cost (AVC) is $40 when 2 units of output are produced.
   b. average total cost (ATC) is $50 when 2 units of output are produced.
   c. total fixed cost (TFC) is equal to $20.
   d. All of the above are true

4 In the short run, average variable cost can be obtained by each of the following ***except***:

   D

   a. ATC – AFC.
   b. (TC/Q) - (TFC/Q).
   c. TVC/Q.
   d. ATC - MC.

Use the information below to answer questions 5 and 6.

The average total cost (ATC) of producing a bell is $5 when Jenny's Jingles produces 100 bells. Total cost when zero bells are produced is $250.

5. The total variable cost (TVC) of producing 100 bells is equal to:

   A

   a. $250.
   b. $500.
   c. $750.
   d. $1,000.

6. Average fixed cost (AFC) when 100 bells are produced is equal to:

   A

   a. $2.50.
   b. $5.00.
   c. $7.50.
   d. $25.00.

NAME____SECTION#_______________

PRINT LAST NAME, FIRST NAME

7. Suppose through 10 games Dirk Nowitzki scored, on average, 25 points per game. If in his 11th game he scored 21 points, we know that his:
   a. marginal score is greater than his average score, and his season average will fall.
   b. marginal score is greater than his average score, and his season average will rise.
   c. marginal score is less than his average score, and his season average will fall.
   d. marginal score is less than his average score, and his season average will rise.

C

Use the table below to answer questions 8 through 10.

Output (Q = TP)	TVC	TC
0	$ 0	$80
1	20	100
2	30	110
3	50	130
4	80	160
5	120	200

8. If this firm does not produce any output, it:
   a. must pay fixed costs of $80.
   b. will not have to pay any costs.
   c. is making a long-run decision.
   d. will still have total revenue of $80.

A

9. The total cost of producing 3 units of output is:
   a. $30.
   b. $80.
   c. $110.
   d. $130.

D

10. Average variable cost (AVC) when 4 units of output are produced is:
   a. $16.
   b. $20.
   c. $40.
   d. $80.

B

NAME____SECTION#________________

PRINT LAST NAME, FIRST NAME

SHORT-RUN COST CURVES

Use the graph below to fill in the blanks.

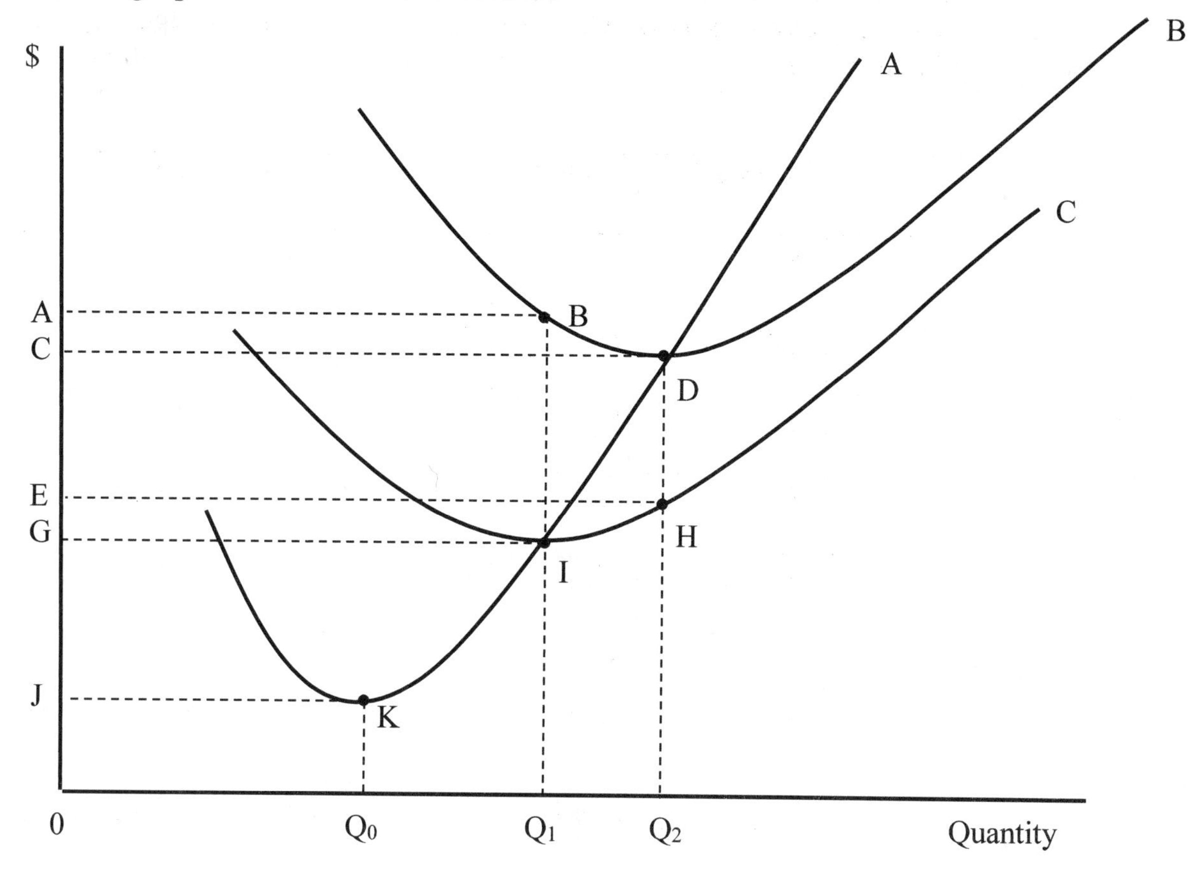

The cost of producing an additional unit of output is given by curve 1) ____________. The average total cost of producing each unit of output is given by curve 2) ____________. The average fixed cost of producing Q_1 units of output is equal to the distance 3) ____________. The total variable cost of producing Q_1 units of output is equal to the area 4) ____________. The total cost of producing Q_1 units of output is equal to the area 5) ____________. The average fixed cost of producing Q_2 units of output is equal to the distance 6) ____________. The total variable cost of producing Q_2 units of output is equal to the area 7) ____________. The total cost of producing Q_2 units of output is equal to the area 8) ____________. Total fixed cost is equal to the area 9) ____________. Total fixed cost is also equal to the area 10) ____________.

NAME____SECTION#______________

PRINT LAST NAME, FIRST NAME

SHORT-RUN COSTS

Fill in the missing values for total cost (TC), total fixed cost (TFC), total variable cost (TVC), average total cost (ATC), average variable cost (AVC), and marginal cost (MC) in the table below; use the data to fill in the blanks.

Q	TC	TFC	TVC	ATC	AFC	AVC	MC
0	$60	$	$	---	---	---	---
1	$	$	$40	$	$	$	$
2	$120	$	$	$	$	$	$
3	$	$	$	$	$	$	$60
4	$	$	$	$70	$	$	$
5	$	$	$	$	$	$68	$

Total fixed costs are equal to 1) $__________, regardless of how much output is produced.

Average fixed costs 2) ____________________ as output is increased. If this firm produces one unit of output, total cost is 3) $__________, total fixed cost is 4) $__________, and total variable cost is 5) $__________.

If this firm produces 3 units of output, average total cost is 6) $__________, average fixed cost is 7) $__________, and average variable cost is 8) $__________.

The marginal cost of the fourth unit of output is 9) $__________ and the marginal cost of the fifth unit of output is 10) $__________.

NAME____SECTION#______________
PRINT LAST NAME, FIRST NAME

LONG-RUN COSTS OF PRODUCTION

1. If a firm is experiencing economies of scale, doubling inputs will:
   a. double output.
   b. more than double output.
   c. have no effect on output.
   d. increase, but less than double, output.

2. In the long run:
   a. all inputs are fixed, and average costs are constant.
   b. some inputs are fixed, and others are variable.
   c. all inputs are variable, and average costs are constant.
   d. all inputs are variable, and average costs may decrease, remain constant, or increase as the scale of production changes.

3. The long-run average cost curve (LRAC) is U-shaped due to:
   a. the law of increasing marginal productivity.
   b. the law of diminishing marginal utility.
   c. the existence of economies and diseconomies of scale.
   d. the existence of barriers to entry.

Use the information below to answer questions 4 through 6.

The table below presents data regarding a firm that is considering expanding its scale of production. The data contains rough estimates of costs associated with four different plant sizes. TC = estimate of annual total cost; Q = estimate of the quantity the plant will produce annually.

	Scale #1	**Scale #2**	**Scale #3**	**Scale #4**
Total Cost (TC)	$500,000	$1,000,000	$2,000,000	$5,000,000
Output (Q)	100,000	400,000	800,000	1,500,000

4. If output is 800,000 units, average cost is equal to:
   a. $4.00 b. $2.50 c. $0.25 d. $0.40

5. Moving from scale #1 to scale #2 will generate for the firm:
   a. economies of scale since long-run average costs fall.
   b. economies of scale since long-run average costs rise.
   c. diseconomies of scale since long-run average costs fall.
   d. diseconomies of scale since long-run average costs rise.

6. Moving from scale #3 to scale #4 will generate for the firm:
   a. economies of scale since long-run average costs fall.
   b. economies of scale since long-run average costs rise.
   c. diseconomies of scale since long-run average costs fall.
   d. diseconomies of scale since long-run average costs rise.

NAME____SECTION#______________

PRINT LAST NAME, FIRST NAME

7. The typical pattern is for a firm to experience:
   a. diseconomies of scale initially, followed by constant returns to scale until reaching a production level high enough for economies of scale to kick in.
   b. economies of scale initially, followed by constant returns to scale until reaching a production level high enough for diseconomies of scale to kick in.
   c. constant returns to scale initially, followed by economies of scale until reaching a production level high enough for diseconomies of scale to kick in.
   d. economies of scale initially, followed by diseconomies of scale until reaching a production level high enough for constant returns to scale to kick in.

Use the graph below to answer questions 8 through 10.

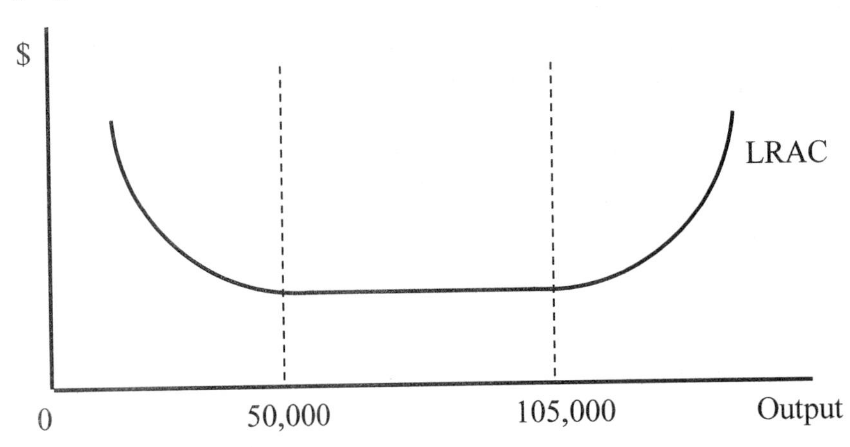

8. This firm experiences economies of scale (or increasing returns to scale):
   a. as output is increased from 0 to 50,000 units.
   b. as output is increased from 50,000 units to 105,000 units.
   c. as output is increased above 105,000 units.
   d. over the entire range of output.

9. The minimum efficient scale for this firm is:
   a. less than 50,000 units of output.
   b. 50,000 units of output.
   c. 105,000 units of output.
   d. more than 105,000 units of output.

10. If this firm increases output from 50,000 to 105,000 units, it will experience:
   a. constant returns to scale, so it has achieved the minimum efficient scale.
   b. economies of scale, so it has not yet achieved the minimum efficient scale.
   c. diseconomies of scale, so communication or monitoring problems exist.
   d. constant returns to scale, so output is increasing faster than costs.

CHAPTER 11 Perfect Competition

Adam Smith published a book in 1776 called *An Inquiry Into the Nature and Causes of the Wealth of Nations*. In it, he argues that each individual naturally pursues his own interest, and that by doing so, an individual is "...led by an invisible hand to promote an end which was no part of his intention." Smith's invisible hand argument leads to the conclusion that society is best served by free markets in which individuals are free to pursue their own interests and government takes a very limited role. Adam Smith's most famous claim, that free markets promote efficient outcomes, rests on a very important assumption; markets must be competitive in order to promote efficiency. The economy in Smith's time was a 'butcher, brewer, baker' economy; in other words, it was made up of many small, competitive businesses.

Smith warned that monopolies tend to be far less efficient because they have no real competitors threatening to break into their market, but he did not develop models of imperfectly competitive markets that are in between perfectly competitive and monopoly. The models of markets that lie between perfect competition and monopoly came into being over 150 years after Smith's time. Joan Robinson introduced the model of monopolistic competition in 1933 and Edward Chamberlin introduced the model of oligopoly in 1957.

All four market models are shown in the diagram below, representing a competitive spectrum.

Perfect Competition	Monopolistic Competition	Oligopoly	Monopoly
many small firms low barriers intense competition lowest profits	many firms low barriers intense competition	a few large firms high barriers competition or collusion	one firm high barriers no real competition highest profits

Competition is the most intense on the far left with perfect competition, and there is a complete absence of competition on the far right with monopoly. The most competitive markets are also the most efficient.

The current chapter focuses on perfect competition, and the next chapter on monopoly. The in-between cases of monopolistic competition and oligopoly, which actually apply to most real-world markets, are examined in chapters 13 and 14.

All firms encounter diminishing returns in the short run and have cost curves that exhibit similar behaviors. The pricing and output decisions of the firm, however, depend not only on the cost functions but also on the demand for the firm's product. The demand curve confronting a firm depends on the competitive conditions in the market in which it operates. The model of perfect competition sets up a situation where individual firms in a market have no market power (price-setting power), and the interaction of all buyers and sellers in the market determines the price at which individual firms sell output.

Perfect competition is the easiest market structure to analyze because the individual firm does not have to determine what price to charge for output. Individual firms are **price-takers,** which means the firm takes the price determined by the market forces of supply and demand. The firm must decide how much output to offer for sale, assuming the goal of the firm is to maximize profit, given the market price. Perfect competition is also used as a benchmark for comparing real-world competitive situations to a perfectly competitive situation in order to assess the efficiency, or inefficiency, associated with real-world markets.

The assumptions or characteristics of the **perfectly competitive model** also include the following:

- the market is comprised of a large number of firms and each firm is small relative to the entire market
- all firms are producing identical (homogeneous) products, making the output of one firm in the market a perfect substitute for the output of every other firm in the market
- there is freedom of entry into the market and exit from the market in the long run because there are no barriers to entry
- consumers have perfect information regarding product price, quality, and availability
- firms have perfect information regarding market prices and opportunity costs

The result of these characteristics is that the firm's demand curve is horizontal, or **perfectly elastic,** at the prevailing market price. The individual firm is small relative to the entire market and can sell all it can produce at the market price and thus is a **price-taker.** The graphs below illustrate the relationship between market price, which is determined by market supply (S_{mkt}) and market demand (D_{mkt}), and the demand curve for the individual firm (d) in the market.

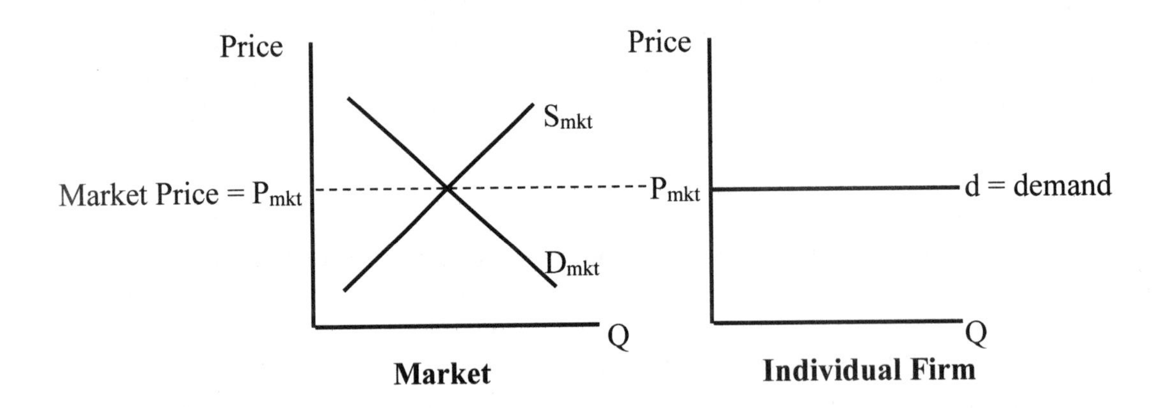

If the firm raises its price above P_{mkt}, its sales will fall to zero because demanders know they can buy the exact same product from another seller at the market price. There is no incentive for the firm to charge a price below P_{mkt} because it can sell all it desires at the market price. Charging a price below P_{mkt} is a violation of the profit-maximizing assumption.

Profit-Maximization in the Short Run

A **perfectly competitive firm** must, in order to maximize profit, make three basic interdependent decisions:

1) How much output to supply (quantity of product)
2) How to produce that output (what production technique to use)
3) How much of each input to demand.

This section focuses on the first decision and assumes that the firm will employ least-cost production techniques and hire inputs accordingly.

There are two approaches to identifying the profit-maximizing level of output:

1) the total revenue minus total cost (TR – TC) approach

2) the marginal revenue equal to marginal cost (MR = MC) approach

Both approaches lead to the same choice of output or quantity supplied, but the marginal approach is generally preferred by economists.

TR – TC Approach

To maximize profit, the firm should supply the level of output (quantity) where total revenue exceeds total cost by the greatest amount. The table below represents a hypothetical grower of tomatoes whose tomatoes are just like those of every other grower in the region. The tomato grower can sell all he takes to market and must decide what quantity of tomatoes, in bushels, to bring to market in order to earn the greatest profit possible.

The grower can vary the number of workers used to pick tomatoes and so can vary the output available to sell at the produce market on Saturday morning. However, the number of tomatoes that can be picked is limited by the number of producing plants the grower already has planted; therefore, the fixed input is the number of producing plants.

Price P	Quantity (Q)	Total Revenue (TR = P x Q)	Total Cost (TC)	Profit (TR – TC)
$12	0	$ 0	$ 5	–$5
12	1	12	13	– 1
12	2	24	19	+ 5
12	3	36	29	+ 7
12	4	48	43	+ 5

If the price of tomatoes is $12 per bushel, the farmer should pick 3 bushels of tomatoes (Q = 3) to sell at market because profit is greatest at a quantity of 3 bushels. Profit is less than $7 at any other level of output.

MR = MC Approach

The second approach to finding the profit-maximizing level of output is to apply the marginal benefit equal to marginal cost (MB = MC) rule. Recall that MB = MC is the condition for efficiency developed earlier, so this rule leads to the conclusion that the perfectly competitive outcome is the efficient outcome.

The marginal benefit to the seller is the additional revenue received from the sale of another unit of output. The addition to revenue from the sale of one more unit of output is called **marginal revenue (MR).** Marginal revenue indicates how much total revenue changes when an additional unit of output is sold and is the change in total revenue divided by the change in output.

$$\mathbf{MR = \frac{\Delta TR}{\Delta Q}}$$

A firm selling in a perfectly competitive market can sell all it desires at the current market price. Each additional unit of output sold adds the market price to the firm's revenue, so for an individual firm in perfect competition

$$\mathbf{MR = \frac{\Delta TR}{\Delta Q} = Price}$$

Marginal cost is the addition to the firm's total cost when one more unit of output is produced. Recall that marginal cost is the change in total cost divided by the change in output, or the change in total variable cost divided by the change in output.

$$\mathbf{MC = \frac{\Delta TC}{\Delta Q} = \frac{\Delta TVC}{\Delta Q}}$$

If producing and selling another unit of output adds more to the firm's revenue than it does to the firm's cost, then producing and selling another unit of output will increase the firm's profit. If producing and selling another unit of output adds more to the firm's cost than it does to the firm's revenue, then producing and selling that additional unit will decrease the firm's profit.

Students who have taken or will take business calculus will notice that the profit-maximizing rule, MR = MC, can be derived by setting the first derivative of the profit function equal to zero. It is not necessary to use calculus to understand the rule applied in this course, but it might be helpful to realize that this analysis matches the analysis used in business calculus.

To maximize profit, a firm produces the quantity of output (Q) where **MR = MC**, given that MC is increasing with output.

Quantity	Price = MR	MC = ΔTC/ΔQ
0		
1	$12	$ 8
2	12	6
3	12	10
4	12	14

For our tomato grower, market price and marginal revenue are both equal to $12 per bushel; if picking an additional bushel of tomatoes adds less than $12 to the firm's costs, then that additional bushel will add to the firm's profit. The table above shows that for the third bushel, MR = $12 and MC = $10, indicating that the third bushel will add to the firm's profit. However, for the fourth bushel, MR = $12 but MC = $14, so picking and selling the fourth bushel will result in a lower profit. The tomato grower should supply a quantity of 3 bushels when price is $12. This is the same level of output that maximized profit using the total revenue minus total cost approach.

A profit-maximizing firm will continue to increase production as long as MR is greater than MC, or as long as profit increases when output increases, but will stop at the point where **MR = MC**. To continue beyond this point, where MC is greater than MR, would be to pay more to produce the extra unit of output than the extra unit of output is worth, given the market valuation of the product; this would diminish profit.

The profit-maximizing rule applies to firms in any market structure, including monopoly, but for perfectly competitive firms, the profit-maximizing rule (producing where MR = MC) is equivalent to producing where P = MC, since P = MR when the firm is a price-taker.

The profit-maximizing level of output can be illustrated with graphs. Suppose the market price of the product sold in this perfectly competitive market is $3; MR = MC at point A for the firm. Dropping a line straight down from point A to the quantity axis gives the profit-maximizing level of output, or quantity, which is 90 for the individual firm in this example. Output in the market is always much larger than output for the individual firm since there are many small firms in a perfectly competitive market.

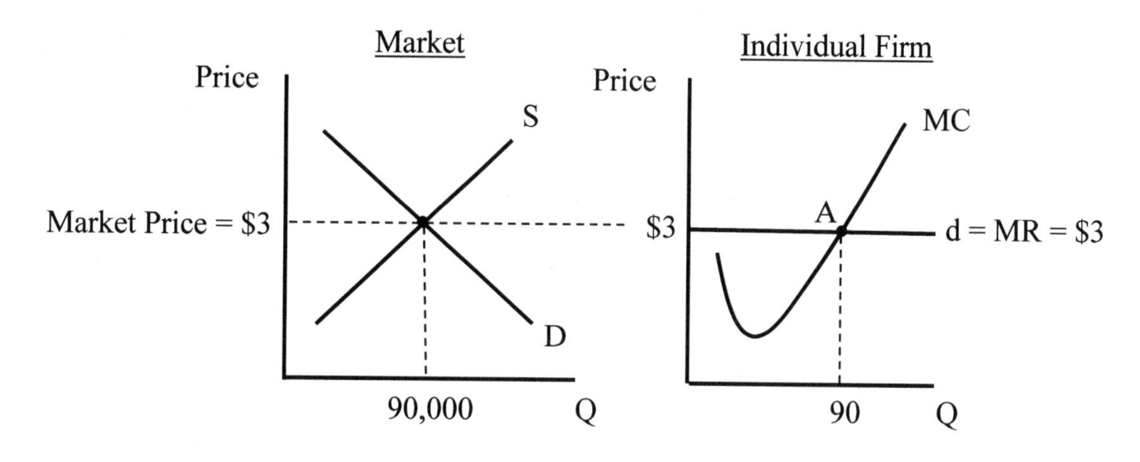

A graph also makes it easier to predict what will happen to the profit-maximizing output and profit for an individual firm in perfect competition when market conditions change. A change in market supply or market demand will change market price, which will change price and marginal revenue for the firm.

Assume market demand increases, shown by a rightward shift from D_0 to D_1 in the graph below. This increase in market demand raises the market price from $3 to $4 in this example.

The higher price results in an upward shift from MR_0 to MR_1 and an increase in the quantity at which MR = MC from 90 to 120 for the individual firm.

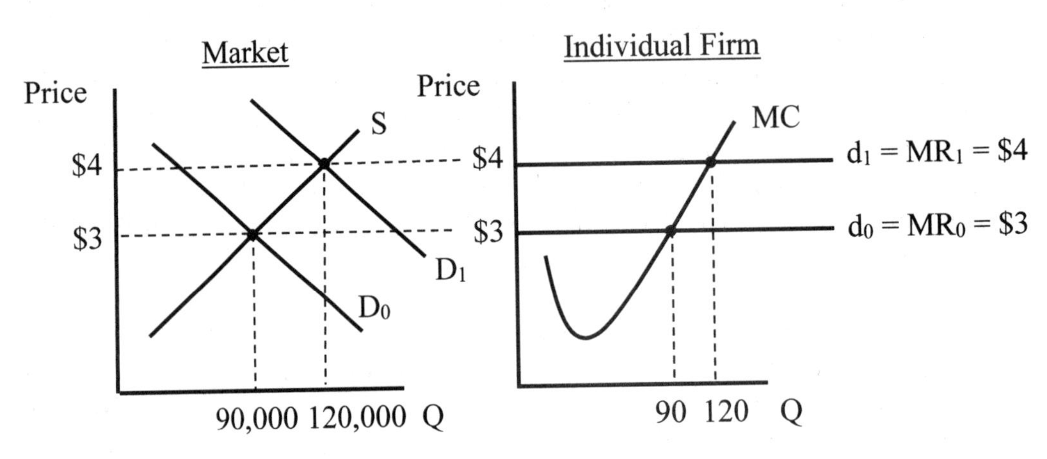

This result is consistent with the **law of supply**, which predicts that firms will produce more output (an increase in quantity supplied) in reaction to an increase in price of the product, ceteris paribus.

Economic versus Accounting Profit

Recall that accounting profit is likely to be positive when economic profit is zero, because economists deduct all costs from revenue when calculating profit.

As an example, suppose Amelia left a job that paid a salary of $40,000 per year in order to start her own flower shop. If her economic profit is equal to zero during the first year, this actually means that she earned enough revenue to cover all of her explicit costs (rent, insurance, utilities, flowers) as well as the $40,000 implicit cost that was her foregone salaray. An accountant might report that Amelia earned $40,000 in profit, but an economist would conclude that she made zero economic profit since she is doing exactly as well running her flower shop as she could have done staying with her job.

For the competitive firm in the short run, economic profit may be positive, zero, or negative. If economic profit is positive, additional firms will be attracted to the market by the chance to earn more money than can be made elsewhere. However, firms cannot enter the market in the short run, only in the long run. If economic profit is negative, some of the firms in the market are likely to exit in the long run. If economic profit is zero, there is no incentive for new firms to enter the market and there is no incentive for existing firms to exit the market, so this is the condition for long-run equilibrium in a perfectly competitive market.

Short-Run Profit Possibilities

The easiest way to identify the short-run profit position of a firm is to compare price to average total cost at the output where **MR = MC**. There are three possibilities:

1) Positive Economic Profit: P > ATC at the quantity where MR = MC

2) Zero Economic Profit: P = ATC at the quantity where MR = MC

3) Negative Economic Profit: P < ATC at the quantity where MR = MC

Graphically, economic profit is positive when the market price exceeds average total cost (ATC) at the quantity where MR = MC, as illustrated in **Figure 1** below.

Recall that the area of a rectangle is found by multiplying base times height; the base of the shaded rectangle is equal to the quantity of output the firm produces and the height of the shaded rectangle is equal to profit per unit, or P – ATC.

Multiplying profit per unit by output yields

$$[P - ATC] \times Q = (P)(Q) - (ATC)(Q) = TR - TC = Profit$$

Since total revenue minus total cost is profit, *the area of the shaded rectangle in the graph below corresponds to the firm's profit.*

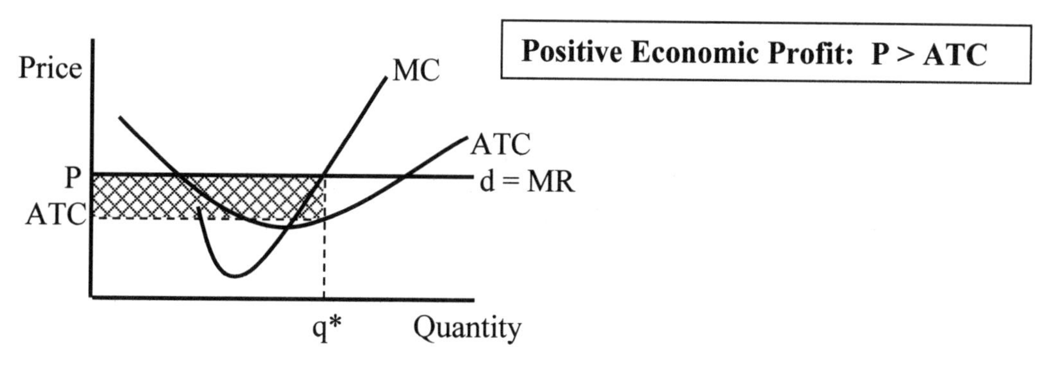

Figure 1

As long as the market price is higher than the minimum point of the ATC curve, the firm will earn a positive economic profit. As shown previously, raising the price causes the firm to produce a higher quantity, consistent with the law of supply, and will also result in a higher profit, ceteris paribus.

Zero economic profit means owners are receiving a reward equal to what they would earn in their next-best alternative opportunity. When price is equal to average total cost at the output where MR = MC, the firm is earning zero economic profit, which is also sometimes referred to as a normal profit or breakeven.

Graphically, economic profit is zero when the market price is equal average total cost, or when the (horizontal) demand line is tangent to the ATC curve at its minimum point, as illustrated in **Figure 2** below.

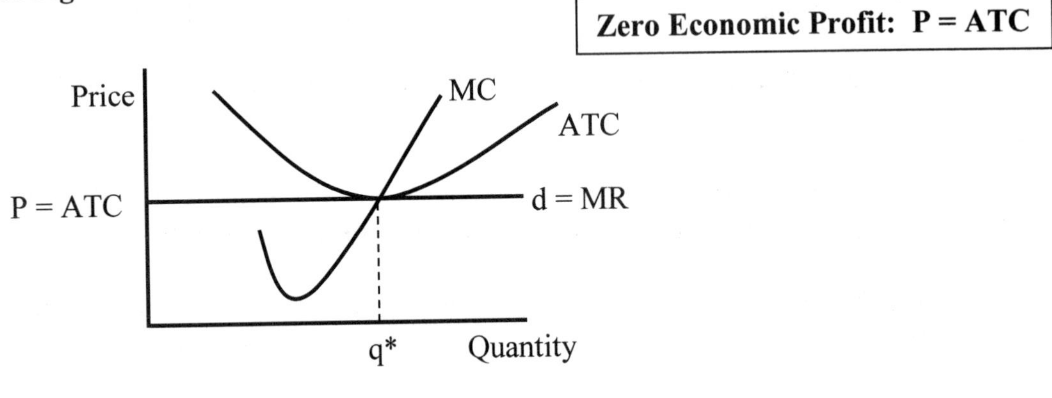

Figure 2

If price is less than average total cost at the output where marginal revenue is equal to marginal cost, then the firm has a **negative economic profit** and is incurring an **economic loss**. *The firm* ***minimizes losses*** *by producing at MR = MC when price is less than average total cost but price is greater than average variable cost.* **Figure 3** below represents a perfectly competitive firm incurring an economic loss equal to the shaded area.

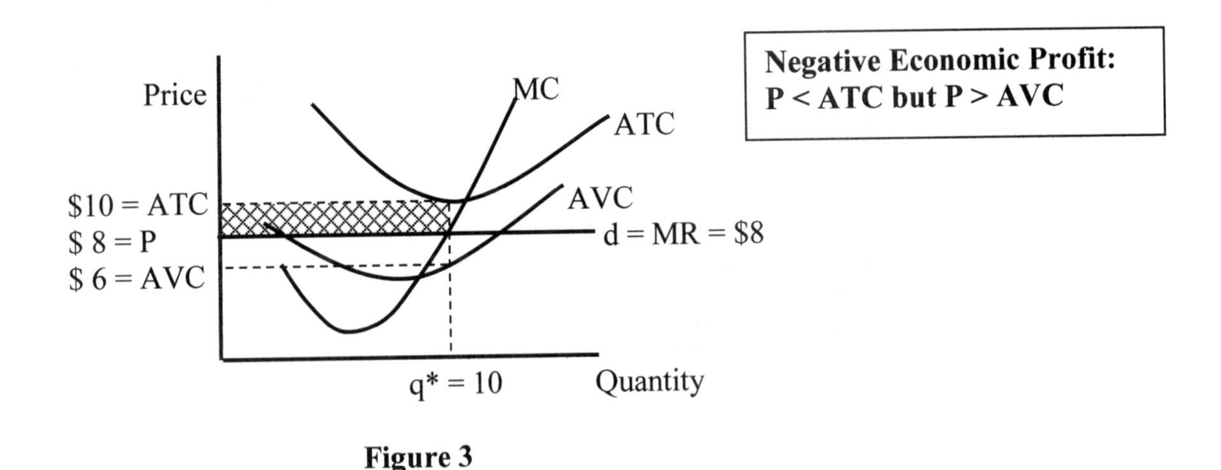

Figure 3

To minimize losses by operating in the short run, a firm must cover **all** variable costs, so price must be above minimum average variable cost. As long as AVC < P < ATC, the firm is losing money, but would lose **more** if it did not produce and sell output because the firm would still have to pay **fixed costs** in the short run even if it did shut down.

The Shut Down Decision

The values assigned to average total cost, market price, average variable cost, and output in **Figure 3** help prove why the firm's best profit-maximizing/loss-minimizing strategy is to produce at MR = MC so long as price exceeds average variable cost. This firm can sell each of the 10 units of output for the market price of $8 to earn total revenue of $80.

$$TR = P \times Q = \$8 \times 10 = \$80$$

The cost of producing each unit of output when 10 units are produced is given by average total cost which is $10 in **Figure 3**. The total cost of producing 10 units of output is therefore $100.

$$TC = ATC \times Q = \$10 \times 10 = \$100$$

The firm earns total revenue equal to $80 and total costs equal to $100, incurring an economic loss equal to $80 - $100 = $20, or economic profit equal to –$20.

$$\pi = TR - TC = \$80 - \$100 = -\$20$$

If the firm shuts down and produces zero output, it must still pay its fixed costs, so the firm's economic loss will be equal to total fixed cost if it shuts down in the short run. According to **Figure 3**, when output is 10 units, average total cost is $10 and average variable cost is $6, so average fixed cost is $4.

$$ATC - AVC = AFC$$
$$\$10 - \$6 = \$4$$

Since total fixed cost is equal to average fixed cost multiplied by quantity, the firms total fixed costs equal $40.

$$(AFC)(Q) = TFC$$
$$(\$4)(10) = \$40$$

In this case shutting down in the short run results in a loss of $40, which is greater than the loss of $20 if the firm produces at MR = MC. Clearly, in the short run, the best strategy for this firm is to produce at MR = MC in order to minimize its loss.

If price falls below average variable cost, total revenue cannot cover all variable costs. A firm will shut down production to minimize losses if price falls below average variable cost because the loss will be greater than total fixed cost if it produces in the short run. Therefore, the minimum point of the average variable cost curve is the short-run **shutdown point**.

To summarize:

- If $P > ATC$, economic profit > 0 so firm should produce where MR = MC
- If $P = ATC$, economic profit $= 0$ so firm should produce where MR = MC
- If $AVC < P < ATC$, economic profit < 0 but firm should produce where MR = MC in the short run since losses are smaller than total fixed costs
- If $P < AVC$, economic profit < 0 and firm should shut down in the short run and pay total fixed costs (losses = TFC)

The graph below summarizes the short-run profit possibilities for a firm operating in a perfectly competitive market.

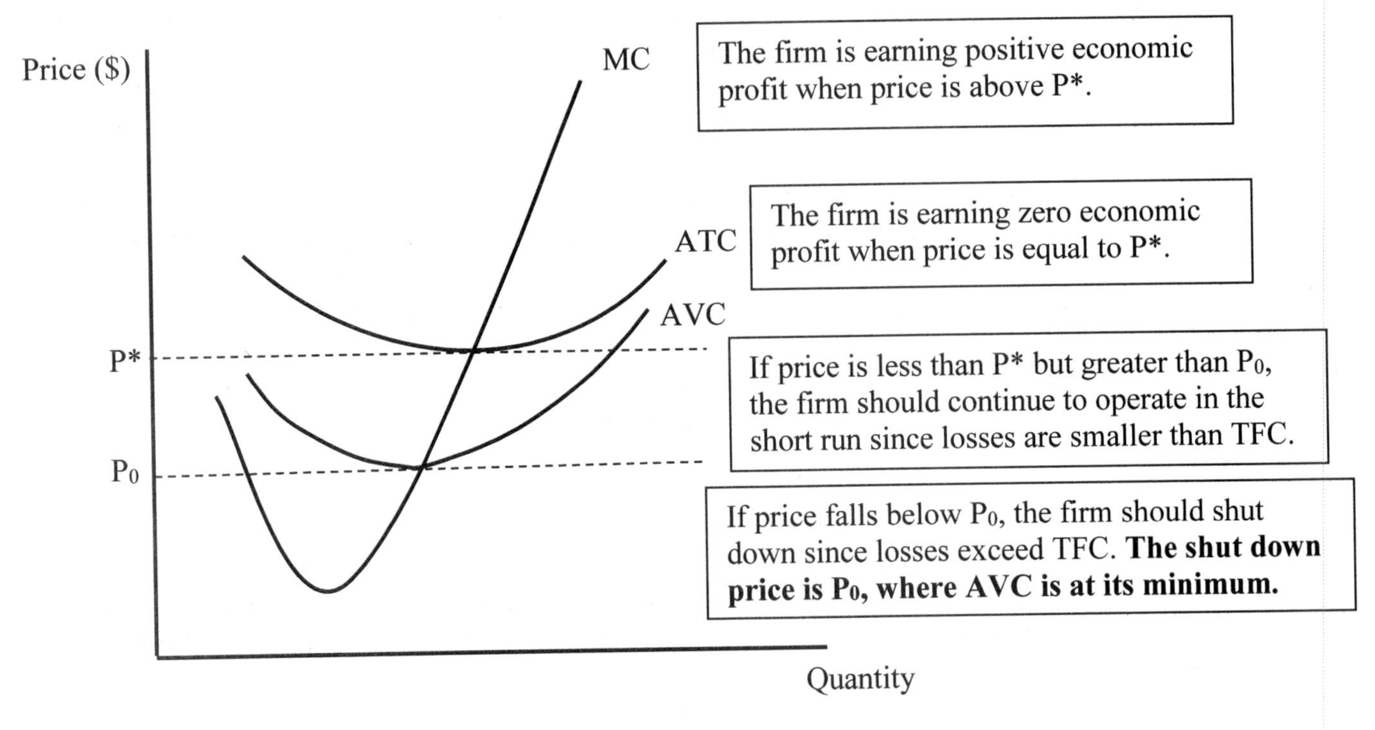

For the perfectly competitive firm, the portion of the marginal cost curve that lies **above** the average variable cost curve (the shutdown price) serves as the firm's **short-run supply curve** because the firm maximizes profit, or minimizes losses, by producing at the output where MR = MC, or P = MC, as long as price is greater than average variable cost (P > AVC). The bold portion of the MC curve in the graph below represents the firm's supply curve.

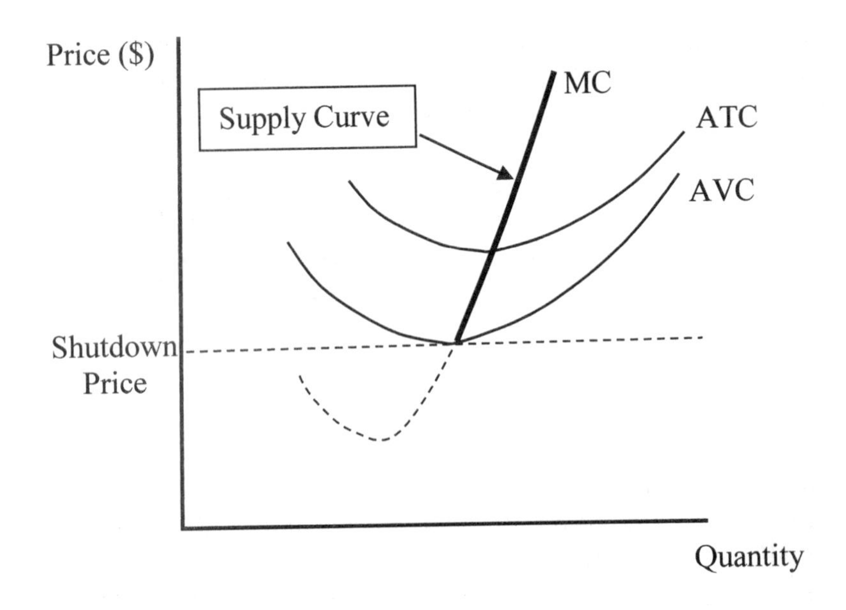

Long Run Equilibrium

In the long run, firms can change all inputs, and all costs are variable. If economies of scale are possible, small firms will increase their scale to lower unit costs. Therefore, one of the conditions for long-run equilibrium is that the firms in the market be at least at the **minimum efficient scale**, or the smallest scale necessary to achieve all economies of scale. There may be firms of different sizes in long-run equilibrium if there is a range of output corresponding to constant returns to scale, but long-run average cost will be the same for each firm in long-run competitive equilibrium.

A short-run economic profit or loss in a competitive industry will lead to long-run industry changes. Remember that the model of perfect competition assumes that firms have **perfect information** and are **free to enter** an industry in the long run. Positive economic profit will attract new firms to the industry, causing the market supply curve to shift to the right.

As shown in chapter 4, when new firms enter a market and market supply shifts to the right, the market equilibrium price falls. A lower market price causes each firm's profit to fall. Industry expansion stops when economic profit is equal to zero for the typical perfectly competitive firm in the market. **Thus, the typical firm in perfect competition earns zero economic profit (normal profit) in long run equilibrium because new firms will enter the market to compete for above normal profit, driving economic profit to zero.**

Negative economic profit (economic loss) will cause some firms to leave the industry in the long run. In the long run, there are no fixed costs, so some firms will exit the market in response to negative profit. As some firms exit, market supply shifts to the left and the equilibrium market price increases. A higher price reduces the losses incurred by the remaining firms. This process continues until the market price is high enough to eliminate all losses, or generate economic profit equal to zero. **Again, the typical firm in perfect competition earns zero economic profit (normal profit) in long run equilibrium because some firms will exit the market in response to below normal profit, driving economic profit to zero.**

The condition for a firm in **long-run equilibrium** in a perfectly competitive industry can be summarized as: **P = MR = MC = ATC = minimum LRAC,** where LRAC is the long-run average cost curve. Long run equilibrium for a perfectly competitive firm is portrayed in the graph below.

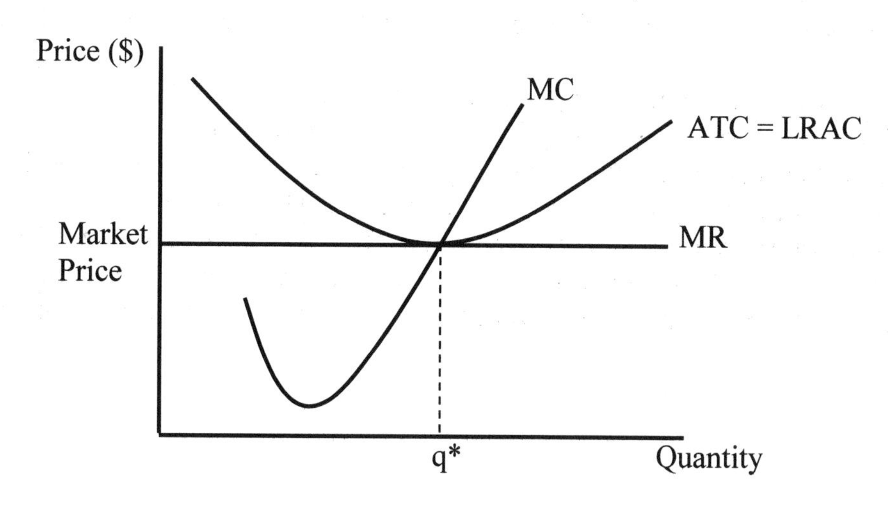

The graphs below represent the relationship between a perfectly competitive market, where quantity produced is measured in millions, and a single firm within the market. If market demand is given by D_1, the equilibrium price is $3 in this market.

Faced with a price of $3, marginal revenue for the individual firm is also $3, so the firm will maximize profit by producing an output level of 50 in the graph on the right. However, if market demand increases or shifts to the right (chapter 4 offered many different possible reasons, including increased consumer income if the product is a normal good, an increase in the number of consumers, a positive change in taste and preferences, an increase in the price of a substitute, or a decrease in the price of a complement), market price rises to $5 and the firm maximizes profit by producing 65 units.

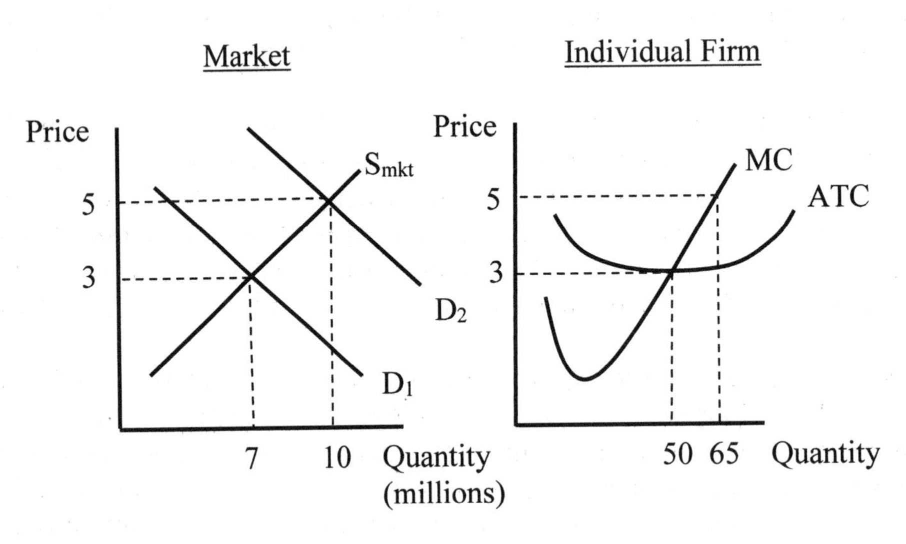

If market price is currently $5, the individual firm is earning positive economic profit since price exceeds ATC. This means that new firms will be attracted to this market. As new firms enter the market in the long run, market supply (S_{mkt}) shifts to the right, resulting in a lower equilibrium price.

Because the minimum point of the ATC curve corresponds to $3 in the individual firm's graph, long run equilibrium price in this market is $3. The position of the market demand function depends on many different variables, but market supply is predicted to react by shifting to the right whenever price is above $3 and shifting to the left whenever price is below $3.

The explanation for long run equilibrium in a perfectly competitive industry leads to the conclusion that consumers are ultimately in charge of the position of the market demand curve and that firms follow market signals to produce as much output as consumers desire, given the constraint that a price of $3 is needed to cover input costs. This result is sometimes called **consumer sovereignty**, since consumer demand dictates output and employment levels in perfectly competitive markets. Adam Smith's invisible hand directs resources by signaling firms to enter a market with positive economic profit and exit a market with negative economic profit in the long run.

Perfect Competition and Efficiency

Economists use this model to make a strong case for a free market system. Adam Smith, who published *The Wealth of Nations* in 1776, believed that market forces work like an invisible hand to guide resources to their best uses and give consumers the goods and services they want and need at the lowest possible price. Adam Smith wanted to eliminate unnecessary government intervention and rely on free markets.

Learning about cost curves and marginal revenue curves may seem to be a cumbersome way to understand business principles, but this theory is crucial to those who strive to understand economic policy issues. This background helps you understand market failures and evaluate public policy proposals. Economists generally agree that when markets are working right, the outcome is efficient so no government intervention can be justified as a means of improving efficiency. However, efficiency is not society's only goal and government intervention may be justified as a means of promoting a more equitable outcome. When markets are not working the way they should due to some market failure, it is possible for government intervention to promote both efficiency and equity, if government policy is properly designed. The role of economic theory is to help us know when government intervention is called for and to help us design optimal policies when the market outcome is inefficient or inconsistent with society's other goals.

Under assumptions of perfect competition, market forces drive economic profit to zero in the long run and price is equal to marginal cost. Resources are allocated efficiently as long as MB = MC. Price is a good measure of the consumer's marginal benefit, therefore P = MB. For a perfectly competitive firm, marginal revenue is equal to price, P = MR. This means P = MB = MR = MC. Output increases as long as the marginal benefit to consumers of having one more unit of output exceeds the marginal cost to producers of providing one more unit of output, and the optimal output is where marginal benefit and marginal cost are equal. Producing to the point where marginal benefit equals marginal cost results in maximization of net benefits from society's perspective. This condition is met with perfect competition because P = MC, P = MR, and P = MB.

Price is also equal to minimum average cost in the long run in perfect competition. Satisfaction of the condition P = ATC also indicates that consumers are able to purchase the product at the lowest possible price. Note that since the demand curve for the individual firm is horizontal (perfectly elastic), the condition P = ATC is necessarily satisfied at the minimum point of the ATC curve (recall that MC intersects the ATC curve at its minimum point); firms are producing the product at the lowest possible per unit cost, and that is the price consumers pay in the long run.

Another way to measure efficiency is to determine if the level of production results in a deadweight loss to society. Deadweight loss is the reduction in total consumer and producer surplus that occurs when output is less than the output where the marginal benefit to society is equal to the marginal cost to society. When prices are flexible and producers are able to respond to consumer demand, a perfectly competitive market moves toward equilibrium. At competitive market equilibrium, MB = MC, total producer plus consumer surplus is maximized, and there is no deadweight loss to society.

The graphs below illustrate efficiency when a firm and a perfectly competitive market are in long-run equilibrium. The market is in equilibrium when quantity demanded is equal to quantity supplied at the market price, which is at the intersection of the supply and demand curves. The following list summarizes the efficiency criteria:

1) MB = MC and P = MC,
2) P = minimum ATC,
3) No deadweight loss and total producer and consumer surplus is maximized.

Demand represents marginal benefit to society and supply represents marginal cost to society, so at equilibrium MB = MC. At market equilibrium, price is equal to P*; P* is equal to MB, and P* is equal to MC, so P = MC. Individual firms in perfect competition are price-takers which means the firm sells output at P*. The condition of MB = MC and P = MC is met.

The firm maximizes profit by producing where MR = MC; for a perfectly competitive firm, P = MR = MC. There are no barriers to entry so profit is driven to zero and, in the long run, the firm produces at minimum average total cost (ATC). Marginal cost intersects average total cost at minimum average total cost; therefore, it is also true for the firm that P = minimum ATC.

Market output is equal to Q*, which is the level of output that corresponds to MB = MC. At Q*, consumer surplus is equal to the area of triangle P*P'A and producer surplus is equal to the area of triangle 0P*A. Total consumer and producer surplus is equal to the area of triangle 0P'A. At any output below Q*, MB > MC and total consumer and producer surplus will be less than the area 0P'A. 0P'A is the greatest amount that total consumer and producer surplus can be, and there is no deadweight loss to society at output Q*. An output greater than Q* will not be produced because MB < MC. The condition of no deadweight loss to society and maximum total consumer and producer surplus is also met.

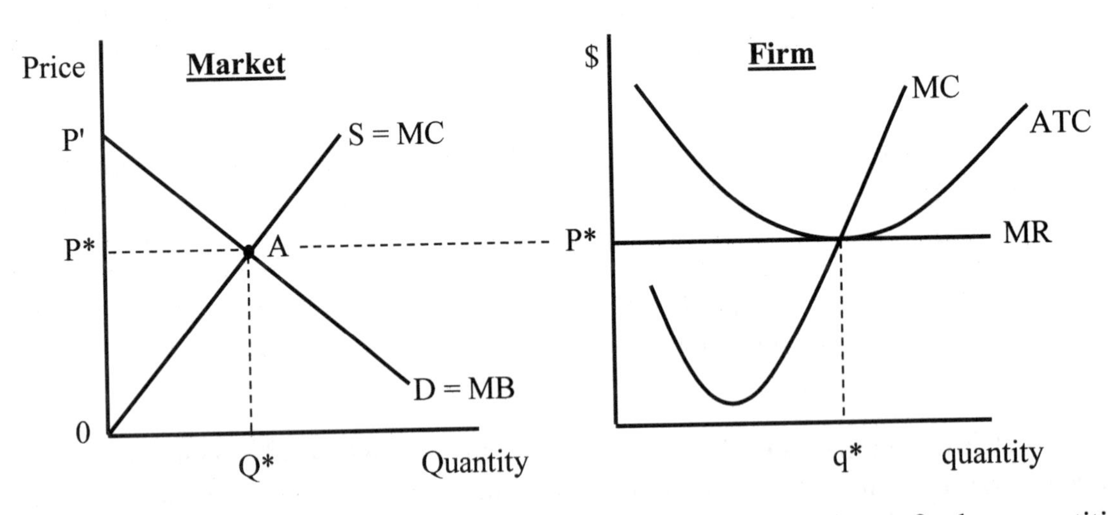

From every perspective, the long-run equilibrium attained under perfectly competitive conditions is efficient. This model is used as a basis for assessing the efficiency of real-world markets. There are not many markets that fit the ideal of perfect competition; local agricultural markets and the daily unannounced trading in the stock market come closest to having the characteristics of perfect competition. The next three chapters look at other market structures and then compare the long run outcome in those market structures to that of perfect competition.

NAME____SECTION#______________
PRINT LAST NAME, FIRST NAME

PERFECT COMPETITION

1. Which of the following real-world markets most closely matches the assumptions of a perfectly competitive market?
   a. Automobiles
   b. Soda
   c. Tomatoes
   d. Cell phones

2. All of the following are assumptions of the model of perfect competition ***except***:
   a. consumers have perfect information regarding product price, quality, and availability.
   b. the output of one firm in the market is a perfect substitute for the output of every other firm in the market.
   c. the market consists of a large number of firms, and each firm is small relative to the entire market.
   d. entry into the market in the long run is restricted by barriers.

3. In a perfectly competitive market:
   a. each firm produces a unique product and chooses a price that maximizes profit.
   b. there are very few firms, and each controls a large segment of the market.
   c. entry into the industry is restricted in the long run.
   d. there are many relatively small firms, and each firm is a price-taker.

4. If a firm is a price-taker, it:
   a. sells its product at the price determined by the market.
   b. sells its product at the price set by the government.
   c. sells its product at the price dictated by the largest firm in the industry.
   d. can sell all it can produce at whatever price it chooses.

5. The marginal revenue curve for a perfectly competitive firm:
   a. lies above the firm's demand curve.
   b. lies below the firm's demand curve.
   c. is the same as the firm's demand curve.
   d. is the same as the market demand curve.

6. The fact that all firms in a perfectly competitive industry are small relative to the industry and produce goods that are perfect substitutes leads to:
   a. each firm in the industry having identical cost structures in the short run.
   b. each firm in the industry facing a perfectly elastic demand curve.
   c. all firms earning only normal profits in the short run.
   d. substantial market power for each firm.

NAME____SECTION#________________
PRINT LAST NAME, FIRST NAME

7. In a perfectly competitive market, the demand curve is ______ for the individual firm, while the demand curve is ________ for the market.
   a. horizontal; downward-sloping
   b. vertical; horizontal
   c. downward-sloping; downward-sloping
   d. horizontal; horizontal

8. A firm that chooses ***not*** to produce in the short run suffers a loss equal to:
   a. marginal cost.
   b. total fixed cost.
   c. total variable cost.
   d. zero.

Use the graph of a perfectly competitive market below to answer questions 9 and 10.

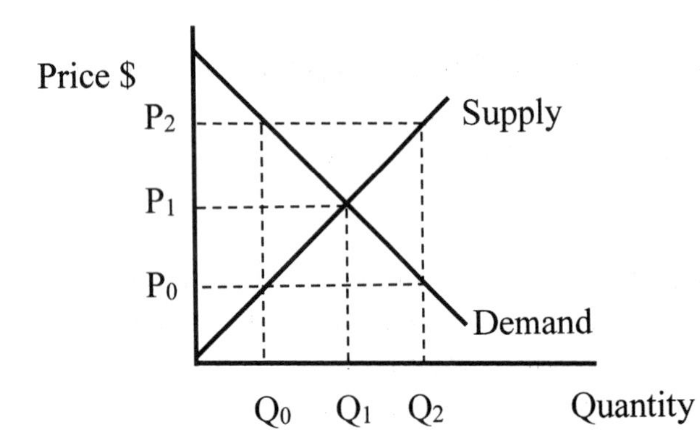

9. The market price for this output will be _______, and the individual firm in this market will sell its output at a price of ______.
   a. P_0; P_1
   b. P_1; P_1
   c. P_1; P_2
   d. P_2; P_2

10. Ceteris paribus, if the market demand for this product increases, the market price:
   a. will not change because it is perfectly competitive.
   b. will increase.
   c. will decrease.
   d. may increase, decrease, or stay the same.

NAME____SECTION#______________
PRINT LAST NAME, FIRST NAME

PERFECT COMPETITION

List the assumptions of the perfectly competitive model.

1) ____

2) ____

3) ____

4) ____

5) Draw and label the perfectly competitive firm's demand and MR function in the graph below assuming the market price is $14.

6) Identify the firm's profit-maximizing or loss-minimizing level of output, Q = ________ Assume the firm produces at this level of output.

7) Calculate the firm's total revenue, TR = $__________

8) Calculate the firm's total cost, TC = $__________

9) Calculate the firm's economic profit = $__________

10) Are firms likely to enter or exit this market in the long run? __________ (yes or no)

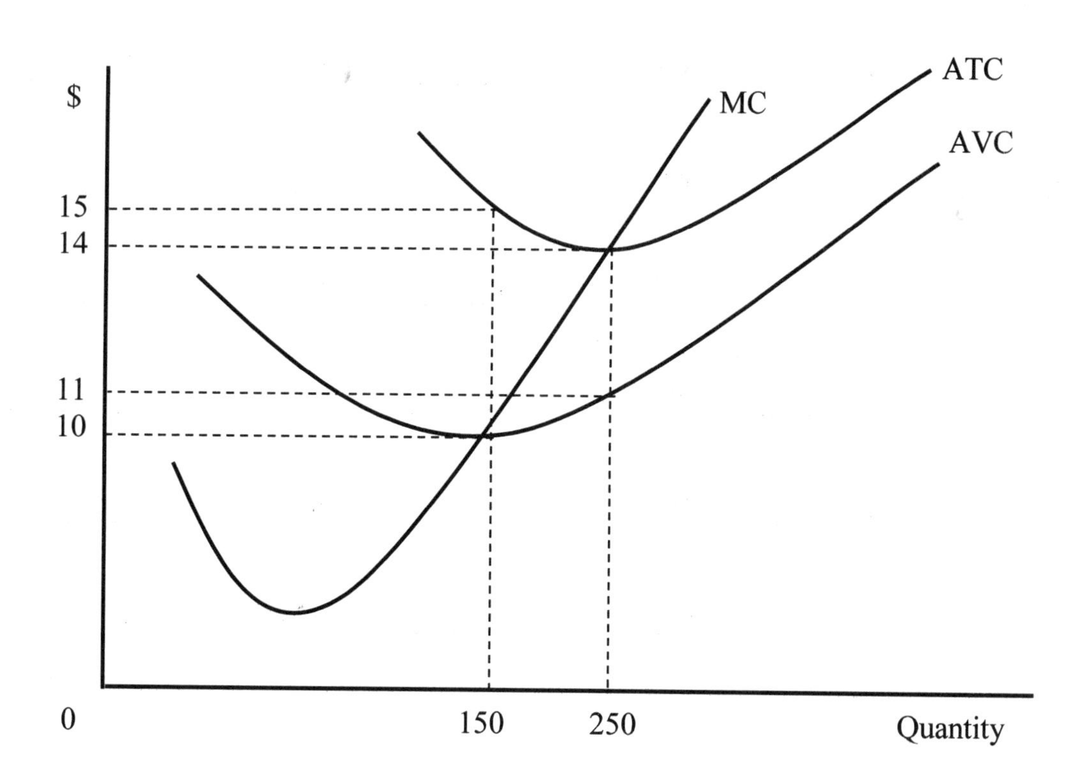

NAME______________________________ SECTION#__________

PRINT LAST NAME, FIRST NAME

PROFIT-MAXIMIZING OUTPUT

The firm represented by the data below sells a product in a perfectly competitive market at a **price of $15**; use this value to fill in the total revenue (TR) and marginal revenue (MR) columns. Use the information provided to fill in missing values for total cost (TC), average total cost (ATC), and marginal cost (MC). Finally, calculate Profit using values for total revenue and total cost. Verify that maximum profit corresponds to the output level where MR = MC.

Q	TR	MR	TC	ATC	MC	Profit
0	$______		$10			$______
1	$______	$______	$15	$______	$______	$______
2	$______	$______	$______	$9	$______	$______
3	$______	$______	$24	$______	$______	$______
4	$______	$______	$______	$______	$8	$______
5	$______	$______	$45	$______	$______	$______
6	$______	$______	$60	$______	$______	$______
7	$______	$______	$77	$______	$______	$______
8	$______	$______	$96	$______	$______	$______
9	$______	$______	$117	$______	$______	$______
10	$______	$______	$______	$______	$23	$______

NAME____SECTION#______________

PRINT LAST NAME, FIRST NAME

PERFECT COMPETITION

1. A firm earns zero economic profit when:
   a. price is equal to average variable cost.
   b. price is equal to average total cost.
   c. price exceeds average total cost by the greatest amount.
   d. marginal revenue is equal to marginal cost.

B

2. A perfectly competitive firm producing where P = MR = MC > ATC in the short run is:
   a. incurring a short-run loss, and would minimize its loss by shutting down.
   b. making an economic profit greater than zero.
   c. making an economic profit equal to zero.
   d. incurring a short-run loss, but minimizes its loss by producing at MR = MC.

B

3. The profit-maximizing rule is for firms to produce the amount of output at which:
   a. ATC = AVC.
   b. MR = MC.
   c. P = ATC.
   d. MR = P.

B

4. The **shutdown** price corresponds to the minimum point of the:
   a. AVC curve because Losses > TFC when P < AVC.
   b. AVC curve because Profit > 0 when P > ATC.
   c. ATC curve because Losses > TFC when P < AVC.
   d. ATC curve because Profit < 0 when P < ATC.

D

5. Suppose at the profit-maximizing/loss-minimizing level of output P = $6, ATC = $7, and AVC = $5. A firm in this situation will:
   a. minimize its losses by continuing to produce where MR = MC in the short run.
   b. minimize its losses by shutting down immediately.
   c. earn a short-run economic profit producing where MR = MC.
   d. produce more than the output where MR = MC.

A

6. The short-run supply curve for the perfectly competitive firm is the portion of the marginal cost curve that lies above the average variable cost curve because:
   a. the firm will maximize profits and minimize losses by producing the quantity where marginal revenue equals marginal cost if price is greater than average variable cost.
   b. the firm is a price-taker and is required to produce and sell output even if it incurs a short-run loss when price falls below minimum average variable cost.
   c. the market supply curve is upward-sloping.
   d. profit is maximized at the level of output where average total cost exceeds average variable cost by the greatest amount.

A

NAME____SECTION#_______________

PRINT LAST NAME, FIRST NAME

7. Bob's Billboard Painting is considering increasing the number of billboards Bob's firm paints per week by one billboard, and the firm is paid $500 for painting a billboard. Bob's total cost will increase as a result from $1,200 to $1,750 per week. In this case:
   a. MR > MC, so the firm's profits will increase as a result of painting one more billboard per week.
   b. MR < MC, so the firm's profits will decrease as a result of painting one more billboard per week.
   c. MR > MC, but painting one more billboard per week will not affect the firm's profits.
   d. MR < MC, but painting one more billboard per week will not affect the firm's profits.

Use the graph below to answer questions 8 through 10.

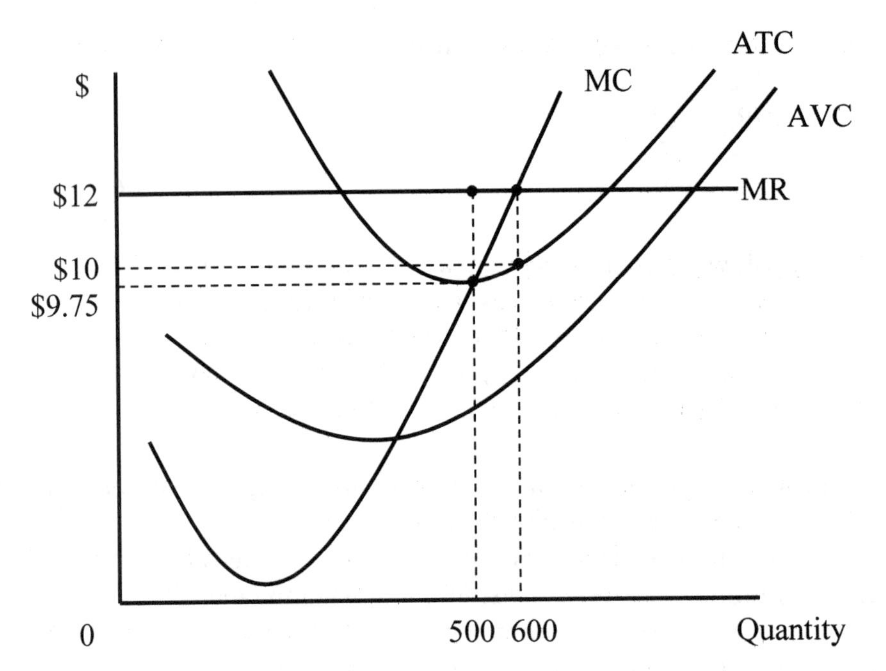

8. This profit-maximizing firm will charge a price of $____ and produce ____ units of output.
   a. 12; 500   b. 12; 600   c. 10; 500   d. 10; 600

9. At the profit-maximizing level of output, total revenue is equal to _____ and total cost is equal to _____.
   a. $6,000; $4,875   c. $7,200; $5,000
   b. $6,000; $5,000   d. $7,200; $6,000

10. This firm is earning economic profit equal to:
   a. $1,200.   b. $1,125.   c. $1,000.   d. $800.

NAME________________________________SECTION#______________
PRINT LAST NAME, FIRST NAME

PERFECT COMPETITION

Use the graph for a perfectly competitive firm to answer questions 1 through 10.

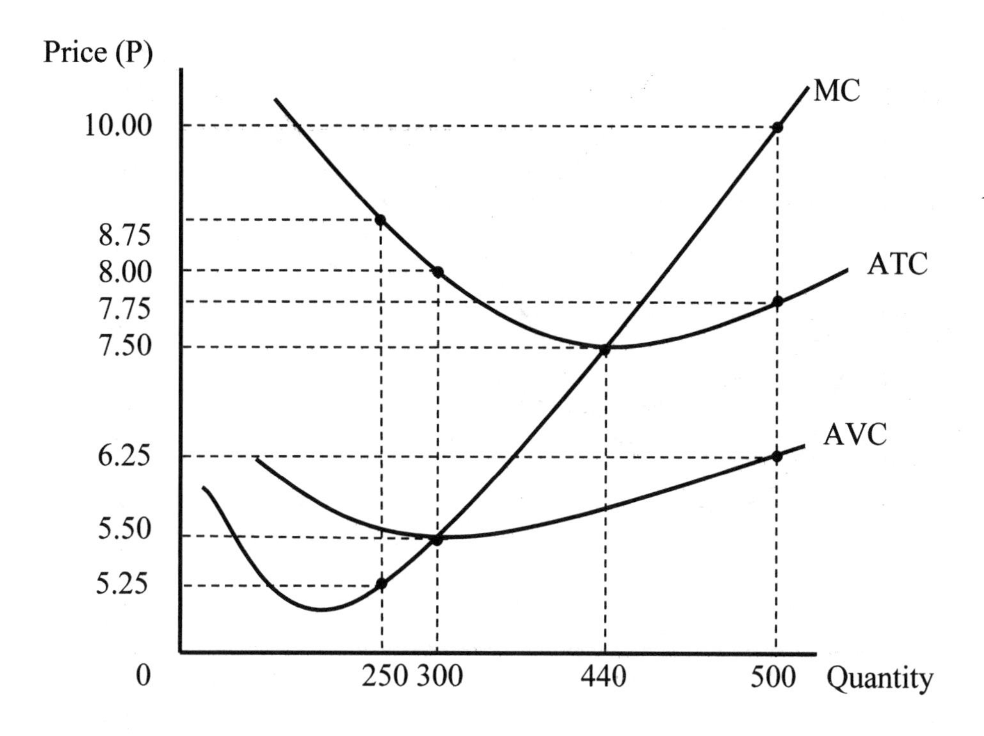

If **price = $10**, the profit-maximizing/loss-minimizing level of output is 1) ___________;

total revenue is equal to 2) $_____________, total cost is equal to 3) $_____________,

and the firm earns economic profit equal to 4) $_____________.

If **price = $7.50**, the profit-maximizing/loss-minimizing level of output is 5) ___________;

total revenue is equal to 6) $_____________, total cost is equal to 7) $_____________,

and the firm earns economic profit equal to 8) $_____________.

If **price = $5.50**, the firm can either shut down immediately and pay fixed costs equal to

9) $_____________ or the firm can produce at output level 300 and incur economic losses

equal to 10) $_____________.

NAME____SECTION#______________

PRINT LAST NAME, FIRST NAME

PERFECT COMPETITION

Use the graph for a perfectly competitive firm to answer questions 1 through 10.

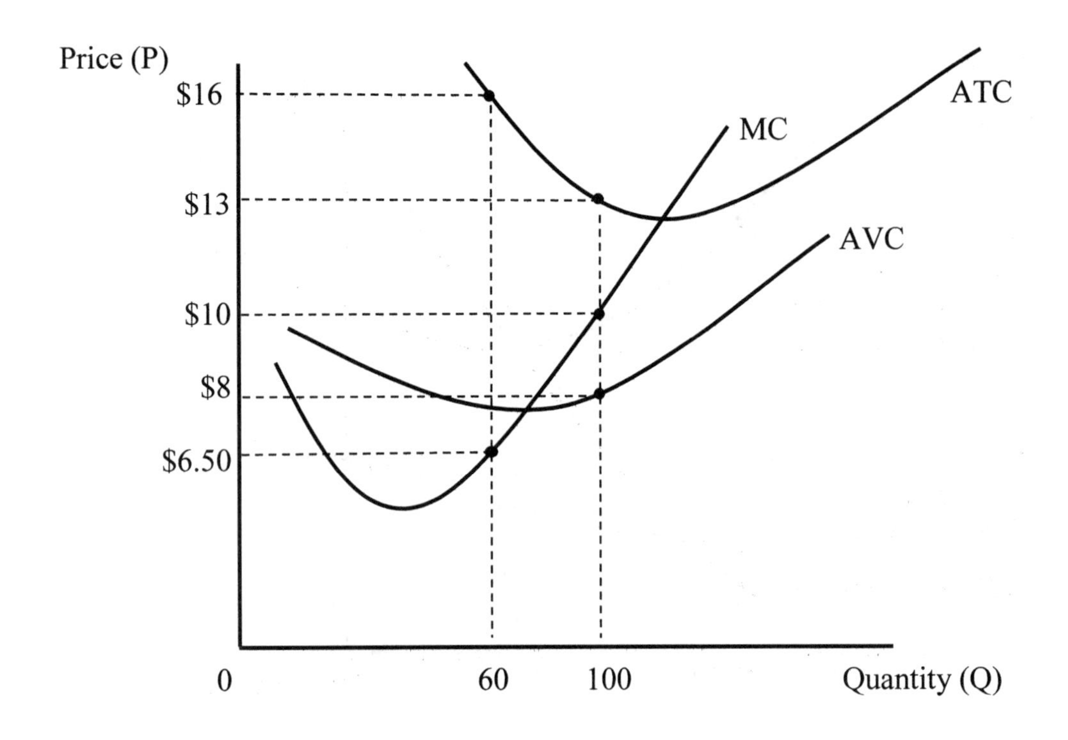

If **price = $10**, the profit-maximizing/loss-minimizing level of output (Q) is 1) ____________;

total revenue is equal to 2) $______________, total cost is equal to 3) $______________,

and the firm has a loss equal to 4) $______________. If this firm does not produce in the short run, it will have a loss equal to 5) $______________.

If **price = $6.50** and the firm produces 60 units of output, total revenue will be equal to

6) $______________, total cost will be equal to 7) $______________, and the firm will

experience a loss equal to 8) $______________. If this firm does not produce in the short run, it will experience a loss equal to 9) $______________ because it must pay its

10) ________________ costs.
fixed/variable

NAME______________________________________ SECTION#______________

PRINT LAST NAME, FIRST NAME

PERFECT COMPETITION

Use the graph below depicting a profit-maximizing, perfectly competitive firm to answer questions 1 through 5.

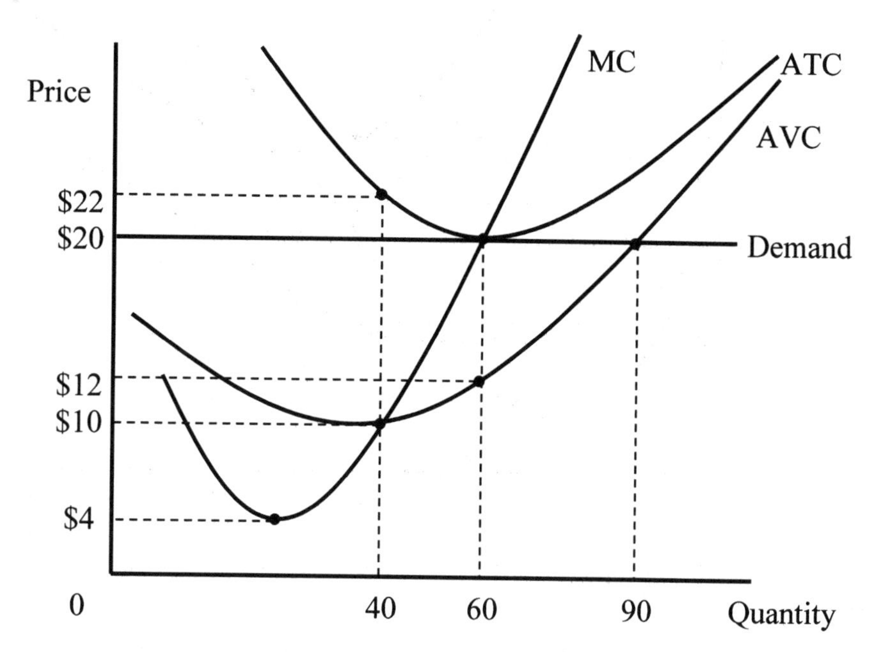

1. Marginal revenue is equal to _____.
   a. $10   b. $12   c. $20   d. $22

2. At the profit-maximizing level of output, total cost (TC) is equal to ______ and total revenue (TR) is equal to ______.
   a. $1200; $720   b. $400; $400   c. $880; $800   d. $1200; $1200

3. Total fixed cost (TFC) is equal to _____.
   a. $400   b. $480   c. $720   d. $1200

4. This firm is experiencing an:
   a. economic loss of $80, and should shut down production to minimize losses.
   b. economic loss of $120, but should continue to produce to minimize losses.
   c. economic profit of $0 (normal profit).
   d. economic profit of $80.

5. This firm minimizes losses by not producing (shutting down) if price falls below:
   a. $4.   b. $10.   c. $12.   d. $20.

NAME____ SECTION#______________

PRINT LAST NAME, FIRST NAME

Use the graph below of a profit-maximizing/loss-minimizing perfectly competitive firm to answer questions 6 through 10.

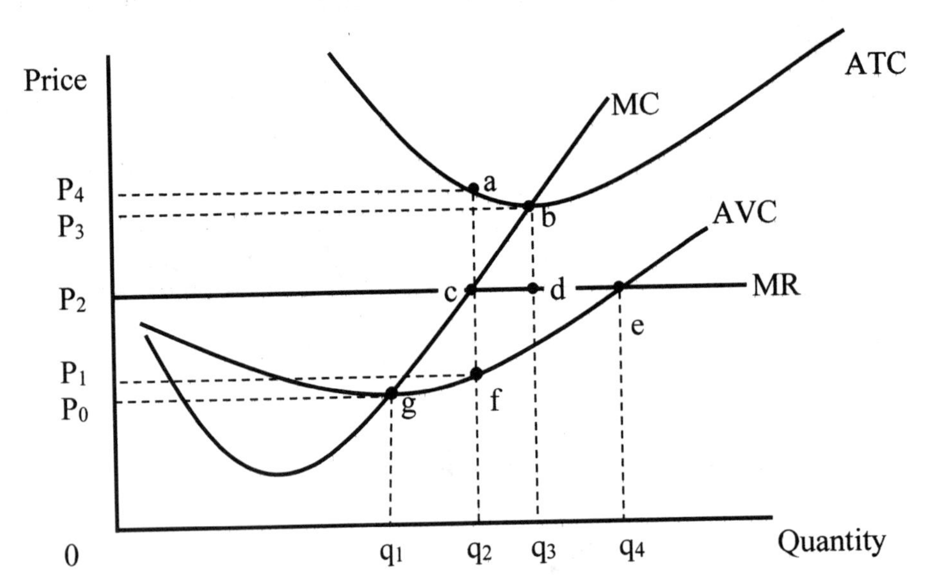

6. At the market-determined price of P_2, the profit-maximizing/loss-minimizing level of output is:
   a. q_1. b. q_2. c. q_3. d. q_4.

7. Total fixed cost (TFC) is given by the area:
   a. $0P_1fq_2$.
   b. P_2P_4ac.
   c. $0P_4aq_2$.
   d. P_1P_4af.

8. Total cost (TC) at the profit-maximizing/loss-minimizing level of output is given by the area:
   a. $0P_1fq_2$.
   b. P_2P_4ac.
   c. $0P_4aq_2$.
   d. P_1P_4af.

9. This firm is experiencing a short run:
   a. profit equal to the area P_2P_3bd.
   b. loss equal to the area P_2P_3bd.
   c. profit equal to the area P_2P_4ac.
   d. loss equal to the area P_2P_4ac.

10. This firm minimizes losses by shutting down if price falls below ________.
    a. P_0
    b. P_1
    c. P_2
    d. P_3

NAME____SECTION#________________
PRINT LAST NAME, FIRST NAME

LONG-RUN EQUILIBRIUM

1. The typical firm in a perfectly competitive industry earns only zero economic profit in the long run because:
   a. it is illegal for firms in the United States to continue to earn excess, or positive economic, profits.
   b. there are no barriers preventing new firms from entering the industry and competing away positive profits in the long run.
   c. firms in competitive industries tend to focus on revenue rather than profits.
   d. U.S. law is designed so that taxes on earnings will eliminate profits.

2. A firm is in long-run equilibrium in a perfectly competitive market when:
   a. $P > MR = MC = ATC$.
   b. $P = MR > MC = ATC$.
   c. $P = MR = MC > ATC$.
   d. $P = MR = MC = ATC$.

3. If, in the short run, perfectly competitive firms are earning positive economic profits, the adjustment to long-run equilibrium will include firms ________ the industry, causing market supply to ________ and market price to ________.
   a. exiting; increase; decrease
   b. exiting; decrease; increase
   c. entering; increase; decrease
   d. entering; decrease; increase

4. Assume soybeans are produced in a perfectly competitive market, and the demand for soybeans increases. This leads to a(n) ______ in the price of soybeans and a(n) _______ in the firm's profit-maximizing level of output.
   a. decrease; increase
   b. increase; decrease
   c. decrease; decrease
   d. increase; increase

5. A decrease in **market** demand for output produced in a perfectly competitive industry:
   a. leads to an increase in the individual firm's marginal revenue.
   b. has no effect on the demand for the individual firm in the industry.
   c. leads to a decrease in the individual firm's marginal revenue.
   d. has no effect on the price charged by the individual firm in the industry.

6. Industry output is efficient when:
   a. $MB = MC$ for each firm.
   b. deadweight loss is maximized.
   c. consumer and producer surplus equal zero.
   d. All of the above statements about efficiency are true.

NAME____SECTION#______________
PRINT LAST NAME, FIRST NAME

Use the graphs below to answer questions 7 through 10.

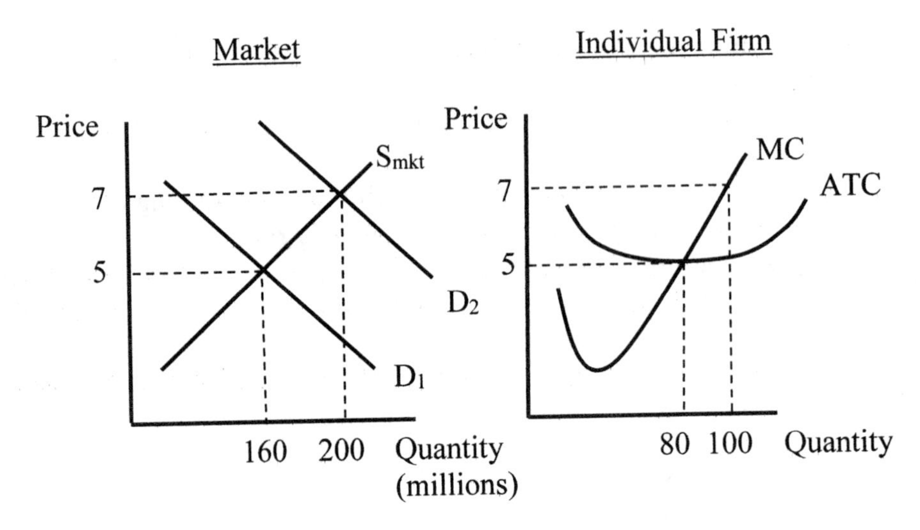

7. If the current market price is $7:
   a. this market is in long-run equilibrium as long as the individual firm is producing and selling 100 units of output.
   b. economic profit is positive, so more firms will enter this industry in the long run, causing market supply to increase.
   c. economic profit is negative, so firms will exit this industry in the long run, causing market supply to decrease.
   d. there is not enough information provided in the graphs to reach any conclusions.

8. If the current market price is $5:
   a. this market is in long-run equilibrium as long as the individual firm is producing and selling 80 units of output.
   b. economic profit is positive, so more firms will enter this industry in the long run, causing market supply to increase.
   c. economic profit is negative, so firms will exit this industry in the long run, causing market supply to decrease.
   d. there is not enough information provided in the graphs to reach any conclusions.

9. An increase in market demand from D_1 to D_2 causes:
   a. MR and MC to increase from $5 to $7 for the profit-maximizing firm.
   b. MR to decrease from $7 to $5, but no shift in MC.
   c. MC to increase to $7, but no shift in MR.
   d. no change in either MR or MC for the profit-maximizing firm.

10. An increase in market demand from D_1 to D_2 causes:
   a. market price to increase from $5 to $7.
   b. market output to increase from 160 million to 200 million.
   c. the individual firm to increase production from 80 to 100 units.
   d. All of the above changes are likely to occur.

PRACTICE EXAM II

The correct answers to this practice exam can be found on page 230.

1. Brett has agreed to sell a rare comic book to a collector who offered to pay $125. Brett's producer surplus is:
   a. zero since he did not negotiate a price higher than what the collector offered.
   b. $125 because it will not cost him anything to sell his comic book.
   c. $25 if the minimum price he would have accepted is actually $150.
   d. $50 if the minimum price he would have accepted is actually $75.

2. Government policies that interfere with the market mechanism and cause price to be different from equilibrium are:
   a. efficient because they reduce total surplus.
   b. inefficient because they reduce total surplus.
   c. efficient because they increase total surplus.
   d. inefficient because they increase total surplus.

3. The difference between the maximum price consumers are willing to pay and the actual price consumers pay in the market measures:
   a. deadweight loss.
   b. equilibrium price.
   c. consumer surplus.
   d. producer surplus.

4. A demand curve can best be interpreted as a:
   a. marginal cost curve.
   b. marginal benefit curve.
   c. horizontal line corresponding to market price.
   d. vertical line corresponding to market quantity.

5. If haircuts are normal goods, then a decrease in consumer income leads to a(n) ________ in the equilibrium price of haircuts, and producer surplus to barbers will ________.
   a. increase; increase
   b. increase; decrease
   c. decrease; increase
   d. decrease; decrease

6. The law of diminishing marginal returns suggests that marginal cost:
   a. increases as output increases.
   b. decreases as output increases.
   c. remains constant as output increases.
   d. behaves in an unpredictable way as output is changed.

Use the graph below to answer the next four questions.

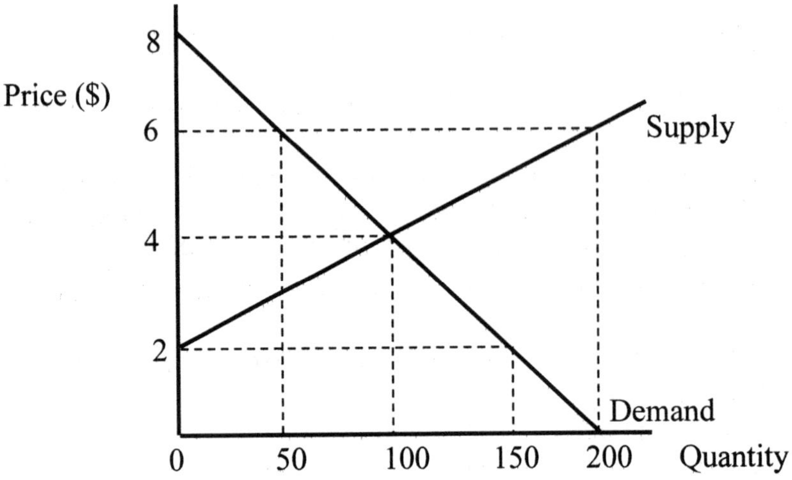

Price ($)
8
6
4
2
0 50 100 150 200 Quantity
Supply
Demand

7. The marginal benefit of the 50th unit is:
   a. $2. b. $4. c. $6. d. $8.

8. Under free market conditions, equilibrium price is ___ and equilibrium quantity is ___.
   a. $2; 150 b. $4; 100 c. $6; 50 d. $6; 200

9. Under free market conditions, consumer surplus is equal to _______.
   a. $100 b. $200 c. $300 d. $400

10. Under free market conditions, producer surplus is equal to _______.
   a. $100 b. $200 c. $300 d. $400

Use the graph below to answer the next question.

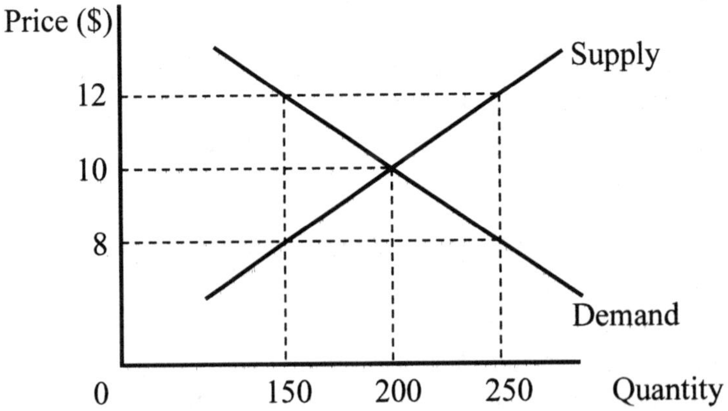

Price ($)
12
10
8
0 150 200 250 Quantity
Supply
Demand

11. An effective (binding) price ceiling of $8 would cause a ____ in the amount of ___ units.
   a. shortage; 50 c. surplus; 50
   b. shortage; 100 d. surplus; 100

12. The purpose of setting a price floor above the equilibrium price is to:
    a. protect consumers from price gouging.
    b. cause market surpluses.
    c. maintain a high price for the sellers in the market.
    d. prevent market shortages.

13. If a product with a relatively elastic demand and a relatively inelastic supply is taxed, the economic burden of the tax is borne:
    a. entirely by the sellers of the product.
    b. entirely by the consumers of the product.
    c. mostly by the sellers of the product.
    d. mostly by the consumers of the product.

Use the graph below to answer the next three questions.

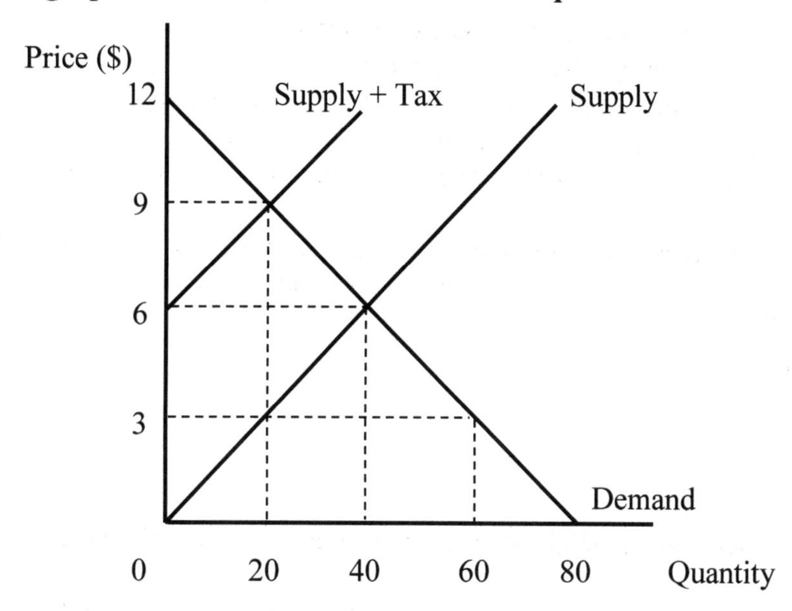

14. In free market equilibrium, consumer surplus is equal to _______.

a.	$60	c.	$240
b.	$120	d.	$480

15. If government imposes a $6 per unit tax in this market, total tax revenues collected will be equal to _______.

a.	$120	c.	$360
b.	$240	d.	$480

16. The deadweight loss resulting from a $6 per unit tax is equal to _______.

a.	$60	c.	$120
b.	$90	d.	$240

17. A good is considered to be a pure public good if it is:
   a. rival and excludable.
   b. non-rival and excludable.
   c. rival and non-excludable.
   d. non-rival and non-excludable.

18. The "free-rider" problem refers to the fact that:
   a. some people receive welfare benefits to which they are not entitled.
   b. the benefits associated with public goods cannot be denied to those who are unwilling to pay for them.
   c. government must subsidize public transportation.
   d. the benefits associated with private goods cannot be denied to those who are unwilling to pay for them.

19. Which of the following is an example of a negative externality?
   a. A boy scout troop cleaning up a neighborhood park
   b. Toxic chemicals dumped into a river that is used as a water supply
   c. A neighbor who plants a beautiful garden in his front yard
   d. A lower crime rate in a neighborhood patrolled by a security company

20. When there is a positive externality, the unregulated market results in a level of output that is ________ than the socially efficient level because the private benefits are ________ than the social benefits.
   a. higher; greater
   b. higher; less
   c. lower; greater
   d. lower; less

21. The Coase theorem states that an efficient outcome will prevail through private bargaining as long as:
   a. property rights are clearly defined and transaction costs are sufficiently low.
   b. property rights are clearly defined and transaction costs are sufficiently high.
   c. there are no spillover costs or benefits.
   d. there are no free riders.

22. Government policy can promote the efficient use of common resources by:
   a. ensuring that these resources are available for everyone to use at no cost.
   b. converting them into private goods with clearly-defined property rights.
   c. providing a subsidy to users.
   d. taking no action.

23. Stella left her $25,000 per year job as an office manager to paint houses and be her own boss. In her first year, Stella received $50,000 in payments from customers and paid $5,000 for paint and supplies. Stella's economic profit in her first year is:
a. $15,000.
b. $20,000.
c. $25,000.
d. $45,000.

24. In the short run, firms:
a. have at least one fixed input.
b. have only fixed inputs.
c. can only vary capital inputs.
d. can vary all inputs.

Use the information in the table below to answer the next two questions.

Number of Workers	Output
0	0
1	10
2	24
3	36
4	44
5	50
6	54

25. When 3 workers are hired, average product is ______.
a. 10
b. 11
c. 12
d. 44

26. The marginal product of the 5th worker is:
a. 4 units of output.
b. 6 units of output.
c. 8 units of output.
d. 10 units of output.

27. All of the following statements are correct ***except***:
a. MP eventually falls in the short run.
b. AP rises when MP is greater than AP.
c. AP falls when MP is less than AP.
d. MP intersects AP at the minimum point on the AP curve.

28. The change in total cost resulting from producing one more unit of output is called:
a. marginal cost.
b. fixed cost.
c. total cost.
d. average cost.

29. Costs that must be paid in the short run even when no output is produced are called:
   a. total costs (TC).
   b. total fixed costs (TFC).
   c. total variable costs (TVC).
   d. marginal costs (MC).

Use the table below to answer the next two questions.

Output (Q = TP)	TVC	TC
0	$ 0	$80
1	80	160
2	130	210
3	190	___
4	___	345
5	370	450

30. The total cost of producing 3 units of output is ______.
   a. $80
   b. $270
   c. $190
   d. $345

31. Average variable cost when 4 units of output are produced is ______.
   a. $60
   b. $74
   c. $66.25
   d. $114

32. The downward-sloping portion of a LRAC curve implies:
   a. economies of scale exist over that range of the curve.
   b. constant returns to scale exist over that range of the curve.
   c. diseconomies of scale exist over that range of the curve.
   d. decreasing returns to scale exist over that range of the curve.

33. All of the following are assumptions of the model of perfect competition ***except***:
   a. firms in the market produce identical outputs.
   b. the demand curve facing the firm is perfectly elastic.
   c. the market consists of a large number of buyers and sellers.
   d. entry into the market in the long run is restricted.

34. The demand curve for an individual seller in a perfectly competitive market is:
   a. upward sloping as a result of the large number of sellers.
   b. vertical (perfectly inelastic) at the market-determined quantity.
   c. horizontal (perfectly elastic) at the market-determined price.
   d. downward-sloping; therefore, its elasticity varies along the curve.

Use the graph below to answer the next two questions.

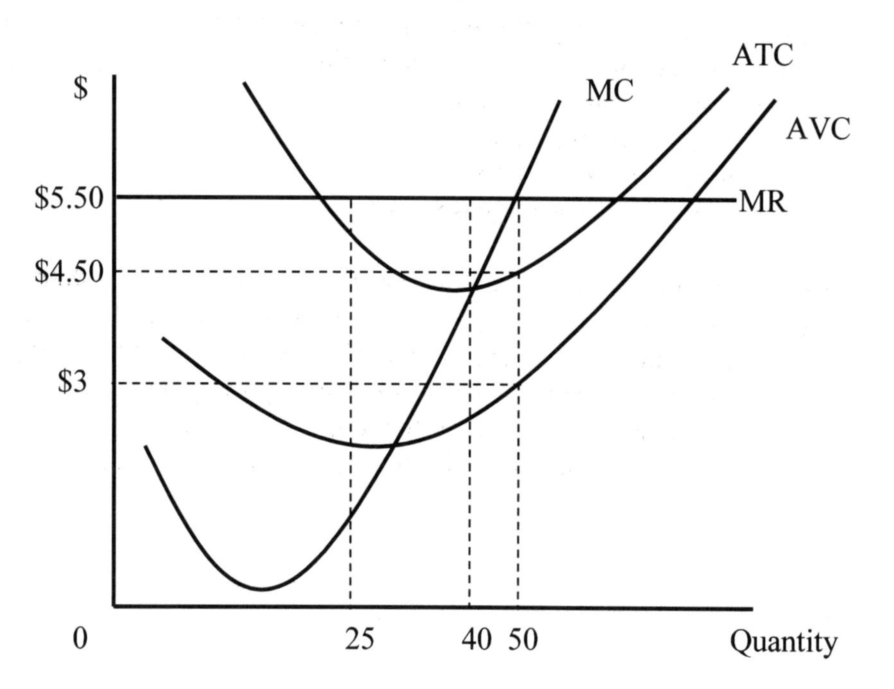

35. This profit-maximizing firm will produce ________ units of output and have total revenue of _________.
    a. 40; $170   b. 40; $220   c. 50; $225   d. 50; $275

36. This profit-maximizing firm is:
    a. in long-run equilibrium.
    b. earning an economic profit of $40 in the short run.
    c. earning an economic profit of $50 in the short run.
    d. earning a normal profit (zero economic profit) in the short run.

37. Firms operating in perfectly competitive markets:
    a. have substantial market power and are price setters.
    b. have no market power and are price takers.
    c. tend to produce differentiated goods for which there are few good substitutes.
    d. rely on advertising to keep other firms out of the market.

38. Suppose at the profit-maximizing/loss-minimizing level of output P = $6, ATC = $7, and AVC = $5. A firm in this situation will:
    a. minimize its losses by continuing to produce where MR = MC in the short run.
    b. minimize its losses by shutting down immediately.
    c. earn a short-run economic profit producing where MR = MC.
    d. produce more than the output where MR = MC.

39. If, in the short run, perfectly competitive firms are earning positive economic profits, the adjustment to long-run equilibrium will include firms ____________ the industry, causing market supply to _______ and market price to ____________.
    a. exiting; increase; decrease
    b. exiting; decrease; increase
    c. entering; increase; decrease
    d. entering; decrease; increase

40. If firms in the market for yogurt are earning positive economic profit in the short run, and there are no barriers to entry into this market, economic theory predicts that:
    a. new entrants into the market will drive down the price of yogurt in the long run.
    b. new entrants into the market will drive up the price of yogurt in the long run.
    c. firms will exit the market in the long run, causing the price of yogurt to fall.
    d. firms will exit the market in the long run, causing the price of yogurt to rise.

Answers to Practice Exam II

1. D	**11. B**	**21. A**	**31. C**
2. B	**12. C**	**22. B**	**32. A**
3. C	**13. C**	**23. B**	**33. D**
4. B	**14. B**	**24. A**	**34. C**
5. D	**15. A**	**25. C**	**35. D**
6. A	**16. A**	**26. B**	**36. C**
7. C	**17. D**	**27. D**	**37. B**
8. B	**18. B**	**28. A**	**38. A**
9. B	**19. B**	**29. B**	**39. C**
10. A	**20. D**	**30. B**	**40. A**

CHAPTER 12 Monopoly

Most industries, or markets, in the real world do not match the perfectly competitive ideal. An **imperfectly** competitive industry is one in which a firm has some control over price, or **market power**. If an individual firm in a perfectly competitive industry raises its price above the market price, it will lose all sales. Firms in imperfectly competitive markets have the ability to raise price without losing all sales, although the quantity demanded of their product will fall unless the demand for the product is perfectly inelastic. The most extreme example of imperfect competition is a **pure monopoly.** A market is a pure monopoly when there is a **single seller** of a **unique product** and **barriers to entry** exist.

A monopoly occurs when **one firm** is the sole producer or seller of a product that has **no close substitutes** (the product is unique). Being the only seller of a product with close substitutes does not make the firm a monopoly. For example, McDonald's is the only seller of Big Macs, due to trademark protection, but it is not a monopoly in the fast food market. McDonald's has some pricing power, but as it raises the price of a Big Mac, ceteris paribus, some consumers will respond to the higher price by purchasing a competitor's output. For a monopolist, there is no competition from firms that offer similar products, and *the demand for the monopoly firm's product is identical to the market demand for that product.*

Industries can remain monopolies only when there are barriers to entry that prevent other firms from entering the market. The primary **barriers to entry** are **government franchises** (e.g., cable service), **licenses, patents** and **copyrights**, **sole ownership of a resource** (e.g., diamond mines) or key input, and substantial **economies of scale**. Another effective barrier comes from **technological lock-in** where one firm's technology becomes the industry standard, making it difficult for other firms to penetrate the market (e.g., Microsoft). Firms that are interested in protecting barriers to entry might engage in **rent seeking behavior** by spending resources to limit competition. For example, a firm might lobby government officials to impose import restrictions and prevent competition from abroad.

Natural Monopoly

Economies of scale exist when average cost falls as output, or the scale of production, increases. If a firm has to be very large to fully exploit economies of scale, then it may be true that one firm can supply the entire market at a lower cost than two or more competing firms. This situation is referred to as a **natural monopoly.** Electricity generation and water distribution are examples of potential natural monopoly. Monopoly firms have market power, which means they can raise price without losing all sales. There are no close substitutes for a monopoly firm's output: the local water provider has no competition and for consumers to use water, they must buy it from the local provider or do without water. In such cases, government may allow the monopoly to exist in order to take advantage of economies of scale. However, to ensure that the benefits of economies of scale (lower per unit costs) are passed on to consumers in the form of a lower price, government may choose to regulate the price the monopoly can charge for its output, or it may operate the monopoly itself. Government may also choose to run a natural monopoly, as with the United States Postal Service.

Like perfectly competitive firms, monopolies maximize profits by producing the quantity where marginal revenue is equal to marginal cost. The profit-maximizing rule of **MR = MC** is true for firms in all market structures. However, unlike perfectly competitive firms, the demand for a monopolist's product is the entire downward-sloping market demand curve. The output decision of the firm depends on whether or not the monopoly firm has the ability to **price discriminate** and can sell the same output to different buyers at different prices when there are no differences in costs. If the firm must sell output to all buyers at the same price and is unable to price discriminate, the firm is a **single-price monopoly**.

Single-Price Monopoly

The demand curve faced by a monopoly firm is identical to the **market demand** curve for its product. Since market demand is likely to be downward-sloping, a single-price monopoly must lower price to sell a higher quantity. The graph below shows that the highest price a demander is willing to pay for the 1st unit of output is $9; the highest price a demander is willing to pay for the 2nd unit is $8. To sell 2 units of output, a single-price monopolist must lower price to $8 for both the 1st and 2nd unit.

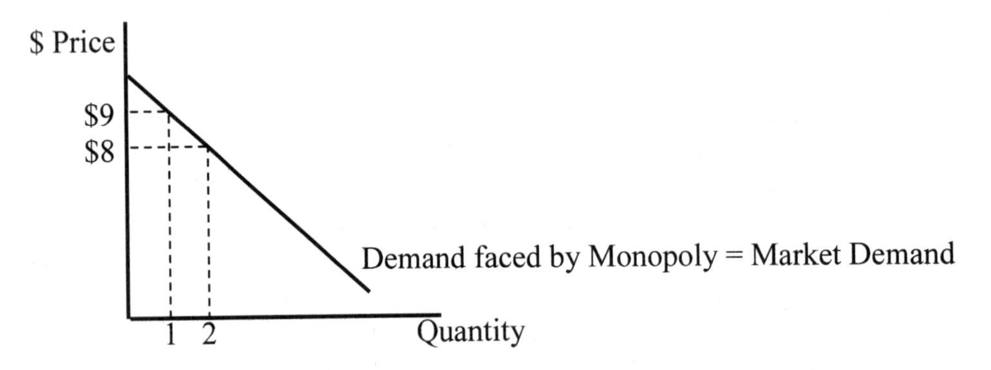

The fact that price must be lowered on all units of output in order to sell a higher level of output means that marginal revenue will not be equal to price for a single-price monopoly. Recall, **marginal revenue** is the change in total revenue divided by the change in quantity sold. Total revenue at a price of $9 is TR = (P)(Q) = ($9)(1) = $9; total revenue at a price of $8 is ($8)(2) = $16. Total revenue increases from $9 to $16 when the second unit is sold. The marginal revenue of the second unit is $16 – $9 = $7, which is less than the price of $8 for the second unit. For a firm with a downward-sloping demand curve, marginal revenue will be less than price if the firm cannot price discriminate, as illustrated in the table below.

Price	Quantity	Total Revenue P x Q	Marginal Revenue ΔTR/ΔQ
$10	0	$ 0	
9	1	9	$9
8	2	16	7
7	3	21	5
6	4	24	3
5	5	25	1
4	6	24	–1

When the firm's demand curve slopes downward, marginal revenue is less than price; the marginal revenue curve lies below the demand curve because the firm must lower price on all units to sell a higher level of output. The profit-maximizing firm produces the level of output where marginal revenue is equal to marginal cost (**MR=MC**). The firm is assumed to charge the highest price the market will bear for that level of output. Price is given by the demand curve, which is above the marginal revenue curve. Therefore, price will be greater than both marginal revenue and marginal cost, or P > MR and P > MC.

The graph below illustrates a single-price monopoly earning a short-run economic profit. Marginal revenue is equal to marginal cost at point A. Follow the vertical line through point A down to the quantity axis to get the profit-maximizing output, which is Q_M. Follow the vertical line through point A up to the demand curve and over to the ($) axis to get the price the monopoly firm will charge for output Q_M. The price that corresponds to point C on the demand curve is P_M. To determine the firm's profit, compare price to average total cost. The cost of producing each unit is given by the ATC curve. Follow the vertical line through point A up to the ATC curve (point B) and over to the ($) axis to get the firm's average total cost, ATC_M. This firm is earning an economic profit since price exceeds average total cost ($P_M > ATC_M$).

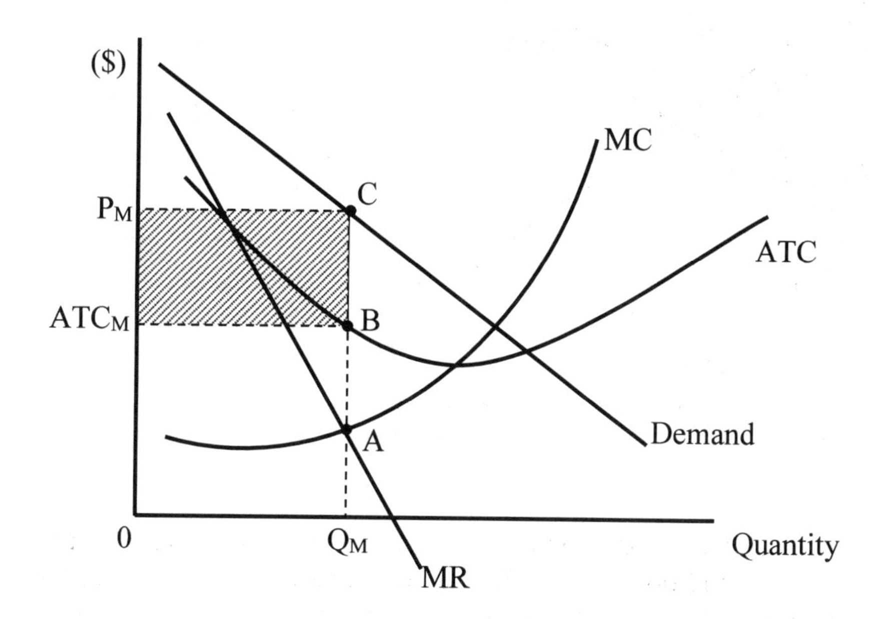

For this firm, total revenue is equal to the area $0P_MCQ_M$ at the profit-maximizing level of output. Total cost is equal to the area $0ATC_MBQ_M$. Profit (π) is the shaded area ATC_MP_MCB, which is the total revenue area minus the total cost area.

As an example, if $Q_M = 100$, $P_M = \$10$, and $ATC_M = \$7$, then:

$$TR = P \times Q = (\$10)(100) = \$1{,}000 \text{ and } TC = ATC \times Q = (\$7)(100) = \$700$$

$$\text{therefore, } \pi = TR - TC = \$1{,}000 - \$700 = \$300$$

Monopoly Profit/Loss

Just being a monopoly is **no guarantee** of positive economic profit. The firm is still constrained by the market demand for its product. It must be able to sell output at a price greater than average total cost in order to enjoy an economic profit. The monopoly firm has the same short-run profit possibilities as the firm in perfect competition.

The firm represented by the graph below chooses the profit-maximizing output by setting MR = MC = \$4, so it will produce and sell 40 units of output, setting price equal to \$9 for total revenue of (P)(Q) = (\$9)(40) = \$360. The average total cost of producing 40 units of output is \$8, so total cost is (\$8)(40) = \$320; economic profit is therefore equal to the difference between total revenue and total cost, or \$360 - \$320 = \$40. Profit can also be calculated by noting that profit per unit is \$1 (the difference between price and ATC), and multiplying profit per unit times output.

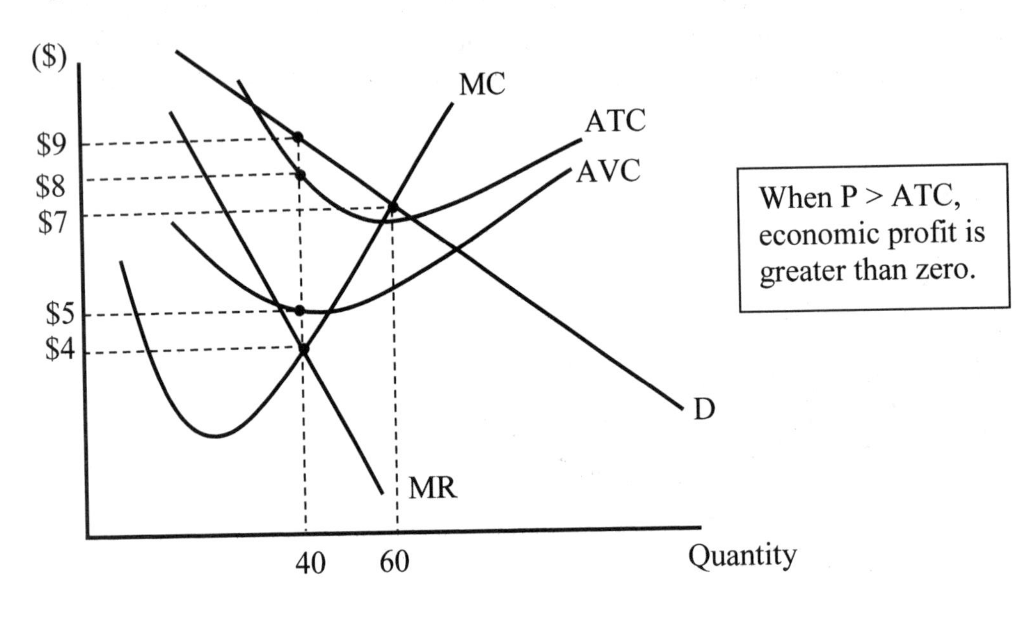

The above graph illustrates a single-price, unregulated monopolist that is able to earn positive economic profit. If market conditions remain favorable and barriers to entry prevent other firms from entering the market, this situation could persist into the long run. Unlike a perfectly competitive market, barriers to entry in a monopoly market prevent new entrants from eliminating positive economic profit. The outcome in a monopoly market is likely to be **inefficient**.

The efficient level of output occurs where marginal benefit (as represented by the market demand curve) is equal to marginal cost. In the above graph, the efficient level of output is 60 units, where MC intersects demand. A profit-maximizing monopolist produces less than the efficient output level and charges a higher price, creating a deadweight loss. The deadweight loss shown in the above graph is approximately equal to ½(20)(\$5) = \$50.

The firm represented by the graph below chooses the profit-maximizing level of output by setting MR = MC = \$5, so it will produce and sell 50 units of output, setting price equal to \$8 for total revenue of (P)(Q) = (\$8)(50) = \$400. The average total cost of producing 50 units of output is \$8, so total cost is (\$8)(50) = \$400, and economic profit is therefore equal to the difference between total revenue and total cost, or \$400 - \$400 = \$0.

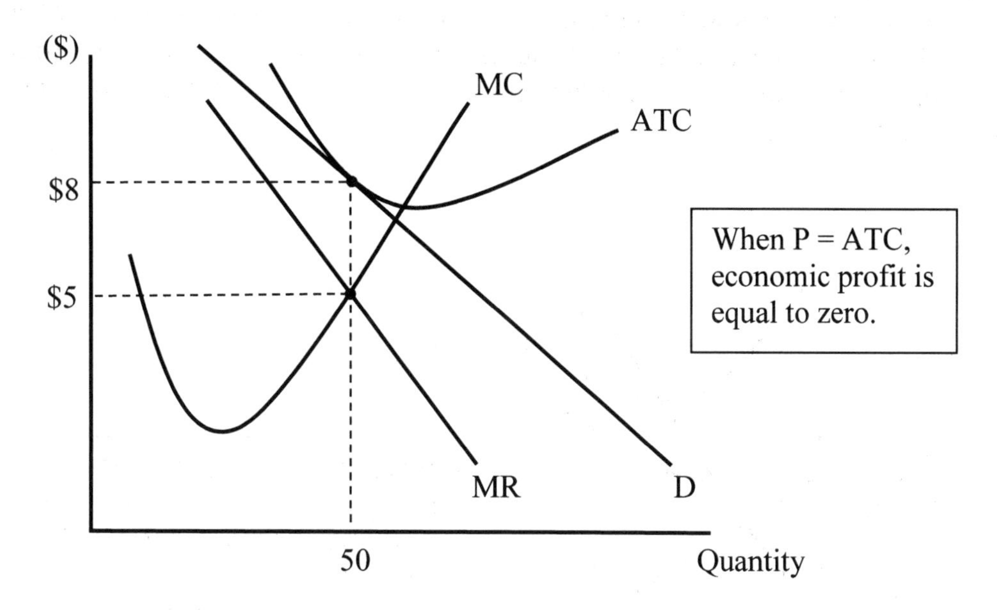

The firm represented by the graph below chooses the loss-minimizing level of output by setting MR = MC = \$4; it will produce and sell 30 units of output, setting price equal to \$8 for total revenue of (P)(Q) = (\$8)(30) = \$240. The average total cost of producing 40 units of output is \$9, so total cost is (\$9)(30) = \$270. Economic profit is equal to the difference between total revenue and total cost, or \$240 - \$270 = -\$30. Since ATC = \$9 and AVC = \$5, the firm's average fixed cost (AFC) is \$4, which means that total fixed cost is equal to \$120, or (AFC)(Q) = (\$4)(30) = \$120. The firm is better off producing 30 units of output and losing \$30 in the short run rather than shutting down and losing \$120, but it is likely to exit the industry in the long run.

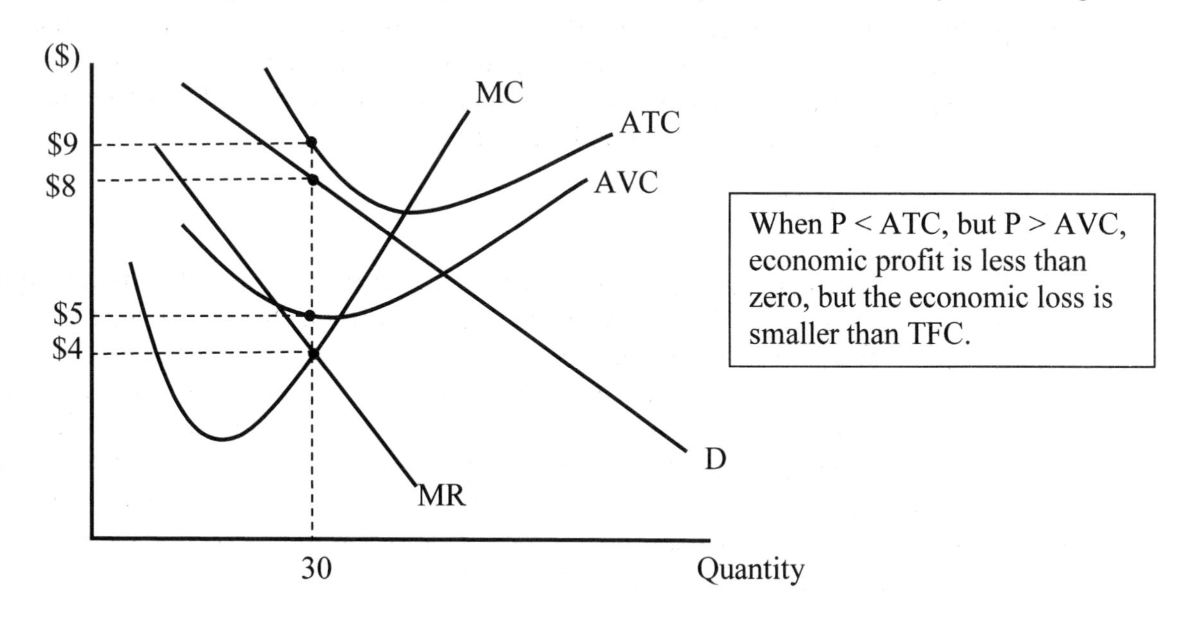

The firm represented by the graph below could produce where MR = MC = \$2, which would indicate an output level of 20 units and a price of \$5, with total revenue equal to (P)(Q) = (\$5)(20) = \$100. The average total cost of producing 20 units of output is \$10, so total cost is (\$10)(20) = \$200; economic profit is therefore equal to the difference between total revenue and total cost, or \$100 - \$200 = -\$100 (loss = \$100). Since ATC = \$10 and AVC = \$6, the firm's average fixed cost (AFC) is \$4, which means that total fixed cost is equal to \$80, or (AFC)(Q) = (\$4)(20) = \$80. The firm is therefore better off shutting down immediately and paying fixed costs, thus incurring an economic loss equal to \$80 since it would lose a greater amount (\$100) by producing where MR = MC.

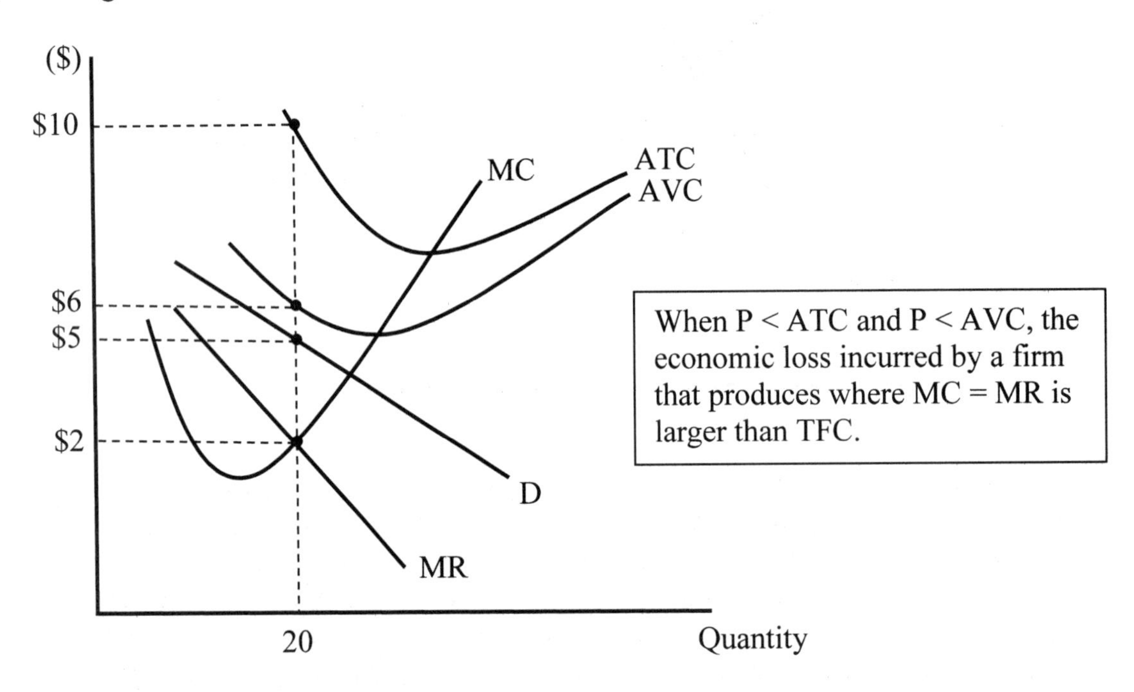

Most people associate monopoly with large and positive profit. This is because any monopoly firms that are actually staying in business and operating in the real world are likely to be highly profitable. If someone gains a patent to sell an item that has a very weak demand or very high production costs, that person is not likely to open for business at all. If market conditions change to create such a situation, the monopolist will either shut down in the short run or exit in the long run in response to economic losses.

Monopoly in the Long Run

Monopoly markets are characterized by significant barriers to entry. If a monopoly firm is earning positive economic profit in the short run, new firms typically cannot enter the market in the long run to compete for the economic profit due to barriers to entry. The monopoly firm can earn a long-run economic profit if it can maintain barriers to entry and has an incentive to engage in rent-seeking behavior in order to establish and maintain barriers to entry. If a monopoly firm is experiencing a short-run loss, it may choose to exit the market in the long run. It may also choose to engage in marketing and advertising in an attempt to increase the demand for its product. This will lead to success only if the firm can pass the cost of the marketing and advertising on to the buyer in the form of a higher price.

Price-Discriminating Monopoly

Price discrimination increases the profit potential of a firm. A firm engages in **price discrimination** when it does not charge the same price to all buyers and there are no differences in the cost of providing the output to all buyers. For example, a 25-year old will be charged a higher price for a ticket to the 7:00 p.m. movie at the local cinema than a 75-year old with a senior citizen discount. It costs the same to show a movie regardless of who is sitting in the seat.

Some groups of buyers may have a more **elastic** demand than other groups of buyers, and the group with more elastic demand is more responsive to a price change (more likely to decide not to buy the product due to a high price). A firm that is able to price discriminate can charge a lower price to the more elastic group and a higher price to the less elastic group. In order to price discriminate, the firm must be able to do two things:

1) separate customers based on the price each is willing to pay
2) prevent customers who pay a low price from re-selling to high-price customers

In some markets, it is relatively easy to separate customers into groups by identifying which buyers have elastic demands and which buyers have inelastic demands. For example, working adults tend to have less elastic demand for movie tickets, due to higher incomes and less time available to go to the movies. It is relatively easy to separate movie goers into groups by age, offering children, students and senior citizens lower ticket prices because their demand is more elastic, while maintaining a higher price for adults with less elastic demand.

The firm that price discriminates must also be able to prevent the lower-price group from buying low and reselling to the higher-price group. If the full price ticket for a movie is $10 and the senior citizen price is $7.50, the cinema doesn't want senior citizens buying tickets for $7.50 each and then reselling them to other movie-goers for $10 each. Senior citizens could make a profit of up to $2.50 per ticket if they could re-sell tickets, but this can be prevented by marking the tickets and checking them at the entrance to the theater. When firms are able to separate customers into groups and charge different prices, as in the case of movie tickets, this is called **third-degree** price discrimination. Another example of third-degree price discrimination occurs when sellers offer cents-off coupons. Customers with more elastic demand use coupons to obtain lower prices, but customers with more inelastic demand do not bother with coupons.

Another type of price discrimination is volume discounting (also called **second-degree** price discrimination). For example, a firm might set the price of a sweater equal to $40, but offer to sell them at the discounted price of 2 for $75, effectively lowering the price of the second sweater to $35 for customers who will purchase two sweaters.

Ideally, a firm would like to charge the highest price each buyer is willing and able to pay for each unit of output. Charging the highest price the market will bear for each unit of output is called **perfect** or **first-degree** price discrimination. The salesperson at a car dealership often begins the interaction with potential buyers by asking them how much they are looking to pay; this is an attempt to charge the individual customer the highest price that customer will pay, or engage in first-degree price discrimination.

The table below compares the total revenue for a single-price monopoly and a monopoly that can engage in perfect price discrimination. For the firm that can perfectly price discriminate, each unit is sold for the highest possible price. For example, total revenue when the firm sells 3 units of output is $9 + $8 + $7 = $24, because the firm charges $9 for the first unit, $8 for the second unit, and $7 for the third unit. The single-price monopolist must lower price on all units in order to sell a higher level of output, and total revenue is P x Q or ($7)($3) = $21 when the firm sells 3 units of output.

Price	Quantity	Total Revenue with Perfect Price Discrimination	Total Revenue for Single-Price Seller
$10	0	$0	$0
9	1	9	9 x 1 = 9
8	2	9 + 8 = 17	8 x 2 = 16
7	3	9 + 8 + 7 = 24	7 x 3 = 21
6	4	9 + 8 + 7 + 6 = 30	6 x 4 = 24

Total revenue for the firm that can price discriminate is greater than total revenue for the single-price firm at every level of output beyond the first unit. If total cost is the same for both sellers, then the price discriminating firm with the greater total revenue will have a greater profit at every level of output. A firm enjoys greater profit when it can price discriminate; however, not all firms can price discriminate because not all firms can separate their customers into groups with different price elasticities of demand and then prevent those groups from trading with each other.

If each unit is sold for the highest price a buyer is willing and able to pay, then price is equal to marginal revenue and there is no **consumer surplus**. The firm discriminates away all consumer surplus. When P = MR, as was the case under perfect competition, the firm will produce the efficient output level; however, consumers are not as well off as they are in a competitive market since all of their consumer surplus is converted into producer surplus.

Monopoly and Government Policy

One of the often cited goals of an economy is efficiency. The inefficiency that often accompanies monopoly provides justification for government regulation or other intervention. There are several approaches government may take, including *doing nothing, promoting competition (blocking mergers), regulating the monopoly firm, or operating the monopoly itself.*

Measures of industry concentration are explored in more detail in chapter 14. These measures can be used by the government to determine when a merger should be challenged on the grounds that it would reduce competition and lead to monopoly power. For example, several proposed mergers between large health insurance providers have recently been blocked by federal judges on the grounds that the mergers would lessen competition in the market and harm consumers. Government action may also be used to break up existing monopolies, creating smaller, now competing, firms. The "Baby Bells" are a result of such an action.

Antitrust legislation is designed to promote and protect competition. These laws make it illegal for firms to restrain trade and engage in harmful and unfair business practices. These laws are also used to stop the behaviors of large firms if the behavior is detrimental to competition. Some of the major pieces of legislation that focus on business are:

1890 The **Sherman Antitrust Act** declared monopoly illegal and prohibited restraint of trade (price-fixing).

1914 The **Clayton Act** specified unreasonable trade restraints or unfair business practices to clarify the Sherman Act.

1914 The **Federal Trade Commission Act** created the Federal Trade Commission (FTC) to investigate unfair business practices and false advertising.

Presently, enforcement of the antitrust laws rests primarily with the Antitrust Division of the Justice Department and the Federal Trade Commission (FTC). Individual business firms harmed by anti-competitive practices can also file lawsuits seeking damages and a court order for the practices to stop.

An unregulated, single-price monopolist produces where $MR = MC < P$, suggesting that it restricts output and charges a higher price when compared to firms in a perfectly competitive industry, assuming economies of scale are not substantial. If economies of scale are substantial and the firm is a **natural monopoly**, government might choose to allow a monopoly to operate in order to take advantage of the cost-savings. However, the price charged may be regulated by government or government might opt to operate the monopoly itself. The USPS is an example of a government-operated monopoly; it is the only legal provider of first-class postal delivery service and can fine or take legal action against private firms attempting to deliver first-class mail to your mailbox.

Government may choose to regulate the price the firm can charge when a private business is allowed to operate a monopoly, as with some utility companies (water, gas, and electricity). Two methods of price regulation are **average cost pricing** and **marginal cost pricing**. Average cost pricing (setting $P = ATC$) prevents a firm from earning positive economic profit, but output is not likely to be at the efficient level, where $MB = MC$. Marginal cost pricing (setting $P = MC$) prevents a firm from choosing an inefficient quantity, but economic profit might turn out to be negative, which would result in the firm going out of business.

The goal of government policy is to avoid the consequences of monopoly inefficiency. The graphs analyzed in this chapter can be used to identify the equilibrium price, quantity, and profit that would emerge in an unregulated monopoly market, as well as the deadweight loss associated with an unregulated equilibrium. The same graph can also be used to illustrate the outcome assuming regulators apply either average cost pricing or marginal cost pricing to force the market to reach a different outcome.

If the graph below represents market conditions for a monopoly firm that produces where MR = MC and sets the highest price the market will bear, output is Q_M and price is P_M. If this market is competitive and there are no economies of scale, the MC curve shown below is equivalent to the market supply curve; therefore, the competitive equilibrium occurs where the demand function intersects the MC function, at Q_C. The difference between the competitive output level and the output level that would be selected by a monopolist forms the base of the **deadweight loss triangle**, which is shaded in the graph below. **Marginal cost pricing** results in $P = MC = P_C$ and motivates the firm to choose the efficient level of output, Q_C, but may result in negative economic profit, depending on the position of the ATC curve. Government would then have to subsidize the monopolist to keep the firm in business.

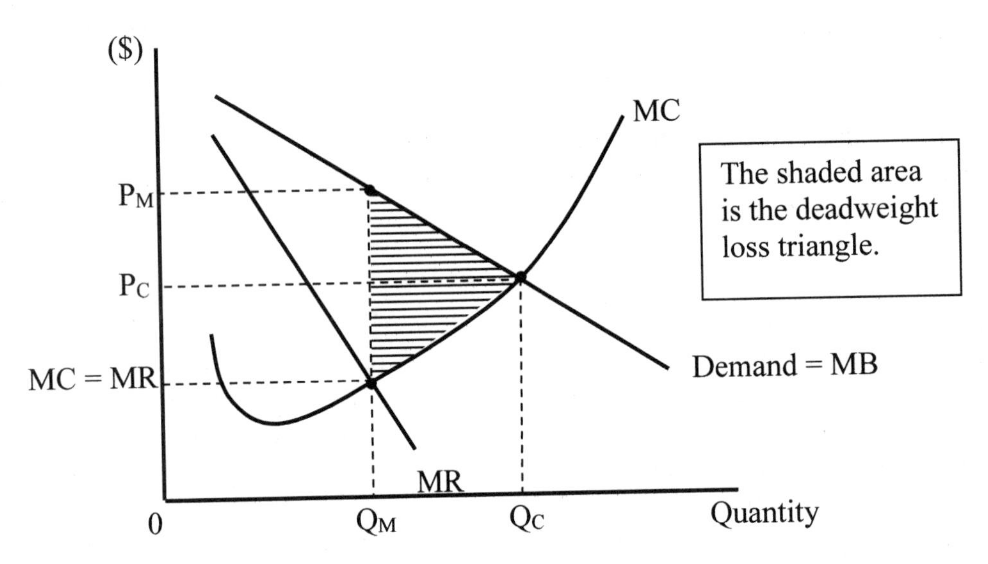

With **average cost pricing**, $P = P_{ATC}$ in the graph below and the firm will produce Q_{REG}, which is not the same as the efficient level of output, Q*. Another issue with average cost pricing, or cost-plus pricing, is that there is no incentive for a firm to keep costs as low as possible. For example, when airline prices were regulated, firms could allow costs to be high by providing expensive meals and service, and this did not lower their profits since the regulated price was set equal to explicit cost per unit plus normal profit per unit.

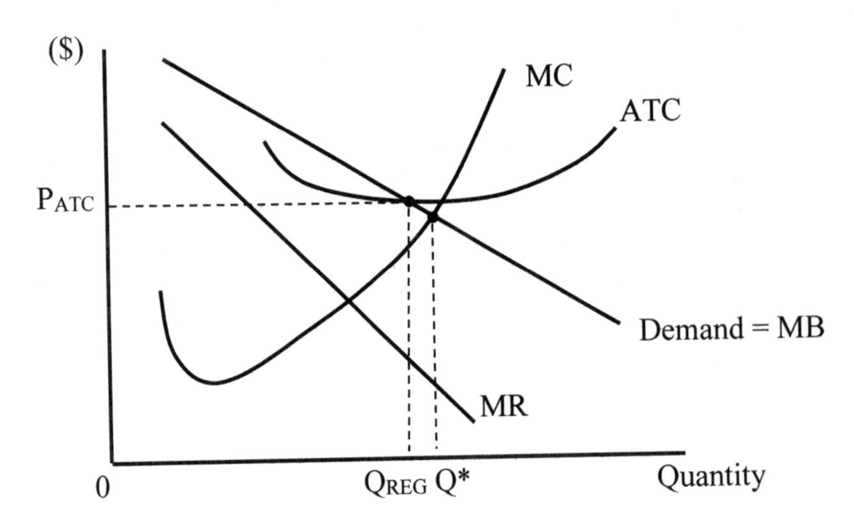

NAME____SECTION#______________
PRINT LAST NAME, FIRST NAME

MONOPOLY

1. Which market comes closest to being a pure monopoly?
   a. Cell phone service
   b. A patented prescription drug
   c. The stock market
   d. E-readers

2. The defining characteristics of a monopoly market are:
   a. many suppliers, unique product, and easy entry.
   b. many suppliers, identical products, and easy entry.
   c. single supplier, product with close substitutes, and barriers to entry.
   d. single supplier, unique product, and barriers to entry.

3. Which of the following is ***not*** an example of a barrier to entry?
   a. Patents and copyrights
   b. Brand awareness
   c. Government franchises and licenses
   d. Sole ownership of key resources

4. A firm gains monopoly power when:
   a. barriers to entry can be erected and maintained.
   b. other firms cannot produce an identical product but are able to produce a close substitute.
   c. it can sell all that it can produce at the price determined by market forces.
   d. it must raise price on all units in order to sell a higher level of output.

5. A natural monopoly can:
   a. supply the entire market at a higher cost than many competing firms.
   b. supply the entire market at a lower cost than many competing firms.
   c. always charge any price it wants since it faces no competition.
   d. use natural resources without being subjected to government regulations.

6. If electrical service can be more efficiently provided to a market by a single supplier than by many competing suppliers, the market is considered to be a(n):
   a. natural monopoly.
   b. unregulated monopoly.
   c. rent-seeking monopoly.
   d. efficient monopoly.

7. In order to price discriminate, a monopoly firm must be able to:
   a. separate customers based on different elasticities of demand.
   b. charge each customer the same price.
   c. incur a different cost for producing each unit of output.
   d. All of the above conditions are necessary.

NAME____SECTION#________________

PRINT LAST NAME, FIRST NAME

8. Government addresses the inefficiency associated with monopoly by:
   a. restricting market power through antitrust laws and regulation.
   b. prohibiting all forms of market power.
   c. requiring all firms to seek government approval before raising prices.
   d. preventing all proposed mergers.

9. The Justice Department:
   a. reviews proposed mergers to ensure that the resulting firm is able to earn a positive economic profit.
   b. reviews proposed mergers to determine if the merger would create excessive market power.
   c. does not interfere with business mergers because the U.S. economy is based on private property and free markets.
   d. does not interfere with business mergers because that is the primary function of the Federal Trade Commission.

10. The Sherman Act of 1890:
    a. was passed to prevent false and deceptive advertising.
    b. established the Federal Trade Commission to deal with unfair business practices.
    c. declared monopoly and unreasonable trade restraints illegal.
    d. specified the conditions under which mergers would be considered anti-competitive.

NAME____SECTION#______________
PRINT LAST NAME, FIRST NAME

MONOPOLY

Fill in the blanks.

A market is a pure monopoly when there is a 1) ______________ seller of a 2) ______________ product and 3) ____________________ to entry exist. The demand curve faced by a monopoly firm is identical to the 4) ______________________________ curve for its product. When demand is downward-sloping, a single-price monopoly must 5) ____________________ price to sell a higher quantity, which means that price will be 6) ____________________ than marginal revenue.

Assume the firm depicted by the graph is an unregulated, profit-maximizing monopolist that cannot price discriminate.

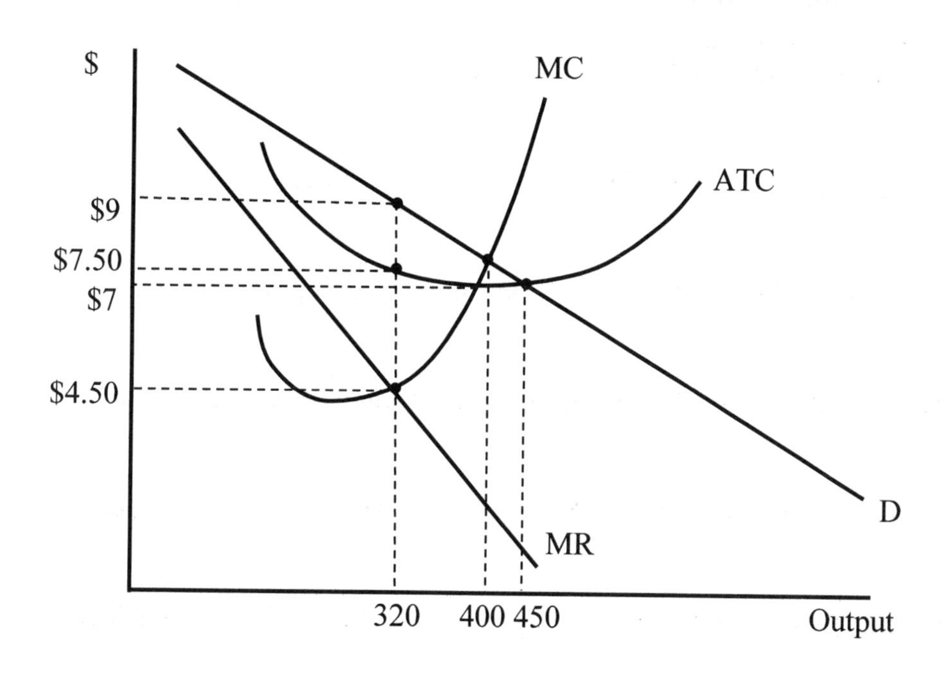

The firm depicted by the above graph will maximize profit by producing 7) ______________ units of output and charging a price of 8) $______________. The efficient level of output in this market is 9) ______________ units, so there is a deadweight loss approximately equal to 10) $____________________ (shade in this area in the graph above).

NAME____SECTION#______________

PRINT LAST NAME, FIRST NAME

SINGLE-PRICE MONOPOLY

Use the graph below to answer questions 1 through 10. Assume the firm depicted by the graph is an unregulated, profit-maximizing monopolist that cannot price discriminate.

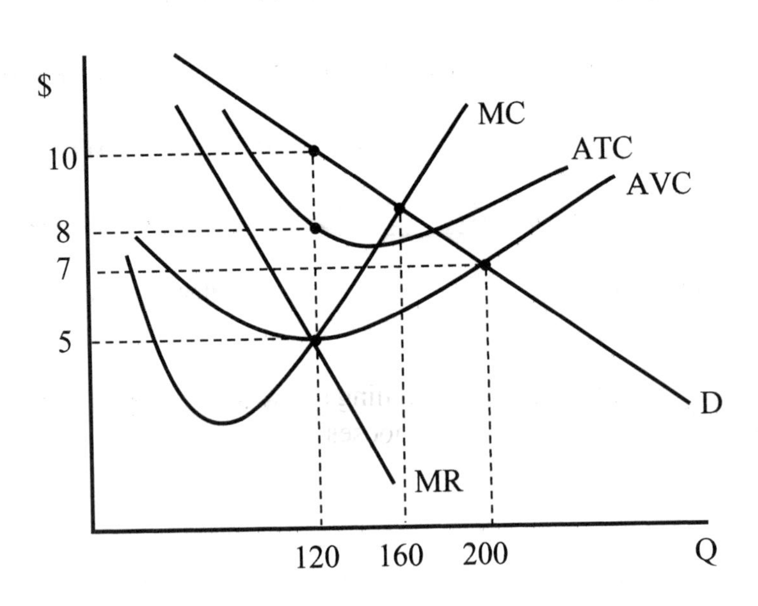

This firm will produce 1) ___________ units of output and set price equal to 2) $___________.

Assuming the firm chooses the profit-maximizing level of output, it will produce where

3) $___________ = MR = MC. At the profit-maximizing level of output, average total cost will

equal 4) $___________; total revenue will equal 5) $___________ and total cost will equal

6) $___________. The firm's profit is equal to 7) $___________. The firm's total fixed costs

are equal to 8) ___________. The efficient level of output in this market is 9) ___________

units; the deadweight loss created by this monopoly is approximately equal to 10) $___________

(shade the area corresponding to deadweight loss).

NAME____SECTION#______________

PRINT LAST NAME, FIRST NAME

MONOPOLY

1. Price discrimination allows a monopolist to:
   a. charge each customer the same high price, even though some customers are willing to pay more than others.
   b. charge those customers with a greater willingness to pay a higher price, resulting in higher profit.
   c. charge a price for its product that exceeds the cost of producing it.
   d. avoid having to make a pricing decision and leave it to government regulators.

2. A firm is a pure monopoly when:
   a. it is the only seller of a unique product and barriers to entry prevent other sellers from entering the market in the long run.
   b. it is the only seller of a product that has very few close substitutes and entry into the market in the long run is unrestricted.
   c. there are only a few other very large firms selling similar products.
   d. it can sell all it can produce at any price it chooses.

3. Barriers to entry:
   a. guarantee that a firm will always earn positive economic profit.
   b. cannot be maintained in the long run because other firms will always find a way to enter a profitable industry.
   c. are obstacles that make it impossible or unprofitable for new firms to enter a market in the long run.
   d. characterize both perfectly competitive and monopoly markets.

4. Suppose MR = MC = $3 at an output level of 2,000 units. If a monopolist produces and sells 2,000 units, charging a price of $6 per unit and incurring average total cost of $5 per unit, the monopolist will earn profit equal to:
   a. $6,000.
   b. $4,000.
   c. $2,000.
   d. $1,000.

5. For a firm with monopoly power that cannot engage in price discrimination:
   a. the marginal revenue curve lies below the demand curve because any reduction in price applies only to the last unit sold.
   b. the marginal revenue curve lies below the demand curve because the firm must lower price on all units in order to sell a higher level of output.
   c. the marginal revenue curve lies above the demand curve because the monopoly firm can charge any price it wishes.
   d. total revenue is a linear function of output because sales are independent of product price.

NAME____SECTION#________________

PRINT LAST NAME, FIRST NAME

6. Assuming government regulators are forcing a monopoly seller to charge a price equal to marginal cost and the firm produces where MR = MC:
   a. economic profit will be equal to zero but production will be inefficient.
   b. economic profit will be greater than zero and production will be inefficient.
   c. the output level will be efficient but economic profit might be negative.
   d. the output level will be inefficient but economic profit will be zero.

Use the graph below to answer questions 7 through 10.

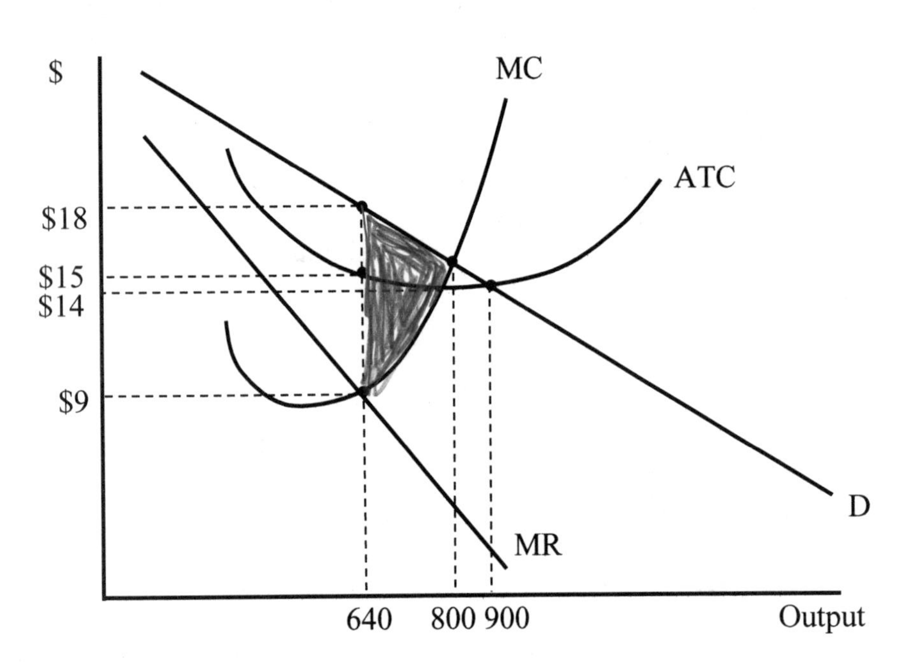

7. If this firm follows the profit-maximizing rule, it will produce _____ units of output; efficiency requires that the firm produce _____ units of output.
   a. 800; 800 b. 640; 900 c. 800; 640 d. 640; 800

8. If this firm follows the profit-maximizing rule, it will earn total revenue equal to:
   a. $9,600, but total cost will equal $5,760.
   b. $9,600, but total cost will equal $9,600.
   c. $11,520, but total cost will equal $5,760.
   d. $11,520, but total cost will equal $9,600.

9. If this firm follows the profit-maximizing rule, it will earn economic profit equal to:
   a. $11,520. b. $12,600. c. $1,920. d. $0.

10. Deadweight loss in this market is approximately equal to:
    a. $1,440 b. $720 c. $2,340 d. $1,170.

NAME____SECTION#______________
PRINT LAST NAME, FIRST NAME

MONOPOLY GRAPHS

Use the graphs below to identify profit-maximizing/loss-minimizing output (Q) and the price the firm will charge (P); calculate total revenue (TR), total cost (TC), and profit. Assume the firms depicted by the graphs are unregulated, profit-maximizing monopolists that cannot price discriminate.

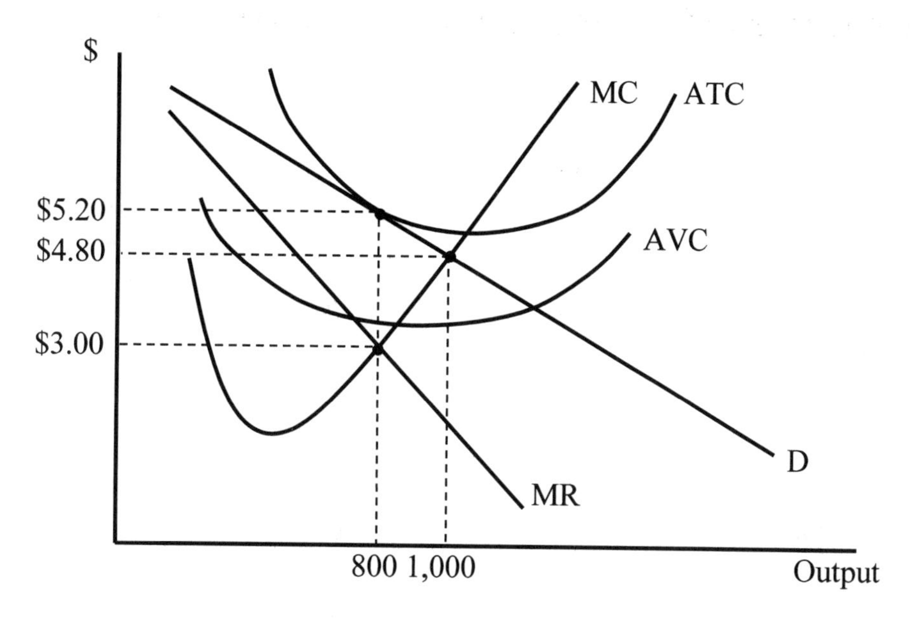

1) Q = _______ 2) P $________ 3) TR = $________ 4) TC = $________ 5) Profit = $________

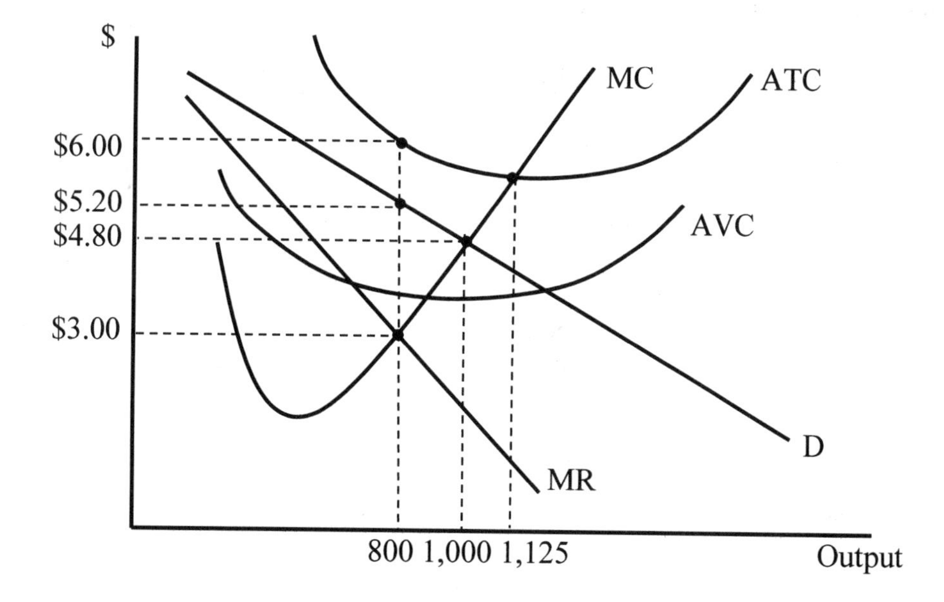

6) Q = _______ 7) P $________ 8) TR = $________ 9) TC = $________ 10) Profit = $________

NAME____________________________________ SECTION#______________

PRINT LAST NAME, FIRST NAME

TOTAL REVENUE AND MARGINAL REVENUE

The chart below gives price and quantity data for a monopolist. Assume the firm is not able to price discriminate, so it must charge every customer the same price. Complete the blanks by calculating Total Revenue and Marginal Revenue.

Price	Quantity Demanded	Total Revenue	Marginal Revenue
$1.90	1	$1.90	
$1.80	2	$3.60	$1.70
.	.	.	.
.	.	.	.
.	.	.	.
$1.30	7	$9.10	$0.70
$1.20	8	$________	$________
$1.10	9	$________	$________
$1.00	10	$________	$________
$0.90	11	$________	$________

The chart below gives price and quantity data for a monopolist. Assume the firm is able to engage in first-degree price discrimination by charging each customer the highest price the customer is willing to pay. Complete the blanks by calculating Total Revenue and Marginal Revenue.

Price	Quantity Demanded	Total Revenue	Marginal Revenue
$1.90	1	$1.90	
$1.80	2	$3.70	$1.80
.	.	.	.
.	.	.	.
.	.	.	.
$1.30	7	$11.20	$1.30
$1.20	8	$________	$________
$1.10	9	$________	$________
$1.00	10	$________	$________
$0.90	11	$________	$________

NAME____SECTION#______________

PRINT LAST NAME, FIRST NAME

MONOPOLY

1. If DeBeers has a monopoly in the diamond market, then:
   a. DeBeers must be engaging in perfect price discrimination if it is charging every customer the same price for a diamond.
   b. the marginal revenue of selling one more diamond is greater than the price of that diamond if DeBeers cannot price discriminate.
   c. the marginal revenue of selling one more diamond is less than the price of that diamond if DeBeers cannot price discriminate.
   d. the market demand for diamonds is perfectly elastic.

2. The Sudsy Soap company places coupons in the local newspaper giving consumers 50 cents off the price of a bottle of liquid soap. This strategy makes more sense than simply lowering the price for all consumers because:
   a. the company only wants to sell soap to consumers who are willing to clip coupons.
   b. those consumers who are unwilling to clip coupons are not in the market for soap.
   c. consumers with a more elastic demand will use the coupon to get a lower price, but consumers with inelastic demand are willing to pay full price.
   d. consumers with a more inelastic demand will use the coupon to get a lower price, but consumers with elastic demand are willing to pay full price.

3. A monopolist that earns positive economic profit in the short run will:
   a. always continue to earn positive economic profit in the long run.
   b. earn positive economic profit in the long run if it can maintain barriers to entry, assuming no changes in costs or market demand.
   c. earn higher economic profit in the long run because of economies of scale.
   d. earn zero economic profit in long-run equilibrium.

4. From society's perspective, assuming economies of scale are not substantial:
   a. monopoly markets are more efficient than competitive markets.
   b. it is never good to have only one firm service an entire market.
   c. competition leads to lower prices, higher output, and greater efficiency than monopoly if the firm is a natural monopoly.
   d. competition leads to lower prices, higher output, and greater efficiency than monopoly provided the firm is not a natural monopoly.

5. When government sets price equal to average total cost for a natural monopoly:
   a. the firm will experience losses.
   b. economic profit is equal to zero.
   c. price will also be equal to marginal cost.
   d. the outcome is efficient since marginal benefit equals marginal cost.

NAME____ SECTION#________________

PRINT LAST NAME, FIRST NAME

Use the following table to answer questions 6 and 7.

Price per unit	Quantity Demanded
$800	0
700	1
600	2
500	3
400	4

6. If a firm that is able to price discriminate produces and sells 3 units, it will receive total revenue equal to:
   a. $300. b. $500. c. $1,500. d. $1,800.

7. If a firm that is not able to price discriminate produces and sells 3 units, it will receive total revenue equal to:
   a. $300. b. $500. c. $1,500. d. $1,800.

Use the following table to answer questions 8 through 10.

Price per unit	Quantity Demanded
$50	0
40	1
30	2
20	3
10	4

8. For a monopolist that is able to price discriminate, selling 4 units brings in total revenue of_____; for a monopolist that is unable to price discriminate, selling 4 units brings in total revenue of_____.
   a. $40; $40
   b. $100; $100
   c. $40; $100
   d. $100; $40

9. For a monopolist that is unable to price discriminate, the marginal revenue of the 3rd unit is _____ and the marginal revenue of the 4th unit is _____.
   a. $0; $20
   b. $20; $10
   c. $20; $0
   d. $0; -$20

10. For a monopolist that is able to price discriminate, the marginal revenue of the 3rd unit is _____ and the marginal revenue of the 4th unit is _____.
   a. $0; -$20
   b. $20; $10
   c. $20; $0
   d. $30; $20

CHAPTER 13 Monopolistic Competition

Perfect competition and pure monopoly are on opposite ends of the market structure spectrum; the majority of firms operate in markets that lie somewhere between the two. A market is imperfectly competitive whenever the firms that make up the market have some control over the price of their products, either because of product differentiation or because the firm enjoys a large market share. Firms in imperfectly competitive markets face **downward-sloping demand curves**, indicating that the individual firm has some degree of market power. The demand for an individual firm's output is not the same as the market demand curve for the output.

Monopolistic competition is characterized by **many firms**, **easy entry** into the market in the long run (no barriers to entry), and **differentiated products**. Products are differentiated when there are close, but not perfect, substitutes, like Folgers and Maxwell House brand coffees. A monopolistically competitive firm achieves market power through product differentiation, which may be the result of advertising or brand recognition, superior location or quality, special services or warranties, or other features that distinguish the firm's product from close substitutes offered by competing firms. When product differentiation is successful and customer loyalty is established, the demand for the firm's product will be stronger and less price-elastic. The firms in a monopolistically competitive industry must compete on the basis of price like firms in a perfectly competitive industry, but they also tend to compete on the basis of the other product features that consumers care about.

Marketing and Advertising

A firm in a **perfectly competitive** market has no incentive to advertise its product on an individual basis. Every other firm in the market is offering an identical output and the firm is a price-taker, so the firm will not be able to pass the cost of advertising on to the consumer in the form of a higher price. This does not mean that there will be no advertising in markets where there are many small producers of identical outputs. Firms may band together to advertise in an attempt to increase the demand for the general product. Ad campaigns by the American Dairy Association such as "Got Milk?" and "The Power of Cheese" are examples of such advertising.

Firms in **monopolistically competitive** markets engage in significant marketing and advertising. Each firm is offering a product that is somehow different from the products of other firms in the market, and the firm has an incentive to advertise the product differences. A firm uses marketing and advertising in an attempt to increase demand and decrease the price elasticity of demand for the firm's specific product with the ultimate goal of gaining enough market power to earn positive economic profit. Marketing and advertising informs potential customers of the product differences. Product differences can be real or illusory; successful product differentiation only requires that consumers perceive differences and be willing to pay a higher price for those differences. For example, some deodorant soaps have aloe in them and are different from deodorant soaps without aloe. However, there may be several green and white deodorant soaps made from the same ingredients. The only difference between the soaps may be the packaging. One may come in a shiny box, giving the impression that it is a more luxurious product, and the other in a dull paper wrapper, indicating that it is just soap. The soap in the shiny box is likely to have a higher price.

Profit-Maximizing Output and Price

A monopolistically competitive firm maximizes profit by producing the quantity of output where **MR = MC;** this rule for profit maximization applies to firms in all market structures. Since the firm's demand curve is downward-sloping, the marginal revenue curve lies below the demand curve. The firm sets the price for its product just like a monopolist, charging the highest price consumers will pay for the profit-maximizing level of output, as indicated by the demand for the firm's product. In the graph below, the short-run profit-maximizing quantity is Q_1 (where MR = MC), and the price is P_1, as given by the demand curve at the output where MR = MC. The firm depicted below is earning a short-run economic profit because price is greater than average total cost (P > ATC) at the output where MR = MC.

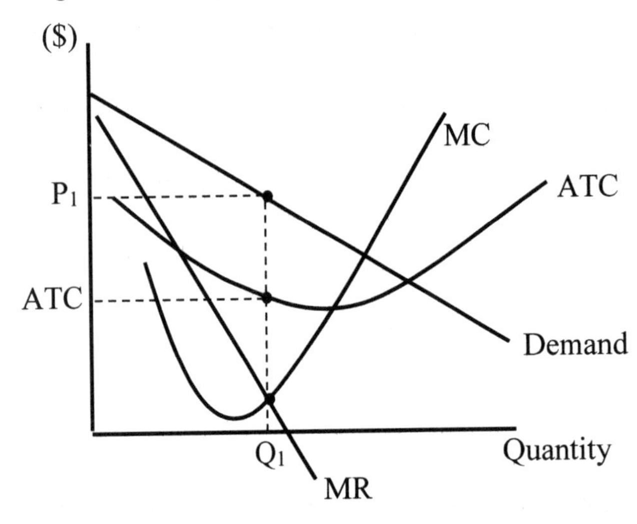

Short-Run Profit Possibilities

The short-run profit possibilities for a firm in a monopolistically competitive market are the same as those for perfectly competitive and monopoly firms. The profit situation is determined by comparing price to average total cost (ATC) at the output where MR = MC. There are three possibilities:

1) Positive Economic Profit: P > ATC, produce where MR = MC to maximize profit
2) Zero Economic Profit: P = ATC, produce where MR = MC to maximize profit
3) Negative Economic Profit: P < ATC
   a) P < ATC but P > AVC; produce where MR = MC to minimize loss
   b) P < AVC; shut down production to minimize loss (pay TFC)

A firm incurring a negative economic profit, or short-run loss, must decide whether to produce and sell output at a loss or shut down production. If the price of output is greater than average variable cost, then the firm's total revenue will cover all variable costs of production and the best option for a profit-maximizing/loss-minimizing firm is to produce at MR = MC. If the price of output is less than average variable cost, then the firm's revenue is not sufficient to pay all variable factors of production and the firm should not hire them. When price falls below average variable cost, the firm should shut down production in the short run; it will incur a loss equal to its total fixed cost.

The graphs below provide three different examples of short-run profit positions for imperfectly competitive firms. The profit-maximizing output, where MR = MC, is denoted Q*; and the price the profit-maximizing firm will charge is denoted by P*.

Example 1: Short-Run Positive Economic Profit

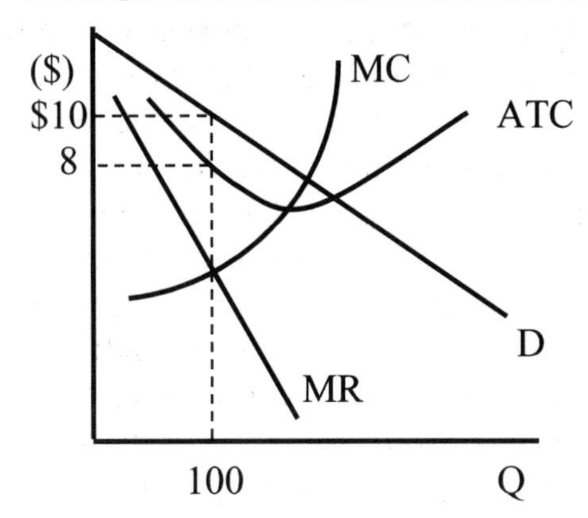

Q* = 100 and P* = $10
At Q*, ATC = $8.

P > ATC and the firm earns a $2 positive economic profit on each of 100 units.

TR = P x Q = ($10)(100) = $1,000
TC = ATC x Q = ($8)(100) = $800
Profit = TR – TC = $1,000 – $800 =$200

Example 2: Short-Run Negative Economic Profit (do not shut down)

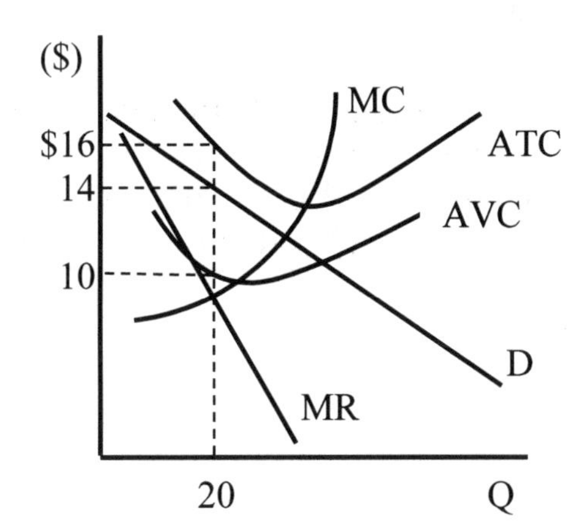

Q* = 20 and P* = $14
At Q*, ATC = $16
ATC = $16 and AVC = $10 at Q = 20, so TFC = $120.

P < ATC and the firm incurs a negative economic profit
P > AVC so the firm should stay in business

TR = P x Q = ($14)(20) = $280
TC = ATC x Q = ($16)(20) = $320
Profit = TR – TC = $280 – $320 = –$40

Example 3: Short-Run Negative Economic Profit (shut down)

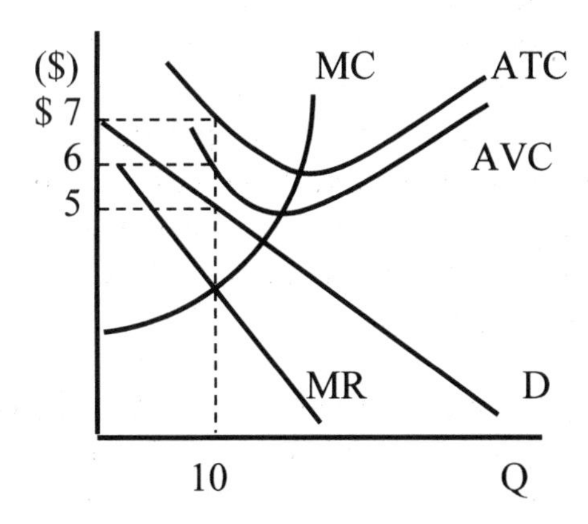

Q* = 10 and P* = $5
At Q*, ATC = $7
ATC = $7 and AVC = $6 at Q = 10, so TFC = $10.

P < ATC and the firm incurs a negative economic profit
Profit is – $20 if the firm produces where MR = MC.

P < AVC so the firm should shut down production and the short run loss is equal to total fixed costs.
Profit is -$10 if the firm shuts down.

One other case not covered on this page is the possibility of zero economic profit. This case is covered in the next section on long-run equilibrium.

Long-Run Equilibrium

In the short run, a monopolistically competitive firm earns a positive economic profit if price is greater than average total cost at the profit-maximizing level of output. There are no significant barriers to entry into the market; positive economic profit attracts new firms to enter the industry in the long run; as in the case of a perfectly competitive industry, long-run economic profits are driven to zero. As new firms enter the industry, the demand for the output of existing firms shifts to the left. Eventually, the demand for the typical firm's product will be tangent to the firm's ATC curve, so that the best the firm can do is earn zero economic profit (normal profit). Long-run equilibrium for a monopolistically competitive firm is shown below, with equilibrium quantity at Q*, where MR = MC, and equilibrium price at P*. Economic profit equals zero in long-run equilibrium because price equals average total cost (P = ATC). However, because price exceeds marginal cost (P > MC), **monopolistically competitive firms produce less than the socially efficient level of output** (where MC intersects Demand). Long-run equilibrium for monopolistic competition is similar to perfect competition since P = ATC and economic profit is zero, but it is also similar to monopoly since there is a **deadweight loss**.

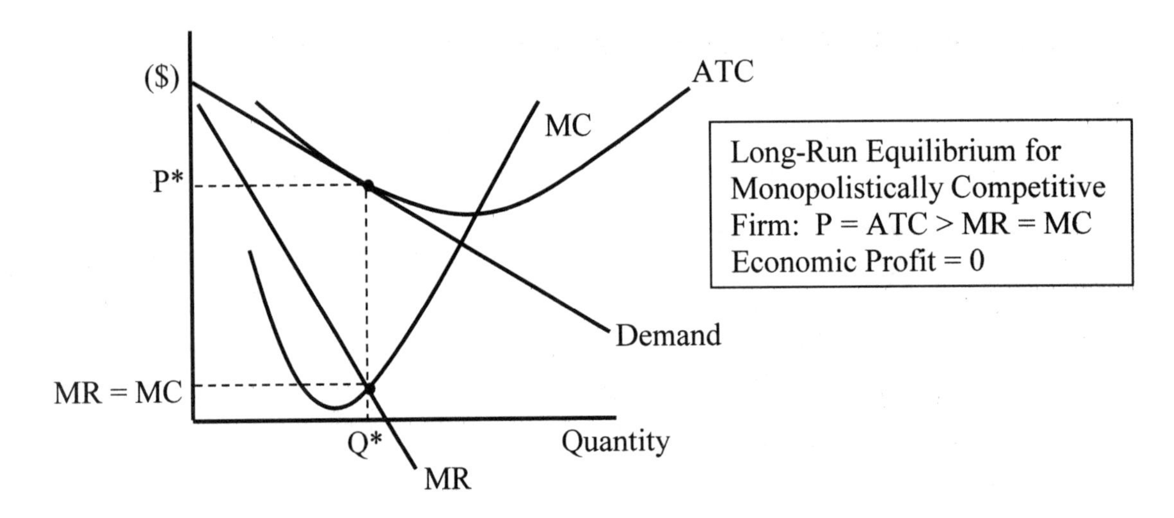

If monopolistically competitive firms have negative economic profit in the short run, the shut down rule used to analyze perfectly competitive models applies. Firms will shut down production in the short run if price is less than average variable cost (P < AVC). If price is between average variable cost and average total cost (AVC < P < ATC), firms will produce at marginal revenue equal to marginal cost because losses are smaller than total fixed cost. If short-run losses persist, some firms will exit the industry in the long run. Thus, negative economic profit causes the industry to contract, resulting in stronger demand for the remaining firms. Adjustment continues until the typical firm is earning zero economic profit.

Firms in a monopolistically competitive industry may work very hard to generate positive economic profit, despite the fact that economic profit will be driven back to zero in the long run. Firms may find ways to strengthen the demand for their own products or lower their costs of production. These efforts may pay off in terms of positive economic profit in the short run, but competitive forces will work to eliminate these profits in the long run, as other firms copy the success of profitable rivals.

NAME____SECTION#________________
PRINT LAST NAME, FIRST NAME

MONOPOLISTIC COMPETITION

1. All of the following are characteristics of a monopolistically competitive market ***except***:
   a. there are many firms in a monopolistically competitive market.
   b. the firms in the industry produce goods that are close, but not perfect, substitutes.
   c. there are significant barriers to entry that prevent new firms from entering the market in the long run.
   d. each firm faces a downward-sloping demand curve and has some control over the price of its product.

   C

2. All of the following are true regarding monopolistically competitive markets ***except***:
   a. firms may advertise to differentiate their products.
   b. there are many firms in the market.
   c. the typical firm earns positive economic profit in the long run.
   d. the number of firms is likely to decline when there are economic losses.

   C

3. A monopolistically competitive firm's demand curve is:
   a. more elastic than a perfectly competitive firm's demand curve.
   b. downward-sloping and marginal revenue lies below demand.
   c. horizontal at the market-determined price.
   d. less elastic than the market demand curve for its product.

   B

4. The typical firm in a monopolistically competitive market:
   a. earns a positive economic profit in the long run due to product differentiation.
   b. is small relative to the entire market for its general product.
   c. generally controls a large share of its market.
   d. cannot earn a positive economic profit in the short run due to the presence of close substitutes.

   B

5. The demand curves of firms in monopolistically competitive markets are relatively elastic compared to market demand due to:
   a. the existence of very close substitutes.
   b. the large size of the typical firm in the market.
   c. marginal revenue exceeding price.
   d. the complexity of production.

   A

6. Jane plans to open her own restaurant and wants to create a strong demand for her product as well as make it less price elastic. All of the following are methods of product differentiation that would help her accomplish her goals ***except***:
   a. setting the price of her meals well below the prices charged by her rivals.
   b. using tasteful furnishings and music to create a pleasant atmosphere.
   c. hiring the best chefs so she can offer the finest quality cuisine.
   d. using different forms of advertising to inform and attract potential customers.

   A

NAME____SECTION#______________

PRINT LAST NAME, FIRST NAME

7. A market is imperfectly competitive when the:
   a. demand curve faced by each individual firm is perfectly elastic.
   b. products offered by the firms are perfect substitutes for each other.
   c. firms that make up the market have no control over the price of their products.
   d. firms that make up the market have some control over the price of their products.

D

8. Ceteris paribus, if a firm in a monopolistically competitive industry raises the price of its product:
   a. sales may drop to zero as consumers switch to the perfect substitutes that are offered by other firms in the industry.
   b. sales may drop to zero as consumers switch to the close substitutes that are offered by other firms in the industry.
   c. sales may drop as consumers switch to the perfect substitutes that are offered by other firms in the industry.
   d. sales may drop as consumers switch to the close substitutes that are offered by other firms in the industry.

D

9. Which of the following is true for ***both*** monopoly firms that do not price discriminate and monopolistically competitive firms in long-run equilibrium?
   a. P > ATC
   b. P > MC
   c. P = ATC
   d. P = MC

C

10. A firm in a monopolistically competitive market is similar to a monopoly firm in that:
   a. neither has control over the price it charges.
   b. both set price equal to marginal cost.
   c. both maximize profit by producing the quantity where marginal revenue equals marginal cost.
   d. both maintain barriers to entry to prevent new firms from entering the market.

C

NAME____SECTION#______________

PRINT LAST NAME, FIRST NAME

MONOPOLISTIC COMPETITION

Fill in the blanks to contrast the assumptions of the two competitive market models.

	Perfect Competition		**Monopolistic Competition**
1)	______________ firm(s) many/few/one	4)	______________ firm(s) many/few/one
2)	______________ products differentiated/identical	5)	______________ products differentiated/identical
3)	______________ barriers to entry significant/no	6)	______________ barriers to entry significant/no

Complete the missing information regarding monopolistic competition.

7) If a firm is able to set price above average total cost (ATC), economic profit will be

______________.
positive/zero/negative

8) Profit-maximizing firms produce where MR = ______________ as long as price exceeds
ATC/MC/AVC
average variable cost (AVC).

9) If economic profit is positive, new firms are likely to enter the market in the long run, which causes the economic profit of existing firms to ______________.
increase/decrease

10) In the long run, economic profit will be ______________ if there are no barriers
positive/zero/negative
to entry.

NAME____SECTION#______________

PRINT LAST NAME, FIRST NAME

MONOPOLISTIC COMPETITION

Use the graph below depicting a profit-maximizing/loss-minimizing monopolistically competitive firm to answer questions 1 through 10.

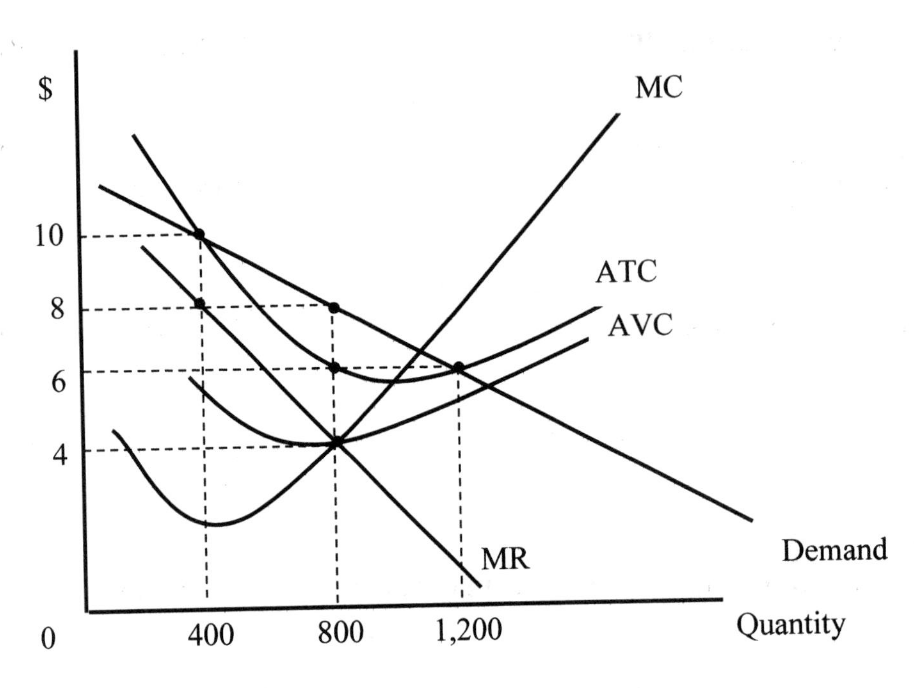

The firm will produce 1) ________ units of output and set price equal to 2) $________.

The firm's total revenue will equal 3) $________, and total cost will equal 4) $________.

The firm's profit will equal 5) $________.

The existence of 6) ________________ (positive/negative) economic profit is likely to cause firms to

7) ______________ (enter/exit) this market in the long run, resulting in 8) ________________ (increased/decreased) demand

for this firm's output. This firm will 9) ________________ (raise/lower) product price in response to the

change in demand, and its profit will 10) ________________ (rise/fall) as a result.

NAME____SECTION#______________

PRINT LAST NAME, FIRST NAME

MONOPOLISTIC COMPETITION

1. Profit-maximizing firms in monopolistically competitive markets:
   a. always charge a price that is equal to marginal cost.
   b. always charge a price that is equal to average total cost.
   c. sell products that are very similar to each other.
   d. tend to earn positive economic profit in the long run.

2. For monopolistically competitive firms in long-run equilibrium, economic profit is:
   a. positive because their products are unique.
   b. positive because their products are differentiated.
   c. zero because there are no barriers to entry.
   d. zero because of strong barriers to entry.

3. If a monopolistically competitive firm is producing where marginal revenue is equal to marginal cost but price is greater than marginal cost, the firm:
   a. should decrease output to increase profit.
   b. should increase output to increase profit.
   c. should continue to produce at this point because it is already maximizing profit.
   d. could increase profit by either increasing or decreasing output.

4. In the long run, it is ***true*** that monopolistically competitive firms produce where:
   a. $P > MC$ and $P >$ minimum average cost
   b. $P > MC$ and $P =$ minimum average cost
   c. $P < MC$ and $P <$ minimum average cost
   d. $P = MC$ and $P =$ minimum average cost

5. A monopolistically competitive firm:
   a. produces where $P > ATC$ in the long run.
   b. earns positive economic profits in the long run.
   c. produces where $MR=MC$ to maximize profit.
   d. All of the above are true

6. Monopolistically competitive firms:
   a. persistently earn positive economic profits in both the short run and the long run.
   b. may earn either profits or losses in the short run, but tend to earn zero economic profits in the long run.
   c. tend to incur persistent losses in both the short run and the long run.
   d. earn zero economic profits in the short run but incur losses in the long run.

NAME____SECTION#______________
PRINT LAST NAME, FIRST NAME

Use the graph below depicting a profit-maximizing/loss-minimizing monopolistically competitive firm to answer questions 7 through 10.

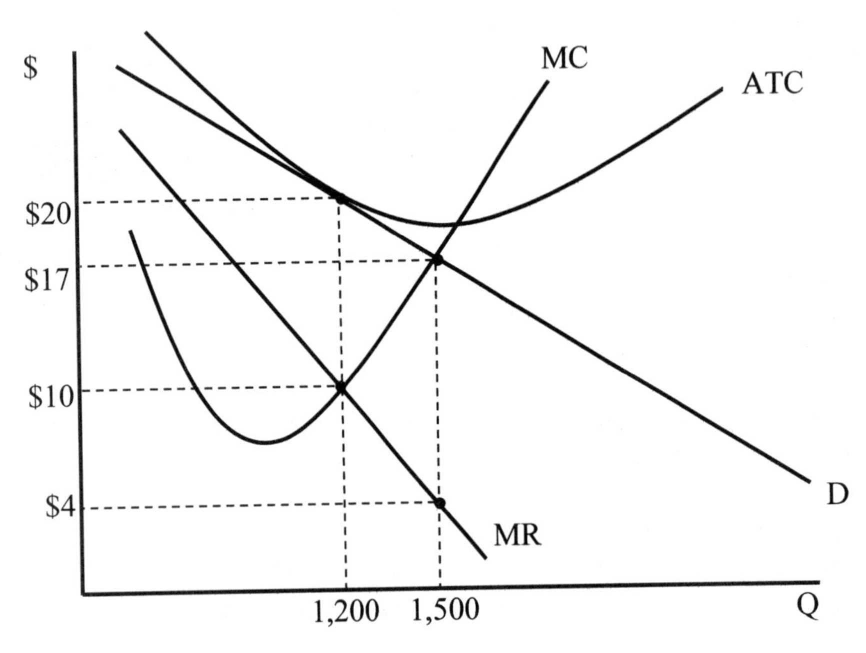

7. The profit-maximizing output is _____ units and the profit-maximizing price is _____.
   a. 1,200; $20
   b. 1,200; $10
   c. 1,500; $17
   d. 1,500; $4

8. At the profit-maximizing/loss-minimizing level of output, total revenue is __________, total cost is __________, and deadweight loss is approximately __________.
   a. $24,000; $12,000; $1,500
   b. $12,000; $12,000; $3,000
   c. $25,500; $6,000; $24,000
   d. $24,000; $24,000; $1,500

9. The graph illustrates a typical firm in a market that is in long-run equilibrium since:
   a. the output level is socially efficient.
   b. price is equal to minimum average total cost.
   c. price is equal to average total cost.
   d. price is equal to marginal cost.

10. Which of the following events would cause this firm's profit to increase?
   a. An increase in labor costs
   b. An increase in consumer demand
   c. A decrease in labor productivity
   d. A decrease in consumer demand

NAME____SECTION#______________

PRINT LAST NAME, FIRST NAME

MONOPOLISTIC COMPETITION

1. Firms in monopolistically competitive markets:
    a. are not likely to engage in advertising.
    b. attempt to differentiate their products.
    c. charge a price that is equal to marginal cost.
    d. All of the above are true

2. Monopolistically competitive markets are comprised of:
    a. many firms selling differentiated products.
    b. many firms selling identical products.
    c. a few firms selling identical products.
    d. a few firms selling differentiated products.

3. Monopolistically competitive firms have some market power because of:
    a. economies of scale.
    b. product differentiation.
    c. barriers to entry.
    d. industry domination.

Use the graph for a monopolistically competitive firm to answer questions 4 and 5.

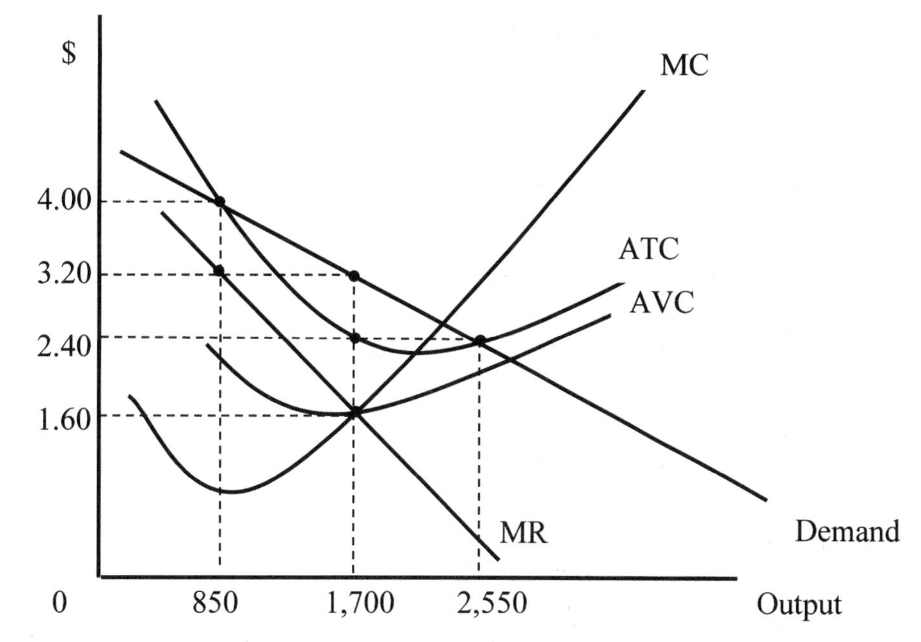

4. The profit-maximizing output is _____ units, and the profit-maximizing price is _____.
    a. 850; $4.00
    b. 1,700; $1.60
    c. 1,700; $3.20
    d. 2,550; $2.40

5. At the profit-maximizing/loss-minimizing level of output, total revenue is _______ and total cost is _______.
    a. $2,720; $4,080
    b. $3,400; $2,720
    c. $5,440; $2,720
    d. $5,440; $4,080

NAME____SECTION#______________
PRINT LAST NAME, FIRST NAME

6. A monopolistically competitive firm is similar to a perfectly competitive firm in that:
   a. both have some control over the price they receive for their products.
   b. both set price above marginal cost.
   c. neither is guaranteed to earn positive economic profit in the short run.
   d. neither uses product differentiation to obtain market power.

C

Use the graph for a monopolistically competitive firm to answer questions 7 through 10.

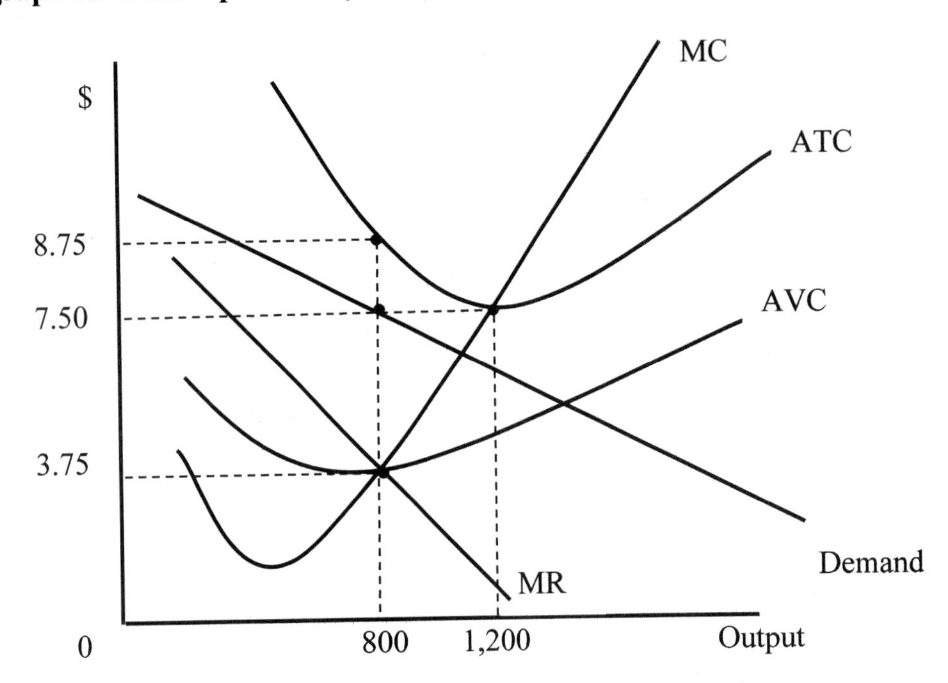

7. Following the profit-maximizing/loss-minimizing rule, this firm will produce _____ units of output and charge a price of _____.
   a. 800; $3.75   b. 800; $7.50   c. 800; $8.75   d. 1,200; $7.50

B

8. This firm's total fixed costs (TFC) are equal to:
   a. $2,000.   b. $3,000.   c. $4,000.   d. $5,000.

C

9. In the short run, this firm:
   a. earns a positive economic profit.
   b. earns zero economic profit.
   c. incurs an economic loss that is larger than the amount it would lose if it shut down and paid fixed costs.
   d. incurs an economic loss that is smaller than the amount it would lose if it shut down and paid fixed costs.

D

10. As the market in which this firm operates adjusts to long-run equilibrium, it is most likely that some firms will _____ this market, causing a(n) _____ in the demand faced by a firm.
   a. enter; increase
   b. enter; decrease
   c. leave; increase
   d. leave; decrease

C

CHAPTER 14 Oligopoly

Oligopoly is an industry dominated by a **few** large firms. In most cases, **barriers to entry** prevent additional firms from entering the industry. The chapter on monopoly included a discussion of barriers to entry. For example, if a firm owns a patent to manufacture a pill that lowers cholesterol, other firms are legally barred from competing with it. This type of barrier would not explain why only a few firms dominate an industry, yet many important U.S. industries can be described as oligopolistic. One explanation is that the start-up costs are so high because manufacturing requires automated equipment, leading to **economies of scale**. There may also be **economies of being established** in some industries that would make it difficult for new firms to enter. For example, an entrepreneur who is thinking about starting a new company selling ketchup might realize that success is unlikely until the new brand is established, a process that would require significant expenditure on advertising. The firms already in the industry have an advantage because they are already established with brand recognition.

An oligopoly may be characterized by either **identical** products (e.g., steel and oil) or **differentiated** products (e.g., automobiles, soda, and cell phones).

Given the small number of participants, oligopoly is characterized by **interdependent decision-making**. Interdependent decision-making means that the decisions of one firm affect the decisions of other firms, and each firm will consider the reaction of rival firms when it makes decisions.

When an industry is dominated by a few large firms, the outcome can range from an inefficient monopoly-like equilibrium based on collusive agreements to a more efficient equilibrium in which sellers keep prices low to avoid loss of market share. There is no single economic model that can predict a long-run equilibrium for oligopolistic markets. Five of the most common models for explaining the interdependent behavior of oligopolistic firms are:

1) **Cartel** – a formal collusive agreement between firms which dictates that each member restrict output in order to keep product price high;

2) **Price Leadership** – implicit (or tacit) collusion that occurs when the dominant firm in the market sets a relatively high product price and other firms follow to avoid a price war;

3) **Kinked-Demand** – a model that predicts rival firms will reach an equilibrium with very stable prices based on concerns that any attempt to change price will reduce profits;

4) **Game Theory** – a model that attempts to explain a firm's best strategy, assuming the firm attempts to anticipate how rival firms will react; and

5) **Contestable Markets** – a model based on the assumption that firms choose a relatively low product price because they believe high profits will attract new entrants into the market.

Regardless of the specific model used, oligopoly firms are assumed to possess a relatively large share of the market and to have the goal of maximizing profit. The models described on the previous page are examined in more detail later in the chapter, with particular emphasis on game theory since this has become such an important aspect of microeconomic analysis.

Industry Concentration

One way to define and identify an oligopoly is by industry concentration. An industry with only two firms, each with 50 percent of the market, is highly concentrated. An industry with ten firms, each with 10 percent of the market, is less concentrated. Economists have attempted to develop a standard for determining how much industry concentration is too much. One measure of industry concentration is the concentration ratio.

The **concentration ratio** is the percentage of total sales accounted for by the top four or eight firms in the industry. The higher the ratio, the more concentrated the industry. For example, the four-firm concentration ratio is 24 for fruit and vegetable canning (showing that the four largest firms in this market account for 24 percent of market sales) and 82 for breakfast cereals (showing that the four largest firms in this market account for 82 percent of market sales). These numbers indicate that the breakfast cereal industry is much more concentrated than the fruit and vegetable canning industry.

Another measure of industry concentration is the **Herfindahl-Hirschman Index** (HHI), which is the sum of the squares of the market shares of each firm in the industry. In an oligopoly, there are only a few firms, each with a relatively large market share, so the HHI tends to be very high for an oligopolistic industry. For example, the HHI for fruit and vegetable canning is 259 as compared to an HHI of 2,445 for breakfast cereals.

If there are 100 firms in an industry, each with 1 percent of the market, then the HHI is equal to 100. The fewer the firms that dominate the market, the larger the index. If there are three firms in the market, two with a 25 percent market share and one with a 50 percent market share, then the HHI is $25^2 + 25^2 + 50^2 = 3{,}750$.

Mergers between two firms in a market are usually challenged by the Department of Justice (DOJ) when the HHI is greater than 1,800. As a recent example, the DOJ did not allow AT&T to acquire T-Mobile, citing the potential negative impact on consumers in the wireless market due to the increased market power of combined firms.

In 2015, the top four wireless provider market shares were Verizon with 34%, AT&T with 34%, Sprint with 16%, and T-Mobile with 15%. Verify that the HHI for the top four was 2,793 by squaring the market shares and adding them up. Note that the four-firm concentration ratio is 99%, so these four firms are effectively the entire market. How would a merger between AT&T and T-Mobile affect the HHI? To answer this question, add the market shares of AT&T and T-Mobile, then repeat the process for calculating the HHI. Verify that the new value for the HHI is 3,813.

Collusion: Cartels and Price Leadership

If the largest firms in an oligopolistic industry join together to maximize their combined profit, each firm can potentially earn more than if they competed against one another. When oligopolies **collude**, or coordinate their production and pricing decisions, they maximize the group's profit like a monopoly, producing where MR = MC for the market and charging a price that is higher than marginal cost (P > MC).

A **cartel** is an example of a formal collusive agreement. In a cartel, the firms make joint price and output decisions. The monopoly model can be combined with information about an oligopoly market to calculate the profit-maximizing level of output that each firm should produce as well as the price that should be charged. The Organization of Petroleum Exporting Countries (OPEC) is an example of a collusive oligopoly, or cartel. U.S. law prohibited cartel agreements for domestic firms by making price-fixing illegal in 1890.

A cartel is an effective way of increasing product price and industry profit as long as each member follows the cartel agreement. Given a downward-sloping market demand curve, firms can choose a point that is associated with a higher price and a lower quantity, compared to where they would end up given competition with one another. Profit maximization requires each member of the cartel to limit production, and the agreement often assigns quotas after calculating how much total output should be produced to maximize industry profit.

There is a strong incentive for an individual member of a cartel to **cheat** by producing extra output to sell at the higher price, but higher output causes price to fall, reducing the profits of other members. Historically, cartel arrangements have not been very stable because of the incentive to cheat. For this reason, cartels are rare even in countries that do not explicitly outlaw them.

Another method of collusion – called tacit or implicit collusion – is price-fixing without any formal agreement, and may allow participants to avoid legal sanctions. One example of informal collusion is the **price leadership** model. In this instance, the firm that dominates the industry (the price leader) sets the product price, and the other firms in the industry follow the dominant firm's pricing policy, even if they believe they could gain market share by lowering price. The firms that follow the price leader are motivated by their desire to avoid a price war, which would most likely be won by the dominant firm. The government has been able to prosecute rare cases of implicit collusion when there is a whistle blower or incriminating evidence. However, proving that firm A set the same price as firm B is not itself evidence of price fixing because competing firms tend to set the same price, when producing identical products, or similar prices, when producing differentiated products.

The extent to which tacit collusion occurs in the U.S. economy is unknown because it is difficult to prove. Some industries may be characterized by some degree of collusion during some time periods, but then enter a new period of competition for any number of reasons, such as new leadership or the threat of discovery by government officials.

Kinked-Demand Model

There are other models that analyze oligopoly behavior under the assumption that the firms are not colluding, but are instead competing with each other. One of these is the **kinked-demand model**. In this model, the demand curve perceived by the firm is kinked because of the assumption that rival firms will **match** a price cut to avoid loss of market share, but will **ignore** a price increase to gain market share.

As an example, assume there are three firms that comprise the market: Firm A, Firm B, and Firm C. If Firm A's price is currently P*, as illustrated in the graph below, Firm A is reluctant to raise price above P* because it assumes that Firm B and Firm C will not raise price (ignoring the price increase); and Firm A believes it will lose market share as customers flock to Firm B and Firm C. Firm A's demand curve is elastic above P*, reflecting a relatively large decrease in its sales when it charges a higher price and loses customers to the rival firms who did not raise price.

Firm A is reluctant to lower price below P* because it assumes that if it lowers its price, Firm B and Firm C will also lower price (matching the price cut); and Firm A will experience a relatively small increase in quantity demanded. If the rival firms did not match the price cut, Firm A could expect to experience a relatively large increase in sales corresponding to a larger share of the market. The fact that the rival firms are unlikely to sit by and allow Firm A to gain market share means that they are very likely to match any price cut implemented by Firm A. If all three firms lower price, the law of demand predicts some increase in quantity demanded, but the increase for Firm A will be much smaller than it would have been if Firms B and C had kept their prices high. Thus, Firm A's demand curve is inelastic below P*, reflecting a relatively small increase in that firm's sales when all of the firms in the industry lower price.

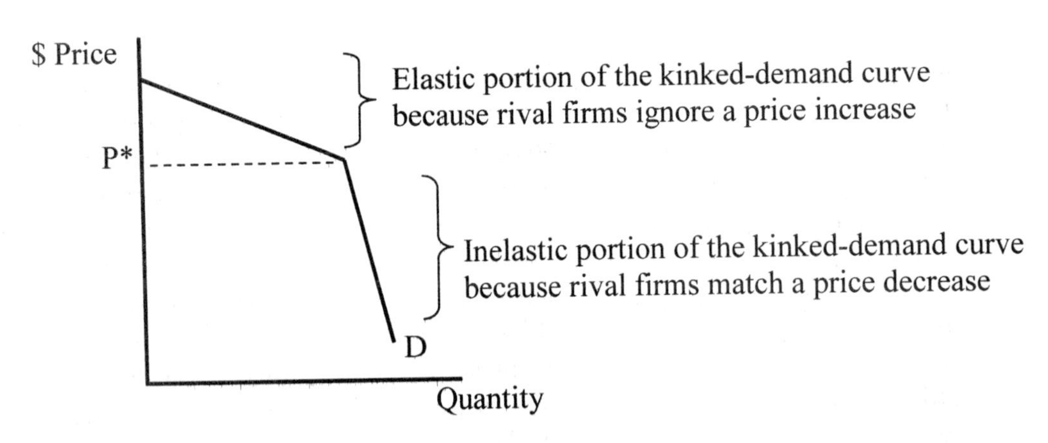

With a kinked-demand curve, firms are reluctant to change product prices because of the reaction they anticipate from their rivals; that is, they are worse off if they raise price and they are worse off if they lower price, so the price is sticky. There are some industries in which product prices have been very sticky, despite volatile production costs, indicating that this model has some validity. However, the model also has some rather severe limitations, foremost being its inability to explain how the initial price was determined or to explain pricing behavior in more volatile industries.

Game Theory

Game theory is the scientific study of interactive, rational decision-making. Game theory models were developed by mathematician John Nash (1928-2015), and have been used to explain the strategic behavior of firms in oligopolistic markets. Game theory models assume that firms anticipate rival firms' decisions and make a series of strategic moves and counter moves.

The classic example of game theory is the **Prisoner's Dilemma**, where two people who have been captured and charged with a crime are immediately separated to avoid the possibility of collusion. One prisoner must decide whether to confess or remain silent based on what he expects the other prisoner to do, so it is a strategic game. Both know that if they remain silent while the other confesses, there is a much greater probability that they will be convicted of the crime and receive a harsh penalty. Even though there is a good chance that both would get away with the crime if neither confessed, there is a strong incentive for each to confess out of fear that the other will confess first.

This model predicts that decision makers will do what is in their own best interest, taking into account the likely behavior of rivals, and this is often different from what is in the group's best interest.

U.S. antitrust legislation prohibits firms from engaging in behaviors that restrain trade and are detrimental to competition, making it illegal for the dominant firms in an oligopolistic industry to collude. Like the prisoners in the example above, each firm in the industry cannot know explicitly how its rivals will act, or at least they cannot enter into a contract that sets forth any collusive terms. Therefore, decisions are made based on the anticipated reaction of rival firms. Game theory has applications in oligopoly pricing, advertising, output, and research and development changes.

Example: An Advertising Game

The example on the next page uses a **payoff matrix** to organize the outcomes for each possible combination of strategies when one firm is trying to decide whether or not to increase its spending on advertising in the hopes of gaining market share and profit. The firm's ultimate decision depends on how it assumes a rival firm will react.

The **players** in this advertising game are two firms, Alpha and Beta. The main **rule** of the game is that Alpha and Beta are prohibited from colluding with each other; in other words, Alpha and Beta cannot discuss their options and then choose to act in a fashion that will lead to the best possible outcome for both. Each player has two possible **strategies:** leave advertising spending unchanged or raise advertising spending. The **payoffs** are the expected economic profits for each firm, and these are given in the payoff matrix on the next page.

The payoff matrix below organizes the players, strategies, and payoffs. Each rectangle reveals the payoff, in expected economic profit, associated with each strategy for both firms.

The top left rectangle gives the payoffs when Alpha and Beta both raise spending on advertising. If both firms raise spending on advertising, neither firm will gain market share. Both will face higher per unit costs as a result of increased spending on advertising, and both earn positive economic profit of $2,000.

The bottom right rectangle assumes both firms leave advertising spending unchanged. If neither firm changes spending on advertising, market shares stay the same and each firm earns an economic profit of $3,000.

The remaining two rectangles show that whichever firm raises advertising spending when the other does not will gain market share and enjoy an economic profit of $4,000 as a result. The firm that leaves advertising spending unchanged when the other firm is raising spending earns an economic profit of $1,000 due to lost market share.

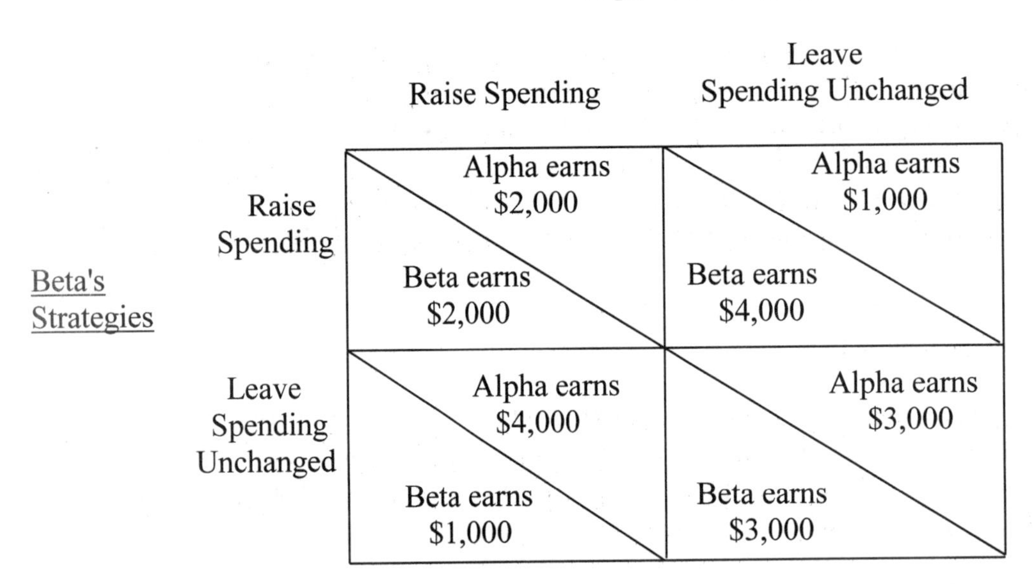

The payoff matrix provides all possible outcomes. The next step is to consider the strategy from the perspective of one of the firms. Alpha's choice depends on Beta's strategy; Alpha will choose the best strategy given Beta's strategy. Beta's choice depends on Alpha's strategy; Beta will choose the best strategy given Alpha's strategy. The game will be in equilibrium when each player chooses its best strategy, given the choice of the other player.

From Alpha's Perspective

If Beta increases spending on advertising, Alpha earns

- $1,000 if it leaves spending unchanged
- $2,000 if it increases spending

so Alpha's best strategy is to **increase spending** if Beta increases spending.

If Beta leaves spending on advertising unchanged, Alpha earns

- $3,000 if it leaves spending unchanged
- $4,000 if it increases spending

so Alpha's best strategy is to **increase spending** if Beta leaves spending unchanged.

From Beta's Perspective

If Alpha increases spending on advertising, Beta earns

- $1,000 if it leaves spending unchanged
- $2,000 if it increases spending

so Beta's best strategy is to **increase spending** if Alpha increases spending.

If Alpha leaves spending on advertising unchanged, Beta earns

- $3,000 if it leaves spending unchanged
- $4,000 if it increases spending

so Beta's best strategy is to **increase spending** if Alpha leaves spending unchanged.

The best strategy for both Alpha and Beta is to increase spending on advertising. This is the most likely outcome and results in both Alpha and Beta earning an economic profit of $2,000.

Notice that in this example *the most likely outcome is not the best outcome for the group.* Alpha and Beta each earn an economic profit of $3,000 if they both leave advertising spending unchanged. However, each firm does not know how the other will react, and it is against the law for them to formally agree not to change spending. Because they cannot collude, each firm makes its choice based on the rival's anticipated behavior.

The outcome reached by analyzing the payoff matrix and predicting what each firm will likely do is called the **Nash equilibrium**. The term is named for Nobel laureate John Nash, subject of the Oscar-winning film *A Beautiful Mind.* Nash won the Nobel Prize for Economic Science in 1994.

Contestable Markets

The **Contestable Market** model is used to explain why some markets are dominated by a small number of firms despite evidence of barriers to entry. According to this theory, it may be possible for a new firm to enter an industry, but the firms that currently control the industry will deliberately keep profits low to avoid the possibility of new rivals entering the market. That is, they will refrain from earning excessive profits because this would attract additional firms into the industry and force them to compete in earnest. When firms in a contestable market behave this way, the outcome will be close to the outcome of a competitive market.

Why are there so few companies that manufacture facial tissue, when this is a product that is relatively easy to produce and always in demand? Perhaps existing firms deliberately keep product price low enough to discourage other entrepreneurs from trying to penetrate the industry.

Although this last model considers the possible existence of a market with few firms, no barriers to entry, and economic profit that is close to zero, this should be considered the exception rather than the rule. In general, oligopoly is characterized by barriers to entry that protect positive economic profit in the long run, just as they do for a monopoly.

The chart on the next page provides an opportunity to summarize the main assumptions and conclusions of all four market structures and should be completed and used as a study tool.

The focus of the last several chapters has been on the relationship between firms and households in **product markets**, where firms are on the supply side and households are on the demand side, as consumers. In the next chapter, the roles are reversed, putting firms on the demand side and households on the supply side of **resource markets**.

NAME____SECTION#______________
PRINT LAST NAME, FIRST NAME

MARKET STRUCTURES

Complete the table using the suggested answers written in parentheses:

	Perfect Competition	Monopolistic Competition	Oligopoly	Monopoly
Number of Firms (one, few or many)				
Type of Product (identical, differentiated, or unique)			could be either identical or differentiated	
Barriers To Entry? (yes or no)				
Industry Example				
Positive economic profit likely in long-run equilibrium? (yes or no)				

NAME____SECTION#______________

PRINT LAST NAME, FIRST NAME

OLIGOPOLY

Suppose that Acme and Ace have formed a cartel, each agreeing to restrict output in order to raise price and increase industry profit. Use the information in the payoff matrix below to answer questions 1 through 6.

Acme \ Ace	Hold to Agreement	Break Agreement
Hold to Agreement	50% market share for Ace; 50% market share for Acme	70% market share for Ace; 30% market share for Acme
Break Agreement	30% market share for Ace; 70% market share for Acme	50% market share for Ace; 50% market share for Acme

If Acme holds to the agreement, Ace will have a 1) ________ percent market share if it also holds to the agreement, but will have a 2) ________ percent market share if it breaks the agreement.

If Acme holds to the agreement, Ace's best strategy is to 3) ______________________________.

If Acme breaks the agreement, Ace will have a 4) ________ percent market share if it holds to the agreement, but will have a 5) ________ percent market share if it also breaks the agreement.

If Acme breaks the agreement, Ace's best strategy is to 6) ______________________________.

Answer questions 7 through 10 based on industry concentration measurements:

If the motor scooter industry is initially made up of four firms, each with 25% of the market, the numerical value of the four-firm concentration ratio is 7) __________ and the Herfindahl-Hirschman Index (HHI) is equal to 8) ________________.

Assume two of the four firms propose a merger, which would leave only three producers in the industry. The projected Industry HHI after the proposed merger is equal to 9) ______________.

Would the Department of Justice be likely to block the proposed merger? 10) ______________

NAME____SECTION#______________
PRINT LAST NAME, FIRST NAME

OLIGOPOLY

1. Oligopoly is a market structure characterized by:
   a. differentiated products in all cases.
   b. identical products in all cases.
   c. a small number of large firms.
   d. a large number of small firms.

C

2. Firms in oligopolistic markets:
   a. tend to earn zero economic profit in the long run due to high barriers to entry.
   b. have no control over the price charged for their product.
   c. consider the reaction of other firms in the market when making a pricing and output decision.
   d. maximize profit where marginal revenue is equal to minimum marginal cost.

C

3. The characteristic that distinguishes oligopoly from the other market models is:
   a. the existence of barriers to entry.
   b. interdependence among firms in pricing and output decisions.
   c. product differentiation.
   d. the ability of firms to earn long-run economic profits.

B

4. All of the following markets fit the characteristics of an oligopoly ***except***:
   a. Breakfast cereals
   b. Cell phones
   c. Automobiles
   d. Fresh fruit

D

5. The percentage of total sales accounted for by the top four or eight firms in the industry is known as the:
   a. concentration ratio.
   b. Herfindahl-Hirschman Index (HHI).
   c. industry differential.
   d. Prisoner's Dilemma.

A

6. The Organization of Petroleum Exporting Countries (OPEC) is an example of:
   a. a competitive oligopoly.
   b. a cartel.
   c. tacit collusion.
   d. all of the above.

B

7. Historically, the success of cartels has been limited by:
   a. the lack of close substitutes for the output of cartel members.
   b. nonmembers charging prices greater than cartel members.
   c. members that produce significantly less than their assigned quotas.
   d. incentives by members to cheat on the collusive agreement.

D

NAME____SECTION#______________
PRINT LAST NAME, FIRST NAME

8. An individual firm in an oligopolistic industry in the U.S. **generally**:
   a. can earn positive economic profit in the long run due to the existence of barriers to entry such as economies of scale.
   b. will not benefit from marketing and advertising because other firms sell similar products.
   c. earns zero economic profit in the long run because there are no barriers to entry.
   d. meets with rival firms to discuss the best price to charge to generate the largest possible industry profit.

A

9. Suppose Bobby's Bait Company is an oligopolistic producer of fishing lures. Bobby's produces at the profit-maximizing level of output, and the price it receives on all the items it produces is below average total cost of production, but above average variable cost. Bobby's is:
   a. making a short-run economic profit.
   b. making a normal profit in the short run.
   c. incurring a short-run economic loss, but is minimizing its losses by producing in the short run.
   d. incurring a short-run loss that is so substantial that it should shut down production immediately to minimize its losses.

C

10. Behavior in which a dominant firm's pricing strategy is followed by other firms in the industry is called:
   a. oligopoly power.
   b. contestable behavior.
   c. price leadership.
   d. cartel membership.

C

NAME____SECTION#______________

PRINT LAST NAME, FIRST NAME

OLIGOPOLY

1. Oligopolistic industries are characterized by:
   a. a few dominant firms and independent decision making.
   b. a large number of firms and independent decision making.
   c. a few dominant firms and interdependent decision making.
   d. a large number of firms and interdependent decision making.

2. If firms in an oligopoly market are able to collude, then:
   a. the market price and output will be very close to the price and output that would prevail under competitive conditions.
   b. the market price is likely to be higher and the output is likely to be lower than they would be if firms could not collude.
   c. all firms in the market will increase output in order to increase profit.
   d. they are not attempting to maximize profit.

3. Once a cartel has successfully achieved a price and output level similar to what would prevail in a monopolized market, some members have an incentive to cheat by:
   a. cutting back production, which causes the market price to fall.
   b. cutting back production, which causes the market price to rise.
   c. increasing production, which causes the market price to fall.
   d. increasing production, which causes the market price to rise.

4. The Kinked-Demand model is based on the notion that an oligopoly firm assumes rival firms will:
   a. match price increases but ignore price decreases.
   b. match both price increases and price decreases.
   c. ignore price increases but match price decreases.
   d. ignore both price increases and price decreases.

5. Game theory assumes that:
   a. firms anticipate rival firms' decisions when they make their own decisions.
   b. firms ignore rival firms' decisions when they make their own decisions.
   c. markets are contestable because there are no barriers to entry.
   d. a firm will always follow the pricing strategy of the dominant firm in the industry.

6. Game theory helps explain:
   a. why firms in oligopoly markets always earn maximum profit.
   b. why firms don't advertise if they operate in oligopoly markets.
   c. the strategic behavior of firms in oligopoly markets.
   d. hiring behavior in professional sports.

NAME____SECTION#________________

PRINT LAST NAME, FIRST NAME

Use the payoff matrix below to answer questions 7 and 8 about two major airlines, Rightway and Leftway, and their pricing decision.

	Rightway sets a low price	Rightway sets a high price
Leftway sets a low price	Rightway's profit is $10 million and Leftway's profit is $10 million	Rightway's profit is $5 million and Leftway's profit is $20 million
Leftway sets a high price	Rightway's profit is $20 million and Leftway's profit is $5 million	Rightway's profit is $15 million and Leftway's profit is $15 million

7. Suppose that Rightway must decide whether to charge a low price or a high price without knowing what Leftway will do. In the Nash equilibrium, Rightway will set a _____ price based on the analysis of the payoff matrix, which indicates that Leftway will set a _____ price.
   a. high; high
   b. low; low
   c. low; high
   d. high; low

8. Which strategy maximizes Rightway's and Leftway's combined profit?
   a. Both airlines set a low price
   b. Both airlines set a high price
   c. Rightway sets a low price and Leftway sets a high price
   d. Rightway sets a high price and Leftway sets a low price

9. An arrangement where there is explicit collusion between competitors to set a common price and adhere to output quotas is referred to as:
   a. a contestable market.
   b. a perfect competitor.
   c. a cartel.
   d. a monopoly.

10. Industry profit is likely to be lowest in an industry that:
    a. has a clear price leader who is followed by all of the other firms.
    b. adheres to a cartel agreement.
    c. is a contestable market.
    d. has significant barriers to entry.

CHAPTER 15 Resource Markets

The circular flow model of chapter 1 shows how firms and households interact in both *product markets* and *resource markets*. In product markets, firms make supply decisions and sell goods and services (outputs), while households, or consumers, make demand decisions and buy goods and services. In resource markets, the roles are reversed. Business firms make demand decisions with respect to inputs by choosing how much labor to employ, how many units of capital to purchase, and the quantities of other resources like energy and raw materials to use in the production process. Households are on the supply side in resource markets and sell labor services and other inputs to firms in order to earn income. Many of the same market principles that are applied to product markets can be easily applied to resource markets, but it is important to remember the new roles taken on by firms and households.

Resources include land, labor, capital, and entrepreneurial ability, and because labor is the most important input for many firms, the theory of labor demand is emphasized in the next section. The demand for labor is a **derived demand** because it depends on, or is derived from, the demand for the output labor helps produce. For example, a factory owner demands assembly line workers to manufacture automobiles because consumers demand automobiles. A university demands the services of professors, tutors, and support staff because consumers (students) demand higher education. Hospitals demand nurses and restaurants demand chefs because they need employees to provide services to their customers. Every business has a (derived) demand for labor of some kind, so there are many different markets for labor, both skilled and unskilled. Some labor markets are competitive, meaning there are many buyers and sellers and all workers are equally qualified. Other markets are non-competitive and the theory of non-competitive labor markets is presented in the appendix.

Labor Markets

The study of competitive labor markets is similar to the study of competitive product markets because the forces of supply and demand determine equilibrium price and quantity. The equilibrium price in a labor market is called the **wage rate (W)**. From an individual firm's perspective, the supply of labor is perfectly elastic at the market wage rate, indicating that each firm in a competitive labor market is a **wage-taker**. A firm hiring in a perfectly competitive labor market can hire as many equally-qualified workers as needed at the going market wage rate.

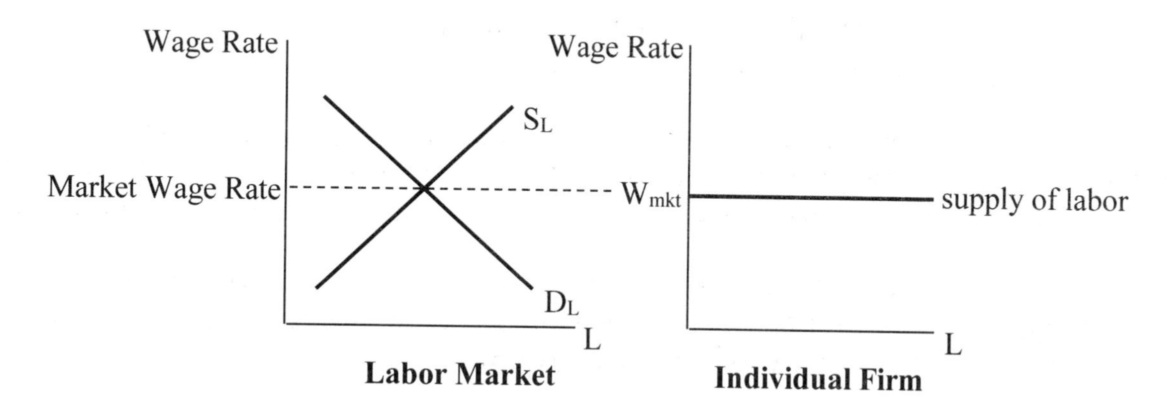

Profit-maximizing firms produce the output level where marginal revenue is equal to marginal cost (MR = MC). By following this rule, a firm will only produce an additional unit of output if the additional revenue earned from the sale of this unit is greater than the additional cost incurred. In other words, a firm will produce additional output only if doing so adds to profit. A similar idea can be applied to the decision to hire an additional worker (labor demand).

Recall from chapter 9 that the **marginal product (MP)** of labor is the additional output produced when one more unit of labor is employed. This additional output is sold at the market price to generate additional revenue for the firm. The **value of marginal product (VMP)** of labor is defined as the additional revenue earned when one additional unit of labor is employed. The equation for the VMP of labor is:

$$\mathbf{VMP_{Labor} = MP_{Labor} \times Price_{Output}}$$

Each additional worker adds the wage rate to the firm's cost, so the marginal cost of labor is the wage rate and the firm faces a perfectly elastic supply of labor. The condition for maximum profit is to hire labor to the point where the value of marginal product is equal to the wage rate **(VMP = W)**. The example below illustrates how the rule is applied.

Workers (L)	Output (Q/hr)	Marginal Product (MP/hr)	Value of Marginal Product (VMP/hr)
0	0		
1	20	20	$40
2	35	15	$30
3	45	10	$20
4	50	5	$10
5	50	0	$ 0

Assume the market price of the product is $2 (P = $2), the wage rate paid to workers is $20 per hour (W = $20), and both the product market and the labor market are perfectly competitive (the firm is a *price-taker* in the output market and a *wage-taker* in the labor market). The VMP for each worker is the worker's marginal product times the price of the product ($2).

Given the production function, product price, and wage rate, the hiring rule for a profit-maximizing employer (firm) is:

- Hire another worker if the VMP ≥ W for that worker
- Do not hire another worker if the VMP < W for that worker.

Based on the above example, the firm should hire three workers, since VMP ≥ W for the first three workers. Hiring the fourth worker would add $10 per hour to revenue and $20 per hour to costs, causing profit to decrease, so a profit-maximizing firm would only hire three workers.

In some examples, VMP and the wage rate may not be exactly equal for the last worker is hired. It would be more realistic to consider hiring fractions of additional workers (part-time employees), but the examples in this book are simplified.

This analysis illustrates one point on the firm's **demand for labor** function: if the wage rate is $20 per hour, then the quantity of labor demanded by this firm is three workers. To derive the entire labor demand function, other points are needed, which requires repeating the analysis at different wage rates. For example, if the wage falls to $10 per hour, then the firm will hire a fourth worker according to the profit-maximizing rule. Other points can be identified by choosing other wage rates, but two points are enough to conclude that the demand for labor is downward-sloping.

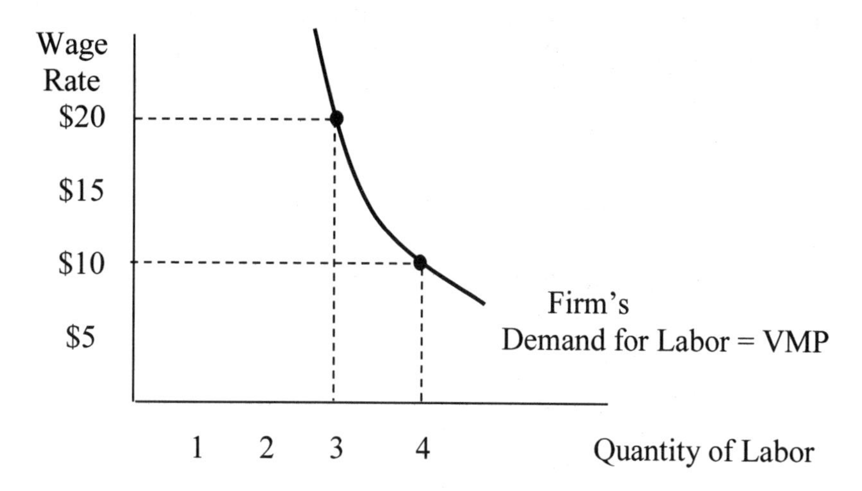

A change in the market wage rate leads to a change in the quantity of labor demanded and a *movement along* the firm's demand for labor curve. The firm's demand for labor curve is its value of marginal product (VMP) curve. The **market demand for labor** curve is the sum of all individual firms' demand for labor in that market.

The demand for labor increases or **shifts to the right** as a result of a change in:

- the price of the product: an increase in consumer demand causes an increase in the product price, which in turn causes the VMP to increase.
- labor productivity: an improvement in labor productivity, brought about by better training or improved technology, causes the VMP to increase.
- the cost of other resources: a decrease in the price of an input that is complementary to labor or an increase in the price of an input that is a substitute for labor causes the VMP to increase.

The demand for labor decreases or **shifts to the left** if there is a decrease in consumer demand and product price, a decline in labor productivity, an increase in the price of a complementary input, or a decrease in the price of a substitute input.

Labor supply decisions are based on several factors, including the wage rate. Ceteris paribus, an increase in the wage rate leads to an increase in the quantity of labor supplied and vice-versa, which means the market supply of labor curve is upward sloping. A change in the wage rate will cause a movement along the labor supply function while other events can cause labor supply to shift. For example, an increase in the number of people earning college degrees is likely to increase supply in skilled labor markets and decrease the supply of unskilled labor.

Wage rates and employment levels are determined by the interaction of labor demand and labor supply in competitive labor markets. A shift in the market labor demand or market labor supply curve leads to a new equilibrium level of employment and wage rate for the market.

Labor Market Equilibrium

The labor market is in equilibrium where labor demand and labor supply intersect. In the graph below, if labor demand is D_1, the market is in equilibrium with L_1 workers employed, and each worker is earning a wage rate of W_1. An increase in labor demand, from D_1 to D_2, causes both employment and the equilibrium wage rate to increase, as shown in the graph.

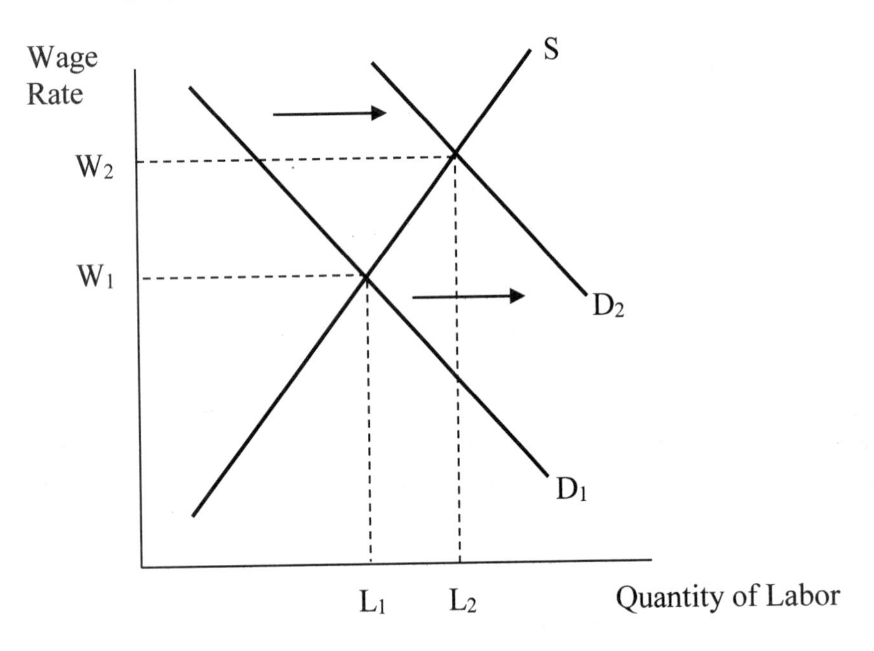

The tools of supply and demand analysis can be applied to the labor market to understand why wages rise or fall and why employment rises or falls in particular markets (or occupations). There are four possible shifts that can lead to a change in labor market equilibrium.

An increase in the demand for labor may be caused by, for example, an increase in the demand for the →good or service labor is employed to produce, often indicating a positive change in consumer preferences or a booming economy. A recession or an adverse change in consumer preferences may cause the demand for a particular kind of labor to fall. A change in technology or a change in the price of other inputs could also cause the demand for labor to shift in either direction.

The supply of labor in a particular market might increase due to factors such as an increase in the number of workers with training for that specific occupation or an increase in immigration that increases the number of qualified workers in that occupation. If there are more young workers entering the labor force than there are retiring workers, then the overall supply of labor increases. A reduction in immigration or an increase in the number of workers retiring or leaving the labor force can cause the supply of labor to fall. Shifts in a specific labor market can also occur as workers leave one labor market to join another.

The graphs below show how equilibrium wage and employment change following each of the four possible shifts.

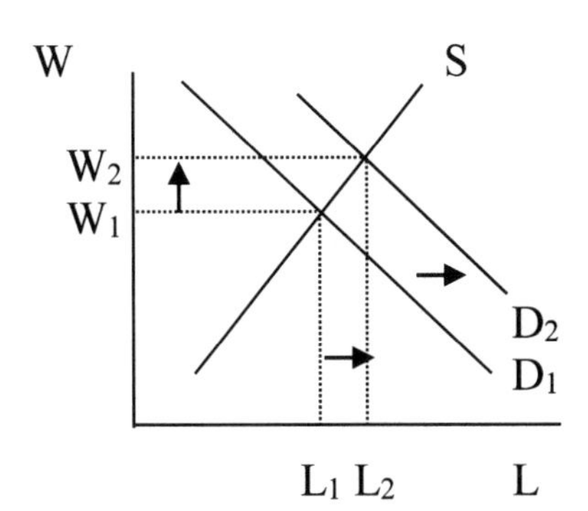

An increase in the demand for labor causes higher wages and employment.

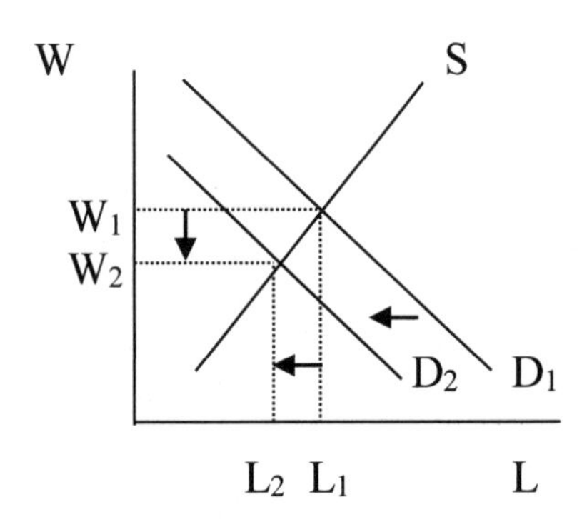

A decrease in the demand for labor causes lower wages and employment.

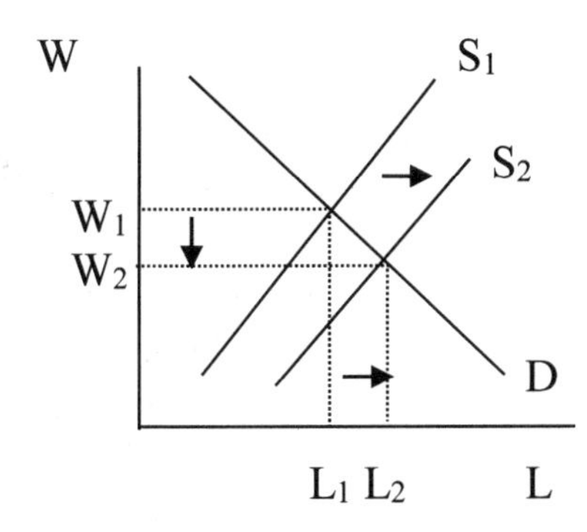

An increase in the supply of labor causes lower wages, but higher employment.

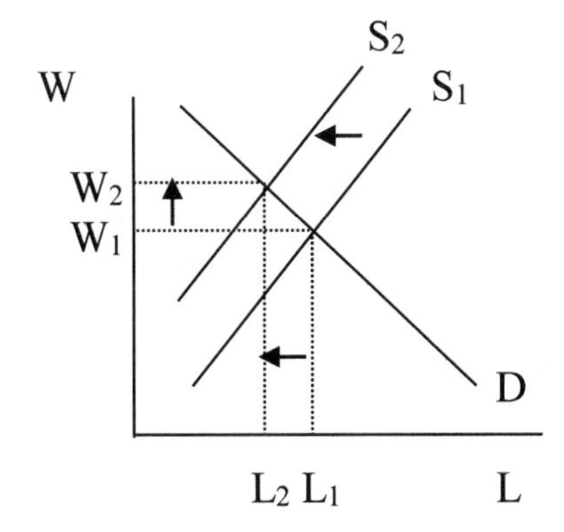

A decrease in the supply of labor causes higher wages, but lower employment.

Wage Differentials

The graphs below illustrate two labor markets in which the equilibrium wage rate is higher in Labor Market 1 than in Labor Market 2.

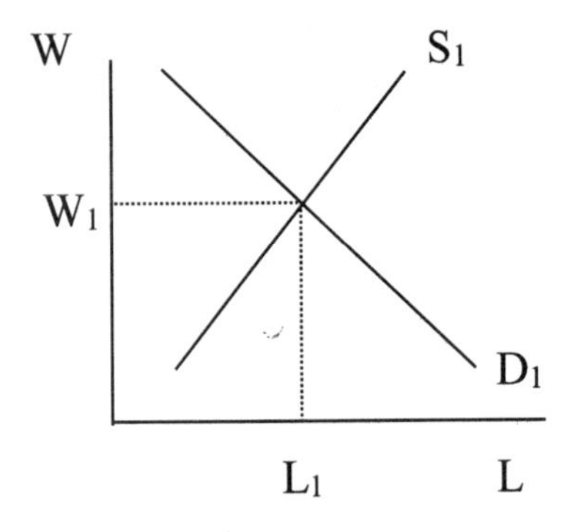

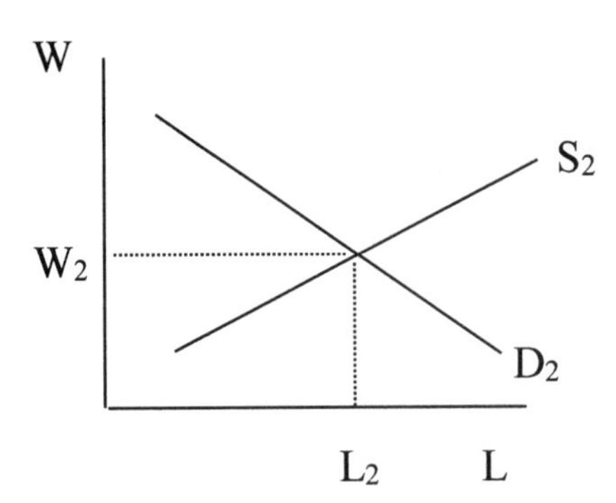

Labor Market 1 **Labor Market 2**

Suppose workers leave Labor Market 2 to join Labor Market 1, attracted by higher wages in Labor Market 1. Then the supply curve S_1 will shift to the right, and supply curve S_2 will shift to the left. The difference between the two wage rates, W_1 and W_2, will disappear as these two shifts occur, causing wages to equalize. The theory of wage differentials (first discussed by Adam Smith) attempts to explain why real-world wages do not equalize across different labor markets. Why do wage differentials persist? There must be something that either prevents workers from moving out of Labor Market 2 into Labor Market 1 or something that makes workers prefer to stay in Labor Market 2 despite relatively low wage rates.

There are many possible explanations for persistent wage differentials. One important factor relates to education and training. For example, workers may not be able to enter labor market 1 (or, in general, a labor market with a relatively high wage rate) because they lack the required credentials, such as a college degree. Another factor has to do with the non-wage aspects of different jobs. For example, the jobs in Labor Market 1 may require working under risky or unpleasant conditions. Or, the jobs in Labor Market 2 may be more flexible or provide better benefits (retirement, vacation time, health insurance). Workers with less desirable job characteristics may require a pay premium (sometimes called a compensating wage differential) to compensate for less pleasant working conditions, more hazardous conditions, or other undesirable job characteristics.

There is evidence of **occupational segregation** between men and women, which partially explains why men earn more than women on average. For example, traditionally more women than men have become teachers than may be earned elsewhere. The teaching occupation offers flexibility and time off, which may compensate for lower salaries. It is difficult to determine if occupational segregation is the result of labor market discrimination, which may bar some groups such as women and minorities, from entering high-wage markets or the result of a preference by certain groups for jobs with desirable characteristics, such as flexible schedules and a pleasant working environment.

Firms use capital (machines, tools, plant, and equipment) combined with other resources to produce output. Over time, firms invest in capital to replace worn out or obsolete plant and equipment or to expand their scale of production. Production usually also involves the use of natural resources, often referred to as land. Combined with our understanding of labor markets, models dealing with capital and natural resource markets help to explain production decisions and income determination in a market economy.

Capital Markets

Capital markets facilitate the flow of **financial capital** between savers and borrowers. Firms demand financial capital in order to purchase **physical capital**. The price of financial capital is the interest rate. The interest rate is determined by supply and demand in the market for financial capital. The supply of financial capital, which comes from household saving, usually increases (shifts to the right) as the population increases and as income increases. The demand for financial capital increases (shifts to the right) as the population grows and technology advances. When the supply of and demand for financial capital both increase, the change in the interest rate depends on the relative size of the two shifts.

The cost of acquiring physical capital has two components: the price of the physical capital and the interest that must be paid, or foregone, to acquire the necessary financial capital. Capital purchases require the firm to compare the cost of the capital incurred today with the earnings expected from the capital in the future. The net present value calculation allows a firm to compare the returns on different capital purchase options in dollar terms.

Present value is the value today of a future stream of income. When nominal (market) interest rates are positive, a given amount of money, if left alone in an interest-bearing account, would grow over time, with a future value exceeding its present value. Looking at the reverse, a sum to be received in the future would have a lower value, or would be **discounted,** in the present period. Future sums can be discounted to present values using a simple calculation that takes into account the impact of interest over time. Assuming compound interest, the present value of a sum of money to be received in the future is determined using the equation:

$$\text{Present Value} = \frac{\text{Future Value}}{(1 + r)^n}$$

where the future value is the sum to be received in the future, r is the interest rate, and n is the number of time periods. For example, how much money would you need to deposit in an interest-bearing account today to have $5,000 for a down payment on a car? The amount will depend on the interest rate and the length of time that the money is left to grow. If the annual interest rate is 6% and the length of time is 4 years, you must deposit approximately $3,968 today since this is the present value (PV) of $5,000.

$$PV = \frac{\$5{,}000}{(1 + .06)^4} = \frac{\$5{,}000}{1.26} = \$3{,}968$$

Net present value (NPV) is the value today of the future income generated by the capital minus the present value of the cost of the capital. For example, assume a delivery firm has two options: a minivan that costs $20,000 and is expected to generate $12,500 per year in revenue for 2 years or a full-size van that costs $25,000 and is expected to generate $15,000 per year in revenue for 2 years. There are other factors that must be considered, such as depreciation. Assume that both vehicles depreciate to zero in two years to simplify the example. Which investment option has the higher net present value assuming the interest rate is 6%?

Step 1: Determine the value today of the future revenue (rounded to the $1)

Minivan:

$$PV = \frac{\$12{,}500}{(1+.06)} + \frac{\$12{,}500}{(1+.06)^2} = \frac{\$12{,}500}{1.06} + \frac{\$12{,}500}{1.12} = \$22{,}953$$

Full-size Van:

$$PV = \frac{\$15{,}000}{(1+.06)} + \frac{\$15{,}000}{(1+.06)^2} = \frac{\$15{,}000}{1.06} + \frac{\$15{,}000}{1.12} = \$27{,}544$$

Step 2: Determine the net present value of each option

Minivan: NPV = $22,953 - $20,000 = $2,953
Full-size Van: NPV = $27,544 - $25,000 = $2,544

Thus, the minivan is a more profitable investment at an interest rate of 6%. The **internal rate of return** is defined as the interest rate at which the net present value of the project would be zero and is used to calculate the rate of return on investments. A given investment is potentially profitable if the internal rate of return exceeds the interest rate, or cost of capital.

Land and Natural Resources

The supply of land is perfectly inelastic, or vertical, at the fixed quantity available. Because supply is perfectly inelastic, the price of land is entirely demand-determined and land earns economic rent. **Economic rent** is the income paid to a resource owner that exceeds the amount necessary to elicit a given quantity supplied of that resource. The quantity of land supplied will be the same at a price of zero as at a price of one million dollars per acre. For this reason, the income earned by owners of land is referred to as **pure economic rent**. Other factors of production, including labor in fields like sports and entertainment, receive economic rent. Most professional basketball players would still be willing to play basketball even at a much lower salary, but they are paid very high salaries due to the high demand and inelastic supply of qualified individuals.

The input category of land also encompasses natural resources, which are either exhaustible or nonexhaustible. **Exhaustible natural resources** are those that can be used only once and cannot be replaced once they are used, such as coal and oil. **Nonexhaustible natural resources** are those that can be used repeatedly, such as rivers and sunshine. A detailed analysis of natural resource markets is complicated and is generally deferred to upper division economics courses, such as environmental economics.

NAME____SECTION#______________

PRINT LAST NAME, FIRST NAME

LABOR MARKETS

1. The demand for labor:
   a. determines the demand for the output that labor helps produce.
   b. is derived from the demand for the output that labor helps produce.
   c. depends entirely on the cost of labor.
   d. is perfectly elastic for the market as a whole, but downward-sloping for an individual employer.

2. Which of the following does **not** reflect labor demand as a derived demand?
   a. The demand for the services of a babysitter by new parents
   b. The demand for teachers by a public school system
   c. The demand for financial planners by Fidelity Investments
   d. The demand for baristas by Starbucks

3. The value of the marginal product of labor (VMP_L) is the:
   a. change in total revenue that results from selling one more unit of output.
   b. change in output that results from employing one more unit of labor.
   c. change in total revenue generated from employing one more unit of labor.
   d. total revenue generated from the use of labor.

Use the information below to answer questions 4 and 5.

ABC Manufacturing produces widgets and sells them in a perfectly competitive market for $2 each. The firm hires workers in a perfectly competitive labor market for $120 per day. ABC's production function is given in the chart below.

Labor	Output Per Day
0	0
1	240
2	420
3	530
4	580
5	600

4. The marginal product (MP) of the second worker is _________ units of output, and the value of the marginal product (VMP) of the second worker is __________.
   a. 180; $90
   b. 180; $360
   c. 210; $420
   d. 210; $105

5. To maximize profit, ABC Manufacturing should hire:
   a. 2 workers.
   b. 3 workers.
   c. 4 workers.
   d. 5 workers.

NAME____SECTION#________________

PRINT LAST NAME, FIRST NAME

6. In competitive labor markets, firms hire:
   a. additional workers as long as the marginal product of labor is positive.
   b. the amount of labor needed to produce the profit-maximizing level of output.
   c. the amount of labor needed to produce the revenue-maximizing level of output.
   d. the number of workers they can afford given a fixed budget.

B

7. In a competitive labor market, an increase in the equilibrium wage rate could result from:
   a. a decrease in the demand for labor.
   b. an increase in the supply of labor.
   c. an increase in the demand for labor.
   d. a decrease in the number of workers represented by labor unions.

C

8. Ceteris paribus, the demand for farm workers will increase in response to all of the following ***except*** an increase in the:
   a. wage paid to farm workers.
   b. price of the agricultural output.
   c. productivity of farm workers.
   d. demand for agricultural output.

A

9. For a competitive firm hiring in a competitive labor market, the profit maximizing rule is to hire labor to the point where:
   a. the marginal cost of the last unit of labor hired is zero.
   b. the value of the marginal product is equal to the wage rate.
   c. marginal product is equal to marginal cost.
   d. the value of the marginal product is at a maximum.

B

10. An increase in the marginal product of autoworkers would be expected to cause a(n) ________ in the value of the marginal product or labor and a(n) ________ in the firm's demand for autoworkers.
   a. increase; increase
   b. decrease; decrease
   c. increase; decrease
   d. decrease; increase

A

NAME____ SECTION#_________________

PRINT LAST NAME, FIRST NAME

THE LABOR MARKET

Suppose Quincy's Quiche Corner operates a restaurant in a mall and sells only various kinds of quiche priced at $3 each (**P = $3**). Employees are primarily high school students with the same skill set and each employee is paid $8.00 per hour (**W = $8**). Assume Quincy's is selling in a perfectly competitive output market and hiring in a perfectly competitive labor market. To simplify, assume that Quincy's has total fixed costs of $18 per hour (**TFC = $18**) and that labor is the only variable input so that total cost is TFC plus total labor costs. Assume also that the goal of Quincy's Quiche Corner is to maximize profit and Quincy follows the profit-maximizing rule.

Complete the table and then answer the questions below the table.

Number of Workers (L)	Output (quiches/hour = Q)	MP_L	VMP_L
0	0		
1	10	________	________
2	18	________	________
3	24	________	________
4	28	________	________
5	30	________	________

1. How many employees should Quincy's Quiche Corner hire? __________________

2. How much is total variable cost per hour for Quincy's? __________________

3. How much is total cost per hour for Quincy's? __________________

4. How much is total revenue per hour for Quincy's? __________________

5. How much profit will Quincy's earn per hour? __________________

NAME____SECTION#______________
PRINT LAST NAME, FIRST NAME

THE LABOR MARKET

Use the graphs below to answer questions 1 through 10.

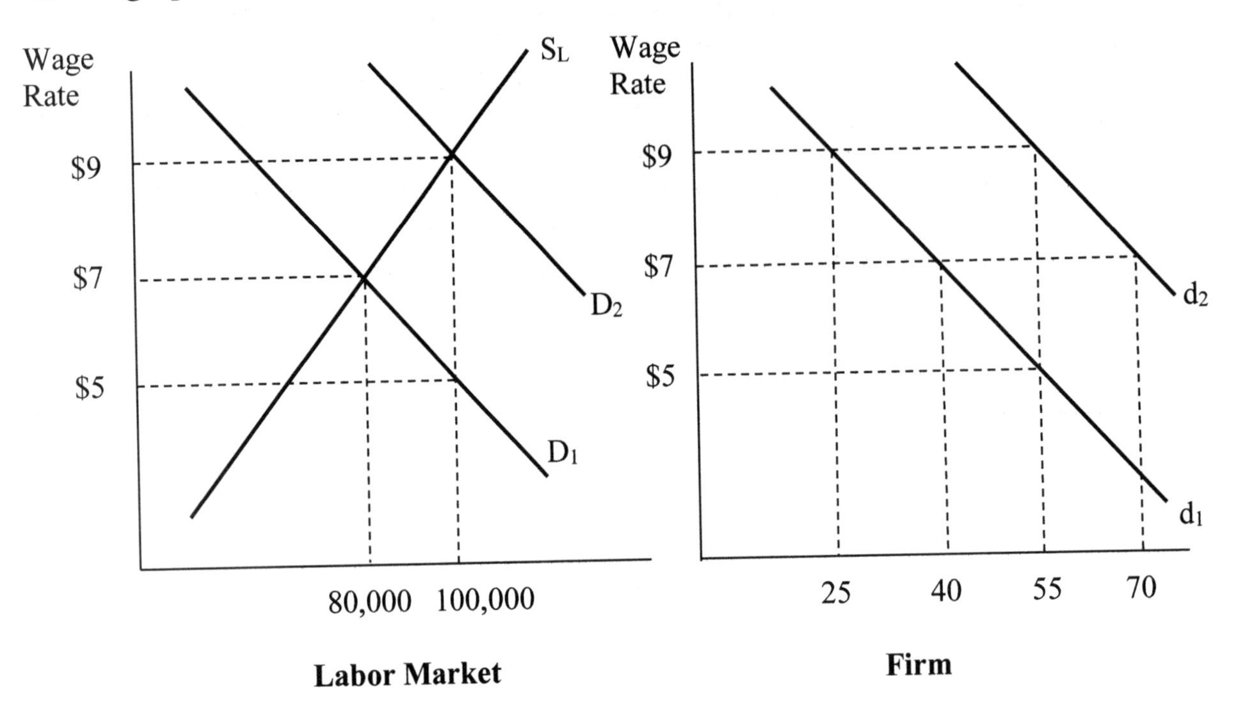

If market demand for labor is D_1 and the market supply of labor is S_L, then 1) __________ workers will be hired in the market. The equilibrium market wage is 2) $__________.

At the equilibrium market wage, the firm will hire 3) ________ workers if its demand for labor curve is d_1, and the firm will hire 4) __________ workers if its demand is d_2.

Suppose the wage is increased to $9 while the market demand for labor remains at D_1 and the firm's demand for labor remains at d_1. Then, the firm will hire 5) __________ workers and the **market** faces a 6) ____________ (shortage/surplus) of labor, which will likely 7) _________ (raise/lower) unemployment.

An increase in worker productivity would cause the firm's demand for labor to shift to the 8) __________ (right/left). If labor demand shifts from D_1 to D_2, the new market wage rate will be 9) $__________ and 10) __________ workers will be employed in this market.

NAME____ SECTION#______________
PRINT LAST NAME, FIRST NAME

RESOURCE MARKETS

1. The supply of financial capital increases as a result of:
   a. an increase in the interest rate, or the price of financial capital.
   b. a decrease in the interest rate, or the price of financial capital.
   c. a decrease in household income.
   d. an increase in household income and wealth.

2. In the market for financial capital:
   a. firms sell financial capital in order to earn high profits.
   b. firms demand financial capital in order to purchase physical capital.
   c. households demand financial capital by saving.
   d. firms borrow and households save at a constant rate of interest.

3. The cost of acquiring physical capital:
   a. is equal to the price of physical capital.
   b. is zero when the nominal interest rate is equal to the inflation rate.
   c. includes both the price of physical capital and the interest that must be paid or foregone to acquire the necessary financial capital.
   d. varies inversely with the rate of interest.

4. Technological advance would be expected to ________ the demand for financial capital, causing the equilibrium interest rate to ________, ceteris paribus.
   a. increase; increase
   b. increase; decrease
   c. decrease; increase
   d. decrease; decrease

5. Other things constant, a decrease in the rate of interest will cause the present value of a given amount of money to be received in the future to:
   a. increase.
   b. decrease.
   c. increase if the money is to be received soon, but decrease if the money will not be received for a long time.
   d. decrease if the money is to be received soon, but increase if the money will not be received for a long time.

6. What is the approximate present value of $5,000 received in 10 years if the annual interest rate is 9%, assuming annual compounding?
   a. $500
   b. $2,112
   c. $4,587
   d. $11,835

NAME____SECTION#______________

PRINT LAST NAME, FIRST NAME

7. Frank estimates that he will need $20,000 in 8 years for a down payment on a new house. Approximately how much money must Frank put into savings today to achieve his goal if the annual rate paid on savings is 8%?
   a. $10,805
   b. $12,388
   c. $18,519
   d. $37,000

8. Net present value is defined as the:
   a. present value of the future income generated by the capital, net of inflation.
   b. total future income generated by the capital minus the cost of the capital.
   c. value today of the future income generated by the capital minus the cost of the capital.
   d. value today of the future income generated by the capital plus the cost of the capital.

9. Bill's Lawn Service is contemplating the purchase of a new lawn mower. A riding lawn mower that costs $3,000 is expected to generate $4,000 in revenue per year for 2 years. A push mower that costs $1,400 is expected to generate $3,000 in revenue per year for 2 years. If the interest rate is 10%, which mower should Bill buy and why?
   a. The push mower because it costs less
   b. The push mower because it has the higher net present value
   c. The riding mower because it generates more revenue
   d. The riding mower because it has the higher net present value

10. If the supply of land is perfectly inelastic, an increase in the demand for land causes:
    a. an increase in the price of land as well as the quantity of land.
    b. an increase in the price of land, but no change in the quantity of land.
    c. a decrease in the price of land and an increase in the quantity of land.
    d. no change in the price of land, but an increase in the quantity of land.

Appendix: Noncompetitive Labor Markets

There are markets where buyers or sellers of labor have control over the wage rate, so the competitive model described in the chapter does not apply. On the demand side of the labor market, market power and the ability to influence the wage rate exists when there is a single or dominant employer in a market. A **monopsony** is a market in which there is only one buyer. In the case of labor, a monopsony exists when a single firm employs all of the labor in a specific market.

Because the monopsonist is the sole employer, it faces the entire upward-sloping supply of labor curve and must pay a higher wage to attract more labor, which means that the marginal cost (MC) of an additional unit of labor is greater than the wage rate. The monopsony firm sets the VMP of labor equal to the marginal cost of labor to maximize profits and, as a result, hires fewer workers and pays a lower wage than would prevail under competitive conditions. This result is illustrated in the graph below.

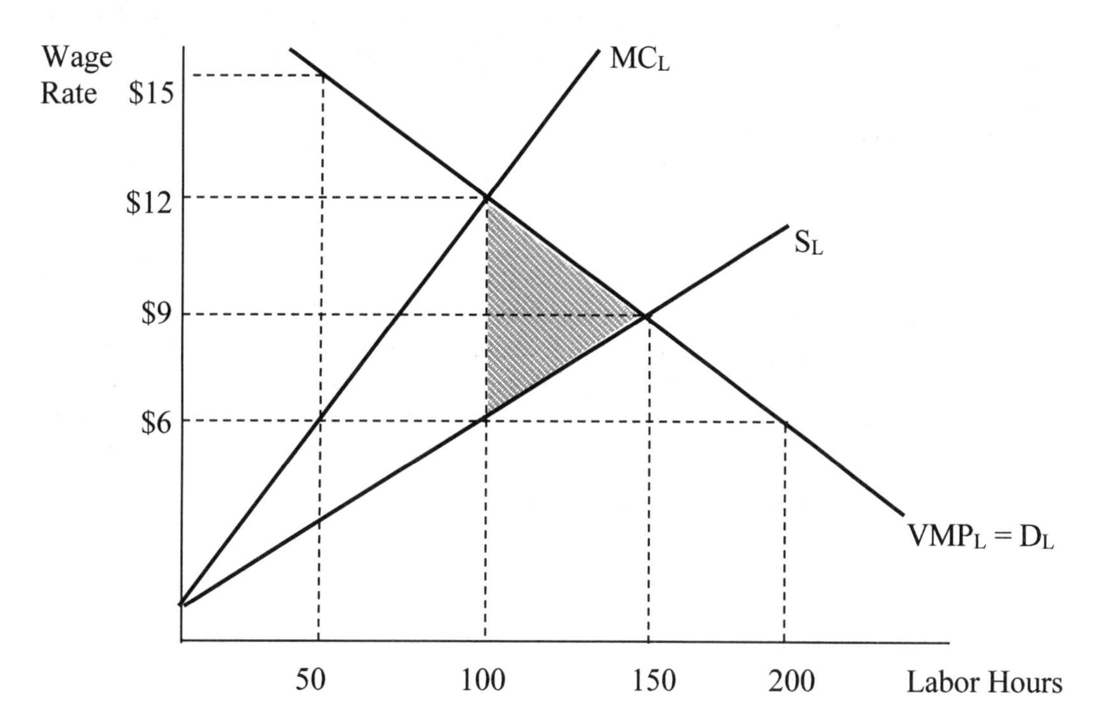

Based on the graph, the monopsony employer continues to hire workers up to the point where the MC of labor curve intersects the VMP curve, which occurs at 100 labor hours. The value of marginal product for the last worker hired is $12; however, the employer does *not* pay a wage rate of $12, because 100 labor hours will be supplied if the wage offered is only $6. The monopsony employer keeps the wage rate and employment low, relative to the competitive outcome (the competitive outcome occurs where supply and demand intersect, at a wage of $9 and labor hours of 150), so there is a deadweight loss as measured by the shaded area in the graph. This model has been used to justify the existence of labor unions as a way of achieving a balance of power in noncompetitive labor markets.

Labor unions possess power on the supply side of the labor market while large employers may exert power on the demand side of the labor market. In the case of labor unions, workers band together in an attempt to increase the wage rate and influence work conditions for union members.

The three main goals of most labor unions are to increase worker compensation, improve working conditions, and create more jobs for union members. In the collective bargaining process, union representatives negotiate with the employer on behalf of members to achieve the best possible outcome for union members.

A **bilateral monopoly** exists when the employer is a monopsony and workers are represented by a monopoly union. The market power on both sides may be balanced in such a way that the outcome is very close to a competitive outcome. The wage rate is determined through a collective bargaining process, with the monopsony firm bargaining for a low wage and the monopoly union bargaining for a high wage. If both sides win some concessions in the bargaining process, then the outcome is neither the high wage associated with monopoly unions nor the low wage associated with monopsony firms, but a wage that is in between and probably quite close to the wage that would have been reached under competitive forces.

Bilateral monopolies exist in professional sports in the U.S. Team owners are the only buyers of the labor services of elite professional players and the players are represented by a players' union.

Based on the graph on the previous page, if a monopsony employer offers a wage of $6, and a monopoly union asks for a wage of $12, they could reach an agreement through collective bargaining that sets the wage rate at or near $9. If the market were competitive, equilibrium would occur at a wage rate of $9 and an employment level of 150 labor hours (this is where labor supply and labor demand intersect), so it is possible that the outcome of bilateral monopoly bargaining could approximate the competitive outcome and eliminate the deadweight loss associated with monopoly or monopsony power.

NAME____SECTION#______________
PRINT LAST NAME, FIRST NAME

IMPERFECTLY COMPETITIVE LABOR MARKETS

Use the graph below to answer questions 1 through 4.

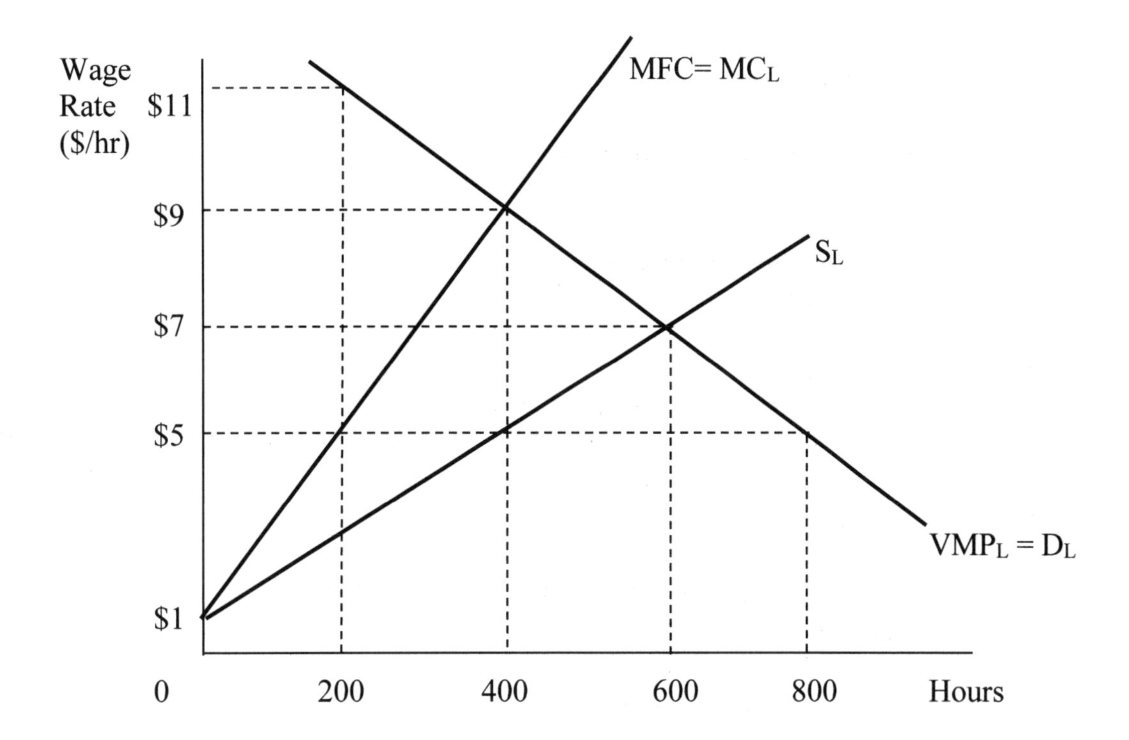

1. If the above diagram represents a perfectly competitive labor market, the equilibrium level of employment will be _____ hours.
   a. 200 c. 600
   b. 400 d. 800

2. If the above diagram represents a perfectly competitive labor market, the equilibrium wage rate will be _____.
   a. $5 c. $9
   b. $7 d. $11

3. If the above diagram represents a monopsony employer, the equilibrium level of employment will be _____ hours.
   a. 200 c. 600
   b. 400 d. 800

4. If the above diagram represents a monopsony employer, the equilibrium wage rate will be _____.
   a. $5 c. $9
   b. $7 d. $11

NAME____SECTION#______________

PRINT LAST NAME, FIRST NAME

5. If all of the workers in a particular market band together to form a labor union, the union possesses power on the ________ side of the labor market.
   a. monopsony
   b. supply
   c. demand
   d. equilibrium

6 . A monopsony is a market in which there is:
   a. a single seller.
   b. a single buyer.
   c. a single seller and a single buyer.
   d. a single seller or a single buyer.

7. A bilateral monopoly exists when:
   a. the market for labor is perfectly competitive.
   b. the employer is a monopolist in both the product market and the resource market.
   c. the employer is a monopsony and workers are represented by a monopoly union.
   d. there are two monopoly labor unions competing for members.

8. The goals of most labor unions include all of the following ***except***:
   a. increasing worker compensation.
   b. increasing the supply of labor.
   c. increasing the demand for labor.
   d. improving working conditions.

9. For a monopsonist, the marginal cost of an additional unit of labor is:
   a. zero.
   b. less than the wage rate.
   c. equal to the wage rate.
   d. greater than the wage rate.

10. If the quantity of labor supplied equals 5 at a wage rate of $10 and 6 at a wage rate of $11, then the marginal cost of hiring a 6th worker for a monopsony employer is _____, assuming all workers are paid the same wage rate.
   a. $10
   b. $11
   c. $16
   d. $22

PRACTICE EXAM III

The correct answers to this practice exam can be found on page 304.

1. A pure monopoly is an industry in which:
   a. one firm is the producer or seller of a product with close, but not perfect, substitutes.
   b. one firm is the sole producer or seller of a product that has no close substitutes.
   c. there are no barriers to prevent other firms from entering the industry.
   d. the price is determined by market forces but output is determined by the seller.

2. All of the following are examples of barriers to entry ***except***:
   a. patents and copyrights.
   b. government franchises and licenses.
   c. constant returns to scale.
   d. sole ownership of key resources.

3. The demand curve for a monopoly firm is:
   a. more elastic than the industry, or market, demand curve for its product.
   b. less elastic than the industry, or market, demand curve for its product.
   c. the same as the industry, or market, demand curve for its product.
   d. perfectly inelastic at the output where MR=MC.

4. If electrical service can be more efficiently provided to a market by a single supplier than by many competing suppliers, the market is considered to be a(n):
   a. rent-seeking monopoly.
   b. unregulated monopoly.
   c. natural monopoly.
   d. efficient monopoly.

5. Which of the following is ***always*** true for a monopolist?
   a. Profit is maximized where marginal revenue equals marginal cost.
   b. Economic profit is positive in both the short run and the long run.
   c. Consumer surplus is zero because the monopoly price is greater than the competitive price.
   d. All of the above are always true for a monopolist.

6. A monopolist that earns positive economic profit in short-run equilibrium will:
   a. definitely continue to earn positive economic profit in the long run.
   b. earn positive economic profit in the long run if it can maintain barriers to entry, assuming no changes in costs or market demand.
   c. earn higher economic profit in the long run because of economies of scale.
   d. earn economic profit equal to zero in long-run equilibrium.

Use the following table to answer the next two questions.

Price per unit	Quantity Demanded
$60	0
50	1
40	2
30	3
20	4

7. For a monopolist that is unable to price discriminate, the marginal revenue of the 2nd unit is _____ and the marginal revenue of the 3rd unit is _____.
   a. $30; $10
   b. $10; $0
   c. $30; –$10
   d. $10; –$10

8. A monopolist that is able to price discriminate by charging each consumer the highest price the consumer is willing to pay would earn total revenue of _____ if it sold 2 units of output and total revenue of _____ if it sold 3 units of output.
   a. $80; $90
   b. $120; $140
   c. $90; $80
   d. $90; $120

9. First-degree (perfect) price discrimination occurs when:
   a. the seller is able to charge each buyer the highest price the buyer will pay.
   b. the seller offers a volume discount to buyers who are willing to purchase more.
   c. the seller is able to separate customers into two different groups and charge one group a higher price than the other group is charged.
   d. the price charged to all buyers is the same as the competitive price.

10. Second-degree price discrimination occurs when:
   a. the seller is able to charge each buyer the highest price the buyer will pay.
   b. the seller offers a volume discount to buyers who are willing to purchase more.
   c. the seller is able to separate customers into two different groups and charge one group a higher price than the other group is charged.
   d. the price charged to all buyers is the same as the competitive price.

11. A seller who is able to separate customers into two different groups and charge one group a higher price than the other group is charged is engaging in:
   a. first-degree price discrimination.
   b. second-degree price discrimination.
   c. third-degree price discrimination.
   d. perfect price discrimination.

Use the graph below, depicting an unregulated, profit-maximizing monopolist that cannot price discriminate, to answer the next three questions.

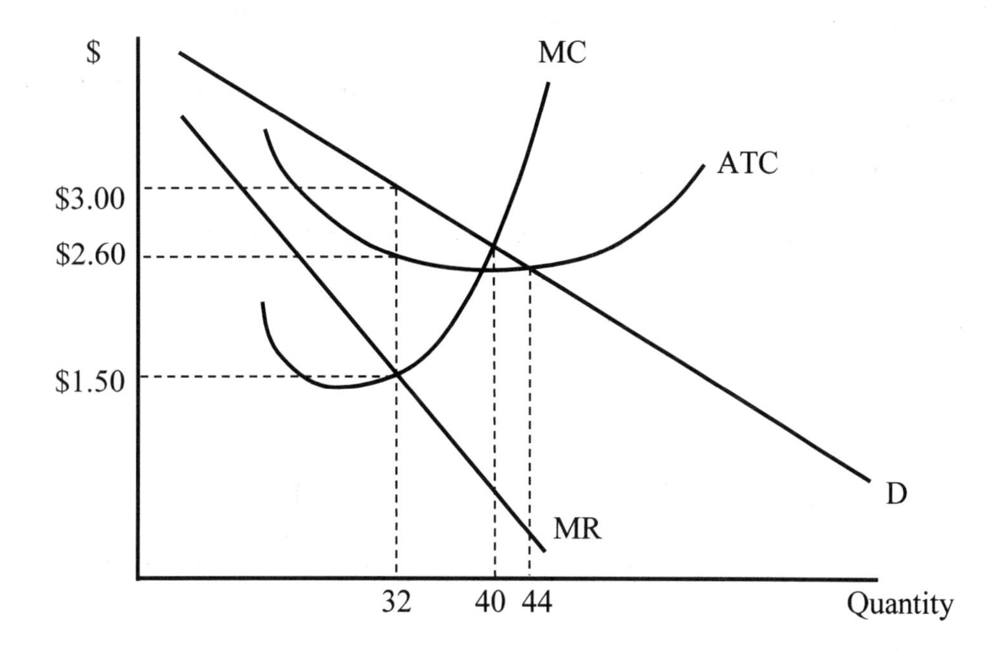

12. This monopolist will produce _____ units of output and charge a price of _____.
    a. 32; $3.00
    b. 32; $2.60
    c. 44; $1.50
    d. 40; $2.60

13. This monopolist is:
    a. earning zero economic profit.
    b. earning positive economic profit equal to $48.
    c. earning positive economic profit equal to $12.80.
    d. incurring economic losses equal to $12.80.

14. The efficient level of output in this market is ____ so the deadweight loss due to monopoly is approximately equal to ____.
    a. 40; $6
    b. 44; $6
    c. 40; $12
    d. 44; $12

15. A producer of widgets is most likely to be a monopolist when:
   a. there are no close substitutes for widgets and there are barriers to entry into the widget industry.
   b. a single firm owns the patent for producing widgets, but other firms can sell gadgets that are a close substitute for widgets.
   c. there are no close substitutes for widgets and there are no barriers to entry into the widget industry.
   d. there are close substitutes for widgets.

16. Which of the following is true for a profit-maximizing monopolist that charges all consumers the same price?
   a. $P > MR = MC$
   b. $P < MR = MC$
   c. $P > MR > MC$
   d. $P = MR = MC$

17. From society's perspective:
   a. monopoly markets are more efficient than competitive markets.
   b. there is no difference between the outcome in monopoly markets and competitive markets.
   c. it is never good to have only one firm service an entire market.
   d. competition generally leads to lower prices, higher output, and greater efficiency than monopoly.

18. A firm that is able to use price discrimination will seek to:
   a. charge customers with more elastic demand a higher price.
   b. charge all customers the same price.
   c. charge customers with more elastic demand a lower price.
   d. set price equal to marginal revenue to determine the profit-maximizing level of output.

19. At the profit-maximizing level of output for an unregulated monopolist:
   a. marginal benefit exceeds marginal cost which creates a deadweight loss.
   b. marginal cost exceeds marginal benefit which creates a deadweight loss.
   c. marginal benefit equals marginal cost which is efficient.
   d. price is equal to marginal cost but price is greater than marginal revenue.

20. Government addresses the potential inefficiency associated with imperfectly competitive markets by:
    a. requiring all firms to seek government approval before raising prices.
    b. blocking all proposed mergers.
    c. restricting market power through antitrust laws and regulation.
    d. protecting monopolies from the forces of competition.

21. All of the following are characteristics of a monopolistically competitive industry ***except***:
    a. there are many firms in a monopolistically competitive industry.
    b. the firms in the industry produce goods that are close, but not perfect, substitutes.
    c. there are no significant barriers to entry into the industry.
    d. the firms in the industry engage in interdependent decision making.

22. A monopolistically competitive firm's demand curve is ___________ elastic than a perfectly competitive firm's demand curve and _____________ elastic than a monopolistic firm's demand curve for the same product.
    a. more; less
    b. less; less
    c. more; more
    d. less; more

23. ***Like*** a perfectly competitive firm, a monopolistically competitive firm:
    a. has some control over the price it charges.
    b. sets price above marginal cost.
    c. maximizes profit by producing the quantity where marginal revenue equals marginal cost so long as price exceeds average variable cost.
    d. All of the above statements are true.

24. For monopolistically competitive firms in long-run equilibrium, economic profit is:
    a. positive because their products are unique.
    b. positive because their products are differentiated.
    c. zero because there are no barriers to entry.
    d. zero because of strong barriers to entry.

Use the graph below depicting a profit-maximizing monopolistically competitive firm to answer the next two questions.

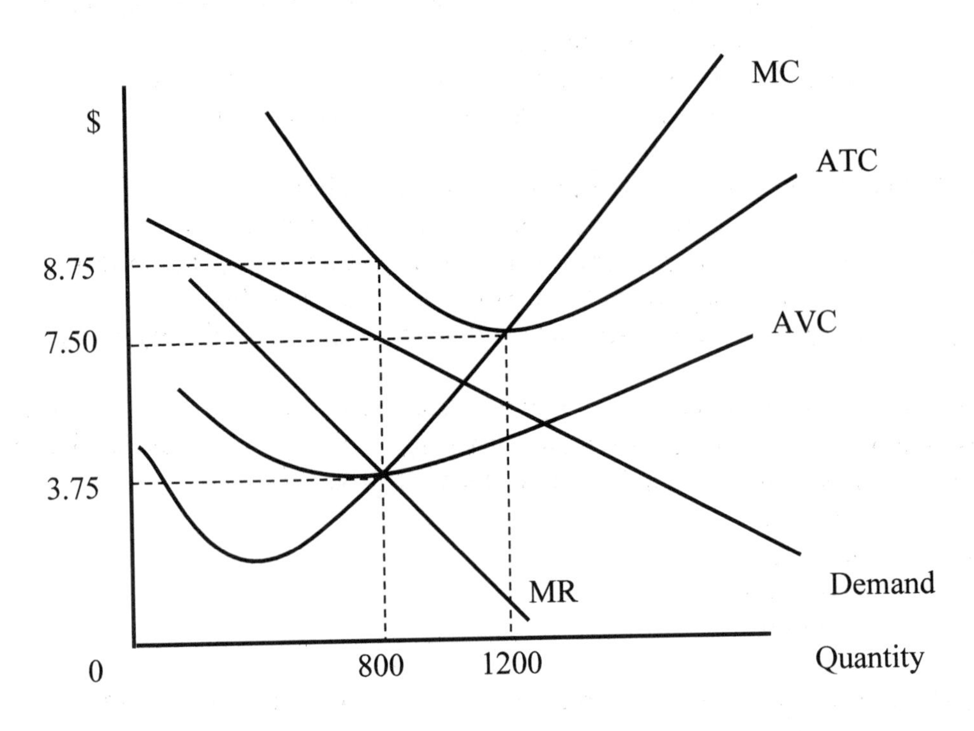

25. This firm's total fixed costs (TFC) are equal to:
    a. $3,000.
    b. $4,000.
    c. $7,000.
    d. $9,000.

26. In the short run, the best this firm can do is to:
    a. shut down and pay total fixed costs.
    b. produce where the ATC curve is minimized to minimize losses.
    c. produce where MR = MC and incur losses equal to $1,000.
    d. produce where MR = MC and incur losses equal to $4,000.

27. An industry dominated by a few large firms whose pricing and output decisions are dependent on one another is:
    a. illegal in the United States.
    b. monopolistically competitive.
    c. monopolistic.
    d. oligopolistic.

28. The characteristic that distinguishes oligopoly from other market structures is:
    a. the existence of barriers to entry.
    b. interdependence among firms in pricing and output decisions.
    c. product differentiation.
    d. the ability of firms to earn long-run economic profits.

29. To be successful in increasing prices for their product, members of a cartel must:
    a. produce as much as they can.
    b. encourage new firms to enter the market.
    c. agree to limit their output.
    d. find ways to lower costs of production.

Use the payoff matrix below to answer the next two questions.

	Acme does not advertise	Acme advertises
Topco does not advertise	Both firms earn profits of $50 million.	Topco earns profits of $30 million and Acme earns profits of $60 million
Topco advertises	Topco earns profits of $60 million and Acme earns profits of $30 million.	Both firms earn profits of $40 million.

30. Suppose Acme and Topco must choose whether or not to advertise without knowing what the other will do. In the Nash equilibrium:
    a. neither Acme nor Topco chooses to advertise.
    b. both Acme and Topco choose to advertise.
    c. Acme advertises, but Topco does not.
    d. Topco advertises, but Acme does not.

31. Which strategies maximize Acme's and Topco's combined profit?
    a. Neither advertises
    b. Both advertise
    c. Acme advertises, but Topco does not
    d. Topco advertises, but Acme does not

32. Behavior in which a dominant firm's pricing strategy is followed by other firms in the industry is called:
    a. oligopoly power.
    b. contestable behavior.
    c. price leadership.
    d. cartel membership.

33. The game theory model assumes that:
   a. firms anticipate rival firms' decisions when they make their own decisions.
   b. firms ignore rival firms' decisions when they make their own decisions.
   c. markets are contestable because there are no barriers to entry.
   d. a firm will always follow the pricing strategy of the dominant firm in the industry.

34. The marginal product of labor (MP_L) is the:
   a. change in total revenue that results from selling one more unit of output.
   b. change in output that results from employing one more unit of labor.
   c. additional revenue generated from employing one more unit of labor.
   d. total revenue generated from the use of labor.

Use the information below to answer the next three questions.

ABC Manufacturing produces widgets and sells them in a perfectly competitive market for $0.25 each and can hire workers in a perfectly competitive labor market for $10 per hour. ABC's production function is given by:

Number of Workers Per Hour	Output Per Hour
0	0
1	150
2	250
3	325
4	375
5	400

35. The marginal product of the second worker is _____ and the marginal product of the third worker is _____.
   a. 150; 250
   b. 100; 150
   c. 250; 325
   d. 100; 75

36. The value of marginal product (VMP) of the second worker is _____ per hour.
   a. $37.50
   b. $18.75
   c. $25
   d. $12.50

37. If ABC Manufacturing maximizes profit, it will hire:
   a. 2 workers and produce 250 units of output per hour.
   b. 3 workers and produce 325 units of output per hour.
   c. 4 workers and produce 375 units of output per hour.
   d. 5 workers and produce 400 units of output per hour.

38. Which of the following ***best*** represents a ***derived*** demand?
   a. The demand for tickets to the World Series by baseball fans
   b. The demand for secretarial services by a publishing firm
   c. The demand for new novels by recreational readers
   d. The demand for the services of a pediatrician by new parents

39. In a competitive labor market, an increase in the supply of labor, ceteris paribus, will:
   a. increase the demand of labor.
   b. decrease the demand of labor.
   c. increase the market wage rate.
   d. decrease the market wage rate.

40. When markets are competitive and no market failures exist, allowing individuals to pursue their own self interest results in:
   a. an efficient outcome in which marginal benefit equals marginal cost.
   b. an efficient outcome in which economic profit is positive for all firms.
   c. an inefficient outcome in which marginal benefit exceeds marginal cost.
   d. an inefficient outcome in which economic profit is zero for all firms.

Answers to Practice Exam III

1. B	21. D
2. C	22. D
3. C	23. C
4. C	24. C
5. A	25. B
6. B	26. C
7. A	27. D
8. D	28. B
9. A	29. C
10. B	30. B
11. C	31. A
12. A	32. C
13. C	33. A
14. A	34. B
15. A	35. D
16. A	36. C
17. D	37. C
18. C	38. B
19. A	39. D
20. C	40. A

PRACTICE FINAL EXAM

The correct answers to this practice exam can be found on page 316.

1. The *ceteris paribus* assumption is used to:
   a. quantify economic relationships by assuming constant values for the variables under consideration.
   b. isolate the relationship between two variables by holding other influences on the relationship constant.
   c. explain the difference between an economic theory and an economic model.
   d. separate normative economics from positive economics.

2. Scarcity exists because:
   a. it is impossible to increase the quantity or productivity of land or labor.
   b. it is impossible to increase the quantity or productivity of the capital stock.
   c. currently available resources are not sufficient to produce everything people want.
   d. currently available resources are sufficient to produce everything people need.

3. Capital as a factor of production is best represented by:
   a. money in a business bank account.
   b. stocks and bonds.
   c. machines in a factory.
   d. trained restaurant managers.

4. If a country is experiencing a high rate of unemployment:
   a. its production possibilities frontier will shift outward.
   b. it is producing at a point on its production possibilities frontier.
   c. it is producing at a point inside its production possibilities frontier.
   d. it is producing at a point outside its production possibilities frontier.

Use the production possibilities schedule below to answer the next two questions.

Combination	Cars	Motorcycles
A	0	11
B	1	10
C	2	8
D	3	_______
E	4	0

5. The opportunity cost of the first car is _____ motorcycle(s), and the opportunity cost of the second car is _____ motorcycle(s).
   a. 1; 2
   b. 2; 3
   c. 3; 4
   d. 4; 5

6. If the opportunity cost of the third car is 3 motorcycles, how many motorcycles can be produced at combination D?
   a. 11
   b. 8
   c. 5
   d. 0

7. A rightward shift of a production possibilities frontier (curve) indicates that:
   a. unemployment has decreased.
   b. economic growth has occurred.
   c. opportunity costs are decreasing.
   d. production went from inefficient to efficient.

8. Two parties can enjoy gains from trade by specializing in the activities for which:
   a. an absolute advantage exists.
   b. a comparative advantage exists.
   c. an unlimited market exists.
   d. a stratified market exists.

9. If country A can produce coffee at a lower opportunity cost than country B, then:
   a. country A has an absolute advantage in the production of coffee.
   b. country B has an absolute advantage in the production of coffee.
   c. country A has a comparative advantage in the production of coffee.
   d. country B has a comparative advantage in the production of coffee.

Use the graph below to answer the next question.

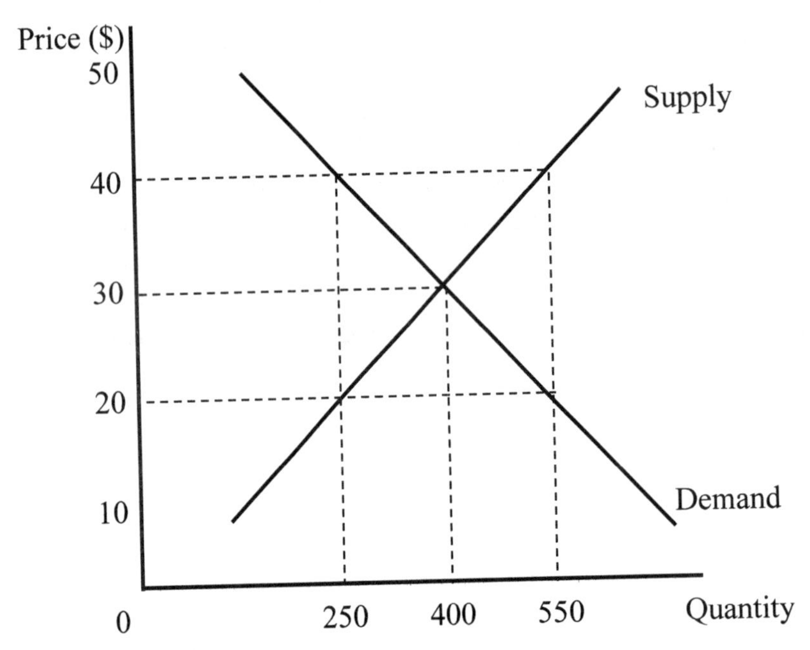

10. If the price in this market is set at $40, a __________ of __________ units will result.
   a. shortage; 150
   b. shortage; 300
   c. surplus; 150
   d. surplus; 300

11. An increase in the quantity supplied of haircuts is most likely to occur as a result of:
   a. a decrease in the supply of baseball caps.
   b. an increase in the popularity of long hair.
   c. an increase in the price of haircuts.
   d. an increase in cost of getting a license to cut hair.

12. An increase in consumer income is expected to cause the demand for milk to:
   a. increase if milk is an inferior good.
   b. increase if milk is a normal good.
   c. decrease if milk is an normal good.
   d. All of the above statements are correct.

13. Improved technology used in the production of cell phones is expected to cause the supply of cell phones to:
   a. shift to the right, resulting in a lower equilibrium price for cell phones.
   b. shift to the right, resulting in a higher equilibrium price for cell phones.
   c. shift to the left, resulting in a lower equilibrium price for cell phones.
   d. shift to the left, resulting in a higher equilibrium price for cell phones.

14. A reduction in the cost of manufacturing smaller personal computers combined with an increase in the demand for smaller personal computers results in an increase in equilibrium:
   a. quantity, but no change in equilibrium price.
   b. price, but no change in equilibrium quantity.
   c. quantity, but the change in equilibrium price depends on the relative size of the shifts.
   d. price, but the change in equilibrium quantity depends on the relative size of the shifts.

15. If the price of soda increases 5% and, as a result, quantity demanded falls 8%, the price elasticity of demand for soda is equal to:
   a. 1.6, so the demand for soda is elastic.
   b. 1.6, so the demand for soda is inelastic.
   c. 0.625, so the demand for soda is elastic.
   d. 0.625, so the demand for soda is inelastic.

16. If an 8% increase in the price of a product results in a 4% decrease in the quantity demanded of the product, then the absolute value of the price elasticity of demand coefficient is _________ and demand is said to be _________.
   a. 2; elastic
   b. 2; inelastic
   c. ½; elastic
   d. ½; inelastic

17. If the demand for movie theater popcorn is inelastic and the movie theater raises the price of popcorn, quantity demanded will _____ and total revenue will _____.
   a. rise; rise
   b. rise; fall
   c. fall; rise
   d. fall; fall

18. Ceteris paribus, the demand for a product will be more elastic when:
  a. the product is a necessity.
  b. there are no close substitutes available.
  c. only a short period of time is allowed for adjustment to a price change.
  d. the spending on the product is large relative to income.

19. If the absolute value of the price elasticity of demand coefficient for juice is 1.6, then the demand for juice is ___________ and a(n) ___________ in price will lead to an increase in total revenue.
  a. elastic; decrease
  b. elastic; increase
  c. inelastic; decrease
  d. inelastic; increase

20. Products that are necessities with no close substitutes tend to have _____ demand curves.
  a. perfectly elastic
  b. unit elastic
  c. elastic
  d. inelastic

21. The difference between the maximum price consumers are willing to pay and the actual price consumers pay in the market measures:
  a. deadweight loss.
  b. equilibrium price.
  c. consumer surplus.
  d. producer surplus.

22. The purpose of setting a price floor above the equilibrium price is to:
  a. protect consumers from price gouging.
  b. cause market surpluses.
  c. maintain a high price for the sellers in the market.
  d. prevent market shortages.

23. If a product with a relatively elastic demand and a relatively inelastic supply is taxed, the economic burden of the tax is borne:
  a. entirely by the sellers of the product.
  b. entirely by the consumers of the product.
  c. mostly by the sellers of the product.
  d. mostly by the consumers of the product.

24. If the price of a bottle of wine increases by $2 due to a $5 per bottle tax, consumers in this market bear _____ of the tax.
  a. 20% b. 40% c. 60% d. 100%

Use the graph below to answer the next three questions.

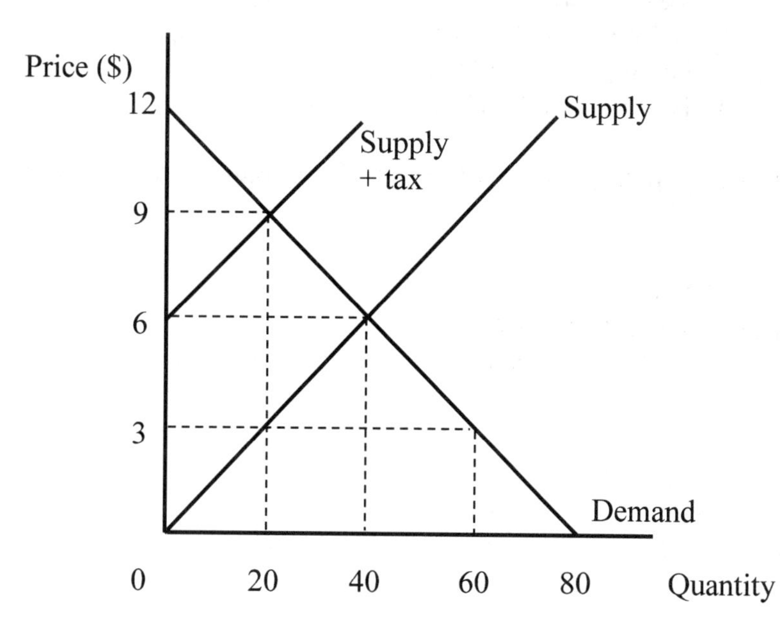

25. With no tax imposed in this market, equilibrium quantity is _____ and consumer surplus is equal to _____.
    a. 20; $240
    b. 20; $120
    c. 40; $240
    d. 40; $120

26. If a $6 per unit tax is imposed in this market, the price consumers must pay changes to _____, while the price sellers retain changes to _____.
    a. $3: $9
    b. $9; $3
    c. $6; $3
    d. $3; $6

27. The deadweight loss resulting from a $6 per unit tax is equal to _______ and the tax revenue generated by this tax is equal to _______.
    a. $60; $120
    b. $90; $240
    c. $120; $60
    d. $60; $240

28. The "free-rider" problem refers to the fact that:
    a. some people receive welfare benefits to which they are not entitled.
    b. the benefits associated with public goods cannot be denied to those who do not pay for them.
    c. government must subsidize public transportation.
    d. the benefits associated with private goods cannot be denied to those who are unwilling to pay for them.

29. Which of the following is one of the functions of government in the U.S.?
  a. Providing a legal framework and protecting property rights
  b. Providing high-paying jobs to all workers
  c. Providing adequate housing and healthcare to all citizens
  d. All of the above are functions of the U.S. government

30. Firms encounter diminishing marginal product (diminishing returns) in the short run because:
  a. all inputs are fixed.
  b. at least one input is fixed.
  c. inputs can only be varied proportionally.
  d. at some point, firms must hire inferior labor to increase output.

31. In the long run, firms:
  a. have at least one fixed input.
  b. have only fixed inputs.
  c. can only vary capital inputs.
  d. can vary all inputs.

Use the information below to answer the next two questions.

Output (Q)	TVC	TC
0	$0	$20
1	$60	$80
2	$100	$120
3	$150	$___
4	$___	$230

32. The total cost of producing three units of output is:
  a. $80. b. $120. c. $170. d. $200.

33. Average variable cost (AVC) when four units of output are produced is:
  a. $50. b. $52.50. c. $57.50. d. $60.

34 Costs that must be paid in the short run even when no output is produced are called:
  a. total costs (TC).
  b. total fixed costs (TFC).
  c. total variable costs (TVC).
  d. marginal costs (MC).

35. The downward-sloping portion of a LRAC curve implies:
  a. economies of scale exist over that range of the curve.
  b. constant returns to scale exist over that range of the curve.
  c. diseconomies of scale exist over that range of the curve.
  d. decreasing returns to scale exist over that range of the curve.

36. If a firm is a price-taker, then it:
   a. sells its product at the price determined by the market.
   b. sells its product at the price set by the government.
   c. sells its product at the price dictated by the largest firm in the industry.
   d. can sell all it can produce at whatever price it chooses.

37. The marginal revenue curve for a perfectly competitive firm:
   a. lies above the firm's demand curve.
   b. lies below the firm's demand curve.
   c. is the same as the firm's demand curve.
   d. is the same as the market demand curve.

38. A firm earns zero economic profit when:
   a. price is equal to average variable cost.
   b. price is equal to average total cost.
   c. price exceeds average total cost by the greatest amount.
   d. marginal revenue is equal to marginal cost.

39. If firms in the market for energy drinks are earning positive economic profit in the short run, and there are no barriers to entry into this market, economic theory predicts that:
   a. new entrants into the market will drive up the price of energy drinks in the long run.
   b. new entrants into the market will drive down the price of energy drinks in the long run.
   c. firms will exit the market in the long run, causing the price of energy drinks to fall.
   d. firms will exit the market in the long run, causing the price of energy drinks to rise.

40. Industry output is efficient when:
   a. MB = MC for each firm.
   b. deadweight loss is maximized.
   c. consumer and producer surplus equal zero.
   d. All of the above are conditions for efficiency.

41. Which of the following statements is *true*?
   a. Monopoly markets are more efficient than competitive markets.
   b. There is no difference between the outcome in monopoly and competitive markets.
   c. It is never good for consumers to have only one firm supplying a market.
   d. Competition generally leads to lower prices, higher output, and greater efficiency than monopoly.

42. For a monopoly, the industry (or market) demand curve is:
  a. more elastic than the monopoly firm's demand curve.
  b. less elastic than the monopoly firm's demand curve.
  c. the same as the monopoly firm's demand curve.
  d. unrelated to the monopoly firm's demand curve.

43. In the long run, monopoly firms:
  a. can earn a positive economic profit if barriers to entry can be maintained.
  b. tend to behave as if they are operating in perfectly competitive markets.
  c. will earn only a normal profit due to the entry of new firms into the market.
  d. will have both fixed and variable costs.

44. If an industry is considered a "natural monopoly," then it must be true that:
  a. production displays diseconomies of scale over a wide range of output.
  b. production displays economies of scale over a wide range of output.
  c. the industry produces only natural resources.
  d. the industry has constant costs at all levels of output.

45. Government addresses the problem of monopoly inefficiency by:
  a. using antitrust laws to promote competition.
  b. regulating the price a monopolist can charge for output.
  c. operating the monopoly itself, especially in the case of natural monopoly.
  d. All of the above are possible policy approaches for government.

46. Suppose a firm has acquired a patent to produce an effective anti-aging drug. If this firm is earning positive economic profit in the short run, then it will:
  a. produce an efficient amount of the drug and charge an efficient price.
  b. earn zero economic profit in long-run equilibrium.
  c. continue to earn positive economic profit in the long run as long as market demand is strong and the patent remains in effect.
  d. continue to earn positive economic profit in the long run even if market demand falls.

Use the information in the table below to answer the next question.

Price per unit	Quantity Demanded
$40	1
30	2
20	3
10	4

47. For a monopolist that is unable to price discriminate, the marginal revenue of the 2nd unit is _____, while the marginal revenue of the 2nd unit for a monopolist that is able to perfectly price discriminate is _____.
  a. $40; $60
  b. $20; $30
  c. $20; $10
  d. $0; -$20

Use the graph below for an unregulated, profit-maximizing monopolist that cannot price discriminate to answer the next two questions.

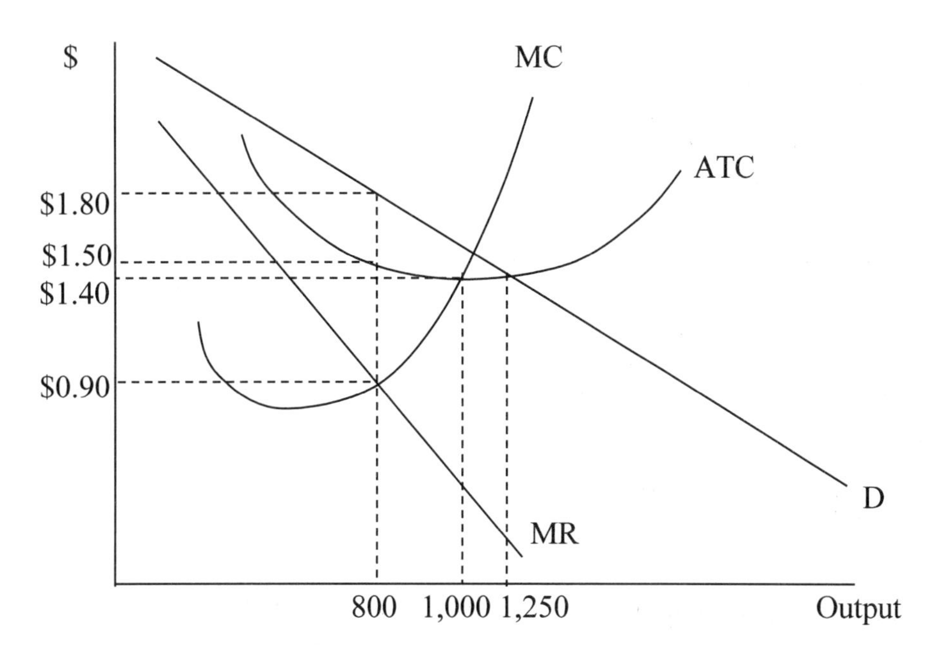

48. This profit-maximizing firm will produce:
    a. 800 units of output and charge a price of $0.90 per unit.
    b. 800 units of output and charge a price of $1.80 per unit.
    c. 1,000 units of output and charge a price of $1.40 per unit.
    d. 1,250 units of output and charge a price of $1.50 per unit.

49. If this firm behaves as a profit-maximizer, its profit will be equal to:
    a. $0.
    b. $200.
    c. $240.
    d. $475.

50. For all firms, profits are maximized and losses are minimized in the short run at the output where:
    a. marginal revenue equals marginal cost so long as price exceeds ATC.
    b. marginal revenue equals marginal cost so long as price exceeds AVC.
    c. total revenue is equal to total cost.
    d. total revenue is maximized.

Use the graph below for a monopolistically competitive firm to answer the next two questions.

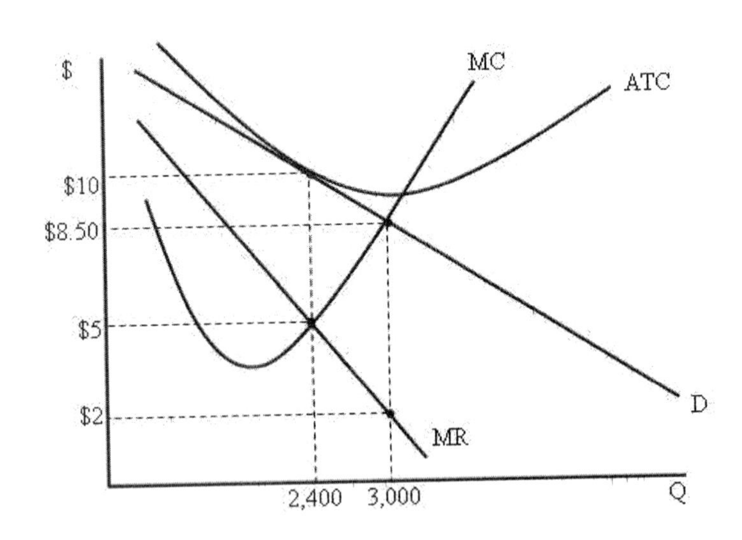

51. The profit-maximizing level of output is _____ and the price charged will be _____.
    a. 2,400; $5
    b. 2,400; $10
    c. 3,000; $2
    d. 3,000; $8.50

52. The monopolistically competitive firm represented in the graph is in:
    a. long-run equilibrium since it is earning zero economic profit, assuming fixed costs are not present.
    b. short-run equilibrium since it is earning zero economic profit, assuming fixed costs are not present.
    c. short-run equilibrium, but not long-run equilibrium since it is earning positive economic profit.
    d. long-run equilibrium, but not short-run equilibrium since it is earning positive economic profit.

53. If a monopolistically competitive firm is producing where marginal revenue is equal to marginal cost but price is greater than marginal cost, the firm:
    a. should decrease output to increase profit.
    b. should increase output to increase profit.
    c. should continue to produce at this point because it is already maximizing profit.
    d. could increase profit by either increasing or decreasing output.

54. Long-run equilibrium for firms in monopolistically competitive industries is similar to long-run equilibrium for firms in perfectly competitive industries in that:
   a. price equals minimum average total cost in both.
   b. price equals average total cost in both.
   c. price equals marginal cost in both.
   d. economic profit is small but positive in both.

55. The percentage of total sales accounted for by the top four or eight firms in the industry is known as the:
   a. concentration ratio.
   b. Herfindahl-Hirschman Index (HHI).
   c. industry differential.
   d. Prisoner's Dilemma.

56. Behavior in which a dominant firm's pricing strategy is followed by other firms in the industry is called:
   a. price leadership.
   b. cartel membership.
   c. contestable.
   d. rent-seeking.

57. According to game theory, firms competing in an oligopolistic market are reluctant to change product price because they anticipate that rivals will:
   a. match a price decrease, but ignore a price increase.
   b. ignore a price decrease, but match a price increase.
   c. match both a price decrease and a price increase.
   d. ignore both a price decrease and a price increase.

Use the table below to answer the next question.

Labor (number of workers)	Output per Hour
0	0
1	5
2	11
3	16
4	20
5	23

58. Assume perfectly competitive markets with product price equal to $2 and the wage rate equal to $8. To maximize profit, this firm should hire:
   a. 2 workers and produce 11 units of output per hour.
   b. 3 workers and produce 16 units of output per hour.
   c. 4 workers and produce 20 units of output per hour.
   d. 5 workers and produce 23 units of output per hour.

59. Which of the following ***best*** represents a derived demand for labor?
   a. The demand for tickets to the World Series by baseball fans
   b. The demand for the services of a personal trainer by individual consumers
   c. The demand for dog food by neighborhood dog owners
   d. The demand for the services of nurses by hospitals

60. In a competitive labor market, an increase in the supply of labor, ceteris paribus, will:
   a. increase the demand of labor.
   b. decrease the demand of labor.
   c. increase the market wage rate.
   d. decrease the market wage rate.

Answers to Practice Final Exam

1. B
2. C
3. C
4. C
5. A
6. C
7. B
8. B
9. C
10. D
11. C
12. B
13. A
14. C
15. A
16. D
17. C
18. D
19. A
20. D
21. C
22. C
23. C
24. B
25. D
26. B
27. A
28. B
29. A
30. B
31. D
32. C
33. B
34. B
35. A
36. A
37. C
38. B
39. B
40. A
41. D
42. C
43. A
44. B
45. D
46. C
47. B
48. B
49. C
50. B
51. B
52. A
53. C
54. B
55. A
56. A
57. A
58. C
59. D
60. D